MENARDS

Ranch HOME PLANS

over 200 home plans

CONTENTS

RANCH HOME PLANS

RANCH HOME PLANS is a collection of our best-selling ranch homes in a variety of styles. These plans cover a wide range of architectural styles. A broad assortment is presented to match a wide variety of lifestyles and budgets. Each plan page features floor plans, a front view of the house, interior square footage of the home, number of bedrooms, baths, garage size and foundation types. All floor plans show room and exterior dimensions.

TECHNICAL SPECIFICATIONS

At the time the construction drawings were prepared, every effort was made to ensure that these plans and specifications meet nationally recognized building codes (BOCA, Southern Building Code Congress and others). Because national building codes change or vary from area to area some drawing modifications and/or the assistance of a professional designer or architect may be necessary to comply with your local codes or to accommodate specific building site conditions. We advise you to consult with your local building official for information regarding codes governing your area.

BLUEPRINT ORDERING - FAST AND EASY

Your ordering is made simple by following the instructions on page 7. See page 6 for more information on which types of blueprint packages are available and how many plan sets to order.

YOUR HOME, YOUR WAY

The blueprints you receive are a master plan for building your new home. They start you on your way to what may well be the most rewarding experience of your life.

Current printing 5 4 3 2

RANCH HOME PLANS is published by HDA, Inc., 944 Anglum Road, St. Louis, MO, 63042. Printed in U.S.A. © 2012.

Artist drawings and photos shown in this publication may vary slightly from the actual working drawings. Some photos are shown in mirror reverse. Please refer to the floor plan for accurate layout.

COVER HOME The house shown on the front cover is plan #M06-072L-1108 and is featured on page 17. Photo courtesy of Lifestyles Home Design.

COVER HOME The house shown on the front cover is plan #M06-072L-1123 and is featured on page 96. Photo courtesy of Lifestyles Home Design.

COVER HOME The multi-family plan shown on the front cover is plan #M06-007D-0022 and is featured on page 223. Color rendering courtesy of HDA, Inc.

LET MENARDS® MAKE YOUR DREAM HOME A REALITY

"Thanks to MENARDS®, finding and building our Dream Home has never been easier."

MENARDS

Thinking about building your dream home? Or, perhaps you are interested in a luxury home or possibly a ranch home? Choosing a home plan can be a daunting task.

This book of Ranch Home Plans has been designed to make the search simple and easy. Browse the pages of this book and look for the style that best suits your family and your needs. These plans have been chosen from top designers from across the country and can provide to you the perfect home that will truly be a place of refuge for your whole family for years to come.

This book is the perfect place to begin your search for the home of your dreams. You will find the expected beauty you want and the functional efficiency you need, all designed with unmatched quality.

Also, keep in mind, this book contains helpful articles for understanding what kind of plan package you may need as well as other helpful building aids to make the process even easier.

When you have made this decision visit your local MENARDS® store to place your order and partner with one of their friendly team members to walk you through the process or order your home plans at www.Menards.com.

MENARDS® is dedicated to assist you through the entire home decision process

SHINGLES
COMPUTER HOUSE ESTIMATING

WHAT'S THE RIGHT PLAN FOR YOU?

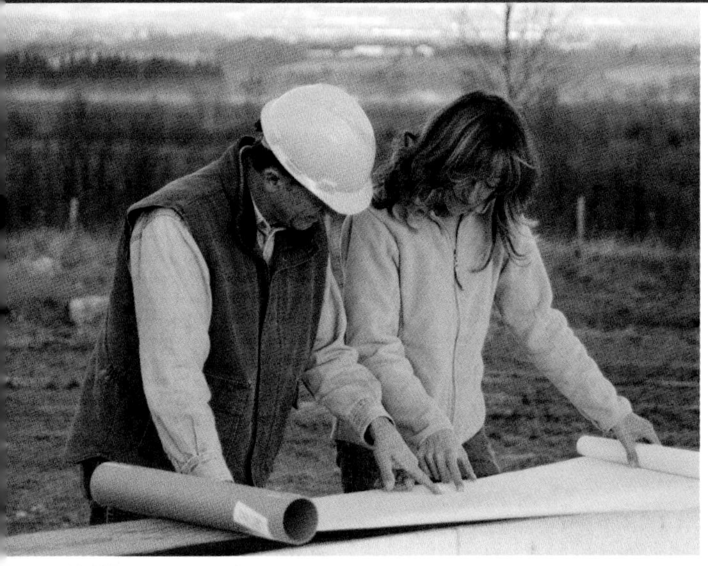

Choosing a home plan is an exciting but difficult task. Many factors play a role in what home plan is best for you and your family. To help you get started, we have pinpointed some of the major factors to consider when searching for your dream home. Take the time to evaluate your family's needs and you will have an easier time sorting through all of the home plans offered in our magazine.

BUDGET: The first thing to consider is your budget. Many items take part in this budget, from ordering the blueprints to the last doorknob purchased. When you find your dream home plan, visit the MENARDS® Building Materials Desk to get a cost-to-build estimate to ensure that the finished product will be within your cost range.

FAMILY LIFESTYLE: After your budget is deciphered, you need to assess you and your family's lifestyle needs. Think about the stage of life you are at now, and what stages you will be going through in the future. Ask yourself questions to figure out how much room you need now and if you will need room for expansion. Are you married? Do you have children? How many children do you plan on having? Are you an empty-nester?

Incorporate in your planning any frequent guests you may have, including elderly parents, grandchildren or adult children who may live with you.

Does your family entertain a lot? If so, think about the rooms you will need to do so. Will you need both formal and informal spaces? Do you need a gourmet kitchen? Do you need a game room and/or a wet bar?

Experts in the field suggest that the best way to determine your needs is to begin by listing everything you like or dislike about your current home.

FLOOR PLAN LAYOUTS: When looking through our home plans, imagine yourself walking through the house. Consider the flow from the entry to the living, sleeping and gathering areas. Does the layout ensure privacy for the master bedroom? Does the garage enter near the kitchen for easy unloading? Does the placement of the windows provide enough privacy from any neighboring properties? Do you plan on using furniture you already have? Will this furniture fit in the appropriate rooms? When you find a plan you want to purchase, be sure to picture yourself actually living in it.

EXTERIOR SPACES: There are many different home styles ranging from Traditional to Contemporary. Flip through and find which style most appeals to you and the neighborhood in which you plan to build. Also think of your site and how the entire house will fit on this site. Picture any landscaping you plan on incorporating into the design. Using your imagination is key when choosing a home plan.

Choosing a home plan can be an intimidating experience. Asking yourself these questions before you get started on the search will help you through the process. With our large selection of multiple styles we are certain you will find your dream home in the following pages.

OUR BLUEPRINT PACKAGES OFFER...

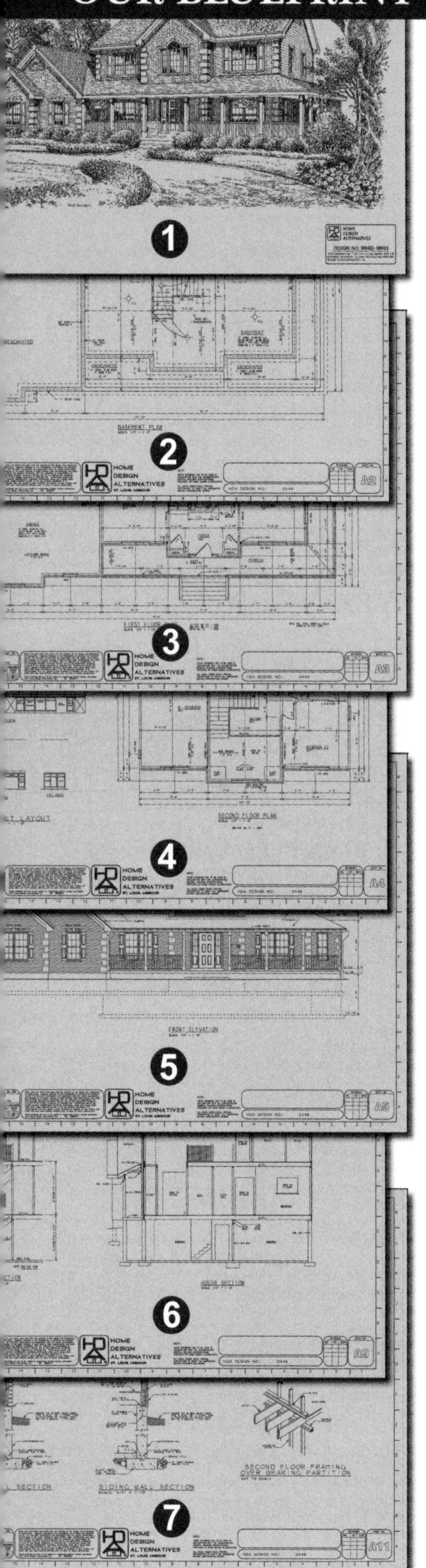

Quality plans for building your future,with extras that provide unsurpassed value,ensure good construction and long-term enjoyment.

A quality home - one that looks good, functions well, and provides years of enjoyment - is a product of many things - design, materials, and craftsmanship.

But it's also the result of outstanding blueprints - the actual plans and specifications that tell the builder exactly how to build your home.

And with our BLUEPRINT PACKAGES you get the absolute best.
A complete set of blueprints is available for every design in this book.
These "working drawings" are highly detailed, resulting in two key benefits:

- Better understanding by the contractor of how to build your home and...
- More accurate construction estimates.

Below is a sample of plan information included for most of the designs in this book. Specific details may vary with each designer's plan. While this information is typical of most plans, we cannot assure the inclusion of all the following referenced items. Please contact customer service for plan specific information, including which of the following items are included.

1. COVER SHEET is the artist's rendering of the exterior of the home and is included with many of the plans. It will give you an idea of how your home will look when completed and landscaped.

2. FOUNDATION plan shows the layout of the basement, crawl space, slab or pier foundation. All necessary notations and dimensions are included. See the plan page for the foundation types included. If the home plan you choose does not have your desired foundation type, see page 8 on how to customize your foundation to suit your specific needs or site conditions.

3. FLOOR PLANS show the placement of walls, doors, closets, plumbing fixtures, electrical outlets, columns, and beams for each level of the home.

4 INTERIOR ELEVATIONS provide views of special interior elements such as fireplaces, kitchen cabinets, built-in units and other features of the home.

5. EXTERIOR ELEVATIONS illustrate the front, rear and both sides of the house, with all details of exterior materials and the required dimensions.

6. SECTIONS show detail views of the home or portions of the home as if it were sliced from the roof to the foundation. This sheet shows important areas such as load-bearing walls, stairs, joists, trusses and other structural elements, which are critical for proper construction.

7. DETAILS show how to construct certain components of your home, such as the roof system, stairs, deck, etc.

OTHER GREAT PRODUCTS

THE LEGAL KIT™

Home building can be a complicated process with many legal regulations being confusing. This Legal Kit was designed to help you avoid many legal pitfalls and build your home with confidence using the forms and contracts featured in this kit. Included are request for proposal documents, various fixed price and cost plus contracts, instructions on how and when to use each form, warranty statements and more. Save time and money before you break ground on your new home or start a remodeling project. Instructions are included on how to use the kit and since the documents are universal, they are designed to be used with all building trades. Since review by an attorney is always advised before signing any contract, this is an ideal way to get organized and started on the process. Plus, all forms are reproducible making it a terrific tool for the contractor and home builder.

Discount Price: $35.00 - Menards SKU 100-3422

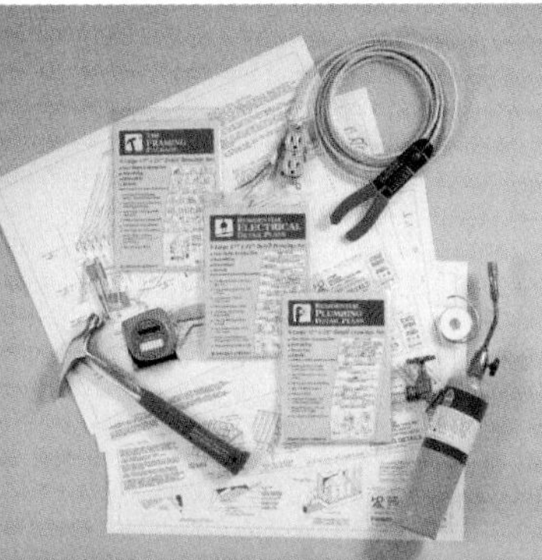

DETAIL PLAN PACKAGES

Framing, Plumbing and Electrical Plan Packages

Three separate packages offer home builders details for constructing various foundations; numerous floor, wall and roof framing techniques; simple to complex residential wiring; sump and water softener hookups; plumbing connection methods; installation of septic systems, and more. Packages include 3-dimensional illustrations and a glossary of terms. These drawings do not pertain to a specific home plan making them perfect for your building situation. Purchase one or all three.

Discount Price: $20.00 each or all three for $40.00 - Menards SKU 100-3422

MORE HELPFUL BUILDING AIDS...

Your Blueprint Package will contain the necessary construction information to build your home. We also offer the following products and services to save you time and money in the building process.

MATERIAL LIST

Material lists are available for all of the plans in this book. Each list gives you the quantity, dimensions and description of the building materials necessary to construct your home. You'll get faster and more accurate bids from your contractor while saving money by paying for only the materials you need. To receive a free home plan estimate call or visit any MENARDS® Building Materials Desk.

Discount Price: $125.00 - Menards SKU 100-3422

NOTE: Material lists are not refundable. A material list can only be sold when at least one set of blueprints has been purchased. They cannot be purchased separately. Material lists are designed with the standard foundation only and will not include alternate or optional foundations.

EXPRESS DELIVERY

Most orders are processed within 24 hours of receipt. Please allow 7-10 business days for delivery. If you need to place a rush order, please call or visit any MENARDS® store to order by 11:00 a.m. Monday-Friday CST and specify you would like express service (allow 1-2 business days).

Discount Price: $50.00 - Menards SKU 194-4356

TECHNICAL ASSISTANCE

If you have questions, call our technical support line at 1-314-770-2228 Monday through Friday, 8am-5pm CST. Whether it involves design modifications or field assistance, our designers are extremely familiar with all of our designs and will be happy to help you. We want your home to be everything you expect it to be.

WHAT KIND OF PLAN PACKAGE DO YOU NEED?

Now that you've found the home you've been looking for, here are some suggestions on how to make your Dream Home a reality. To get started, order the type of plans that fit your particular situation.

YOUR CHOICES

- ☐ **THE ONE-SET STUDY PACKAGE** - We offer a One-set plan package so you can study your home in detail. This one set is considered a study set and is marked "not for construction." It is a copyright violation to reproduce blueprints.

- ☐ **THE MINIMUM 5-SET PACKAGE** - If you're ready to start the construction process, this 5-set package is the minimum number of blueprint sets you will need. It will require keeping close track of each set so they can be used by multiple subcontractors and tradespeople.

- ☐ **THE STANDARD 8-SET PACKAGE** - For best results in terms of cost, schedule and quality of construction, we recommend you order eight (or more) sets of blueprints. Besides one set for yourself, additional sets of blueprints will be required by your mortgage lender, local building department, general contractor and all subcontractors working on foundation, electrical, plumbing, heating/air conditioning, carpentry work, etc.

- ☐ **REPRODUCIBLE MASTERS** - If you wish to make some minor design changes, you'll want to order reproducible masters. These drawings contain the same information as the blueprints but are printed on reproducible paper and clearly indicates your right to alter, copy or reproduce. This will allow your builder or a local design professional to make the necessary drawing changes without the major expense of redrawing the plans. This package also allows you to print copies of the modified plans as needed. The right of building only one structure from these plans is licensed exclusively to the buyer. You may not use this design to build a second or multiple dwelling(s) without purchasing another blueprint. Each violation of the Copyright Law is punishable in a fine.

- ☐ **MIRROR REVERSE SETS** - Plans can be printed in mirror reverse. These plans are useful when the house would fit your site better if all the rooms were on the opposite side than shown. They are simply a mirror image of the original drawings causing the lettering and dimensions to read backwards. Therefore, when ordering mirror reverse drawings, you must purchase at least one set of right-reading plans.

- ☐ **RIGHT READING REVERSE SETS** - Right reading reverse is where the plan is a mirrored image of the original drawings, but all the text and dimensions read correctly. This option may not be available for all home plans, so please check the Home Plan Index on page 224 for availability.

- ☐ **ADDITIONAL SETS** - Additional sets of the plan ordered are available for an additional cost of $45.00 each. Five-set, eight-set, and reproducible packages offer considerable savings.

Note: Available only within 90 days after purchase of plan package or reproducible masters of the same plan.

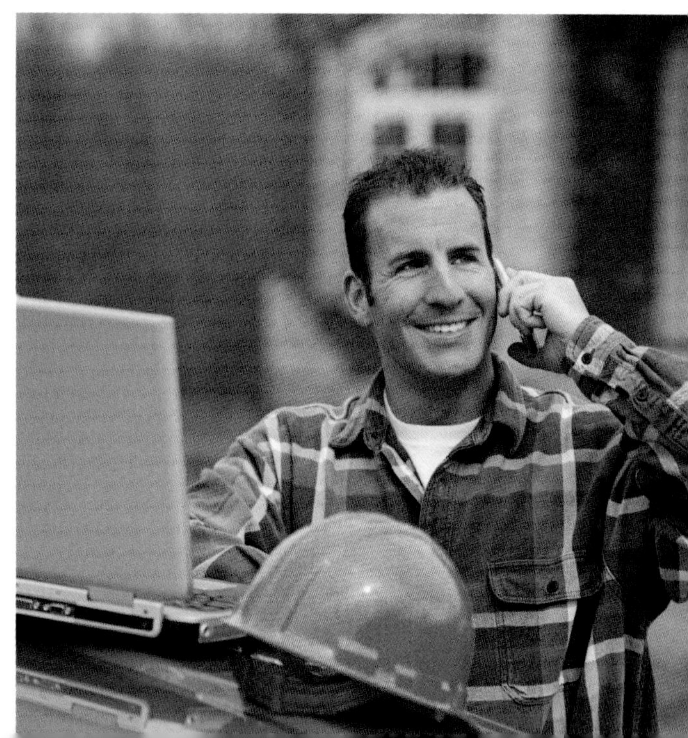

HOW TO ORDER HOME PLANS

You've found your Dream Home, now what?

Follow these simple steps:

1. Review the article on page 6 to decide what type of plan package you need.
2. To order, call or visit any MENARDS® store and go to the Building Materials Desk or visit **www.Menards.com**.

To locate the nearest MENARDS® store, go to **www.Menards.com** and click on the Store locator.

Artist drawings and photos shown in this publication may vary slightly from the actual working drawings. Some photos are shown in mirror reverse. Please refer to the floor plan for accurate layout.

BLUEPRINT SKU PRICING
(PRICES SUBJECT TO CHANGE)

PRICE CODE		1-SET STUDY	5-SET PLAN	8-SET PLAN	REPRO. MASTERS
AAA	Menards SKU	194-3920	194-3933	194-3946	194-3959
	Discount Price	$310	$410	$510	$610
AA	Menards SKU	194-3962	194-3975	194-3988	194-3991
	Discount Price	$410	$510	$610	$710
A	Menards SKU	194-4000	194-4084	194-4165	194-4246
	Discount Price	$470	$570	$670	$770
B	Menards SKU	194-4013	194-4097	194-4178	194-4259
	Discount Price	$530	$630	$730	$830
C	Menards SKU	194-4026	194-4107	194-4181	194-4262
	Discount Price	$585	$685	$785	$885
D	Menards SKU	194-4039	194-4110	194-4194	194-4275
	Discount Price	$635	$735	$835	$935
E	Menards SKU	194-4042	194-4123	194-4204	194-4288
	Discount Price	$695	$795	$895	$995
F	Menards SKU	194-4055	194-4136	194-4217	194-4291
	Discount Price	$750	$850	$950	$1050
G	Menards SKU	194-4068	194-4149	194-4220	194-4301
	Discount Price	$1000	$1100	$1200	$1300
H	Menards SKU	194-4071	194-4152	194-4233	194-4314
	Discount Price	$1100	$1200	$1300	$1400

OTHER PRODUCTS & BUILDING AIDS

MIRROR REVERSE*	
Menards SKU	194-4327
Discount Price	$15
RIGHT READING REVERSE*	
Menards SKU	194-4328
Discount Price	$150
ADDITIONAL SETS**	
Menards SKU	194-4330
Discount Price	$45
MATERIAL LIST**	
Menards SKU	100-3422
Discount Price	$125
EXPRESS DELIVERY	
Menards SKU	194-4356
Discount Price	$50
LEGAL KIT	
Menards SKU	100-3422
Discount Price	$35
DETAIL PLAN PACKAGES *ELECTRICAL, PLUMBING & FRAMING - ALL SAME SKU*	
Menards SKU	100-3422
Discount Price	$20 EA. 3 FOR $40

If at any time you feel you may need assistance in the field while building, HDA offers a technical assistance line for answering building questions pertaining to your specific plan. Please call 314-770-2228 Monday-Friday between 8:00am and 5:00pm CST and our professional design staff will be happy to help.

Please note: All blueprints are printed in response to your order, so we cannot honor requests for refunds. However, if for some reason you find that the plan you have purchased does not meet your requirements, you may exchange that plan for another plan in our collection within 90 days of purchase. At the time of the exchange, you will be charged a processing fee of 25% of your original plan package price, plus the difference in price between the plan packages (if applicable) and the cost to ship the new plans to you. Keep in mind, reproducible drawings can only be exchanged if the package is unopened and material lists can only be purchased within 90 days of purchasing the plan package.

*See page 6
**Available only within 90 days after purchase of plan package of same plan

MAKING CHANGES TO YOUR PLAN

We understand that it is difficult to find blueprints that will meet all your needs. That is why HDA, Inc. is pleased to offer plan modification services.

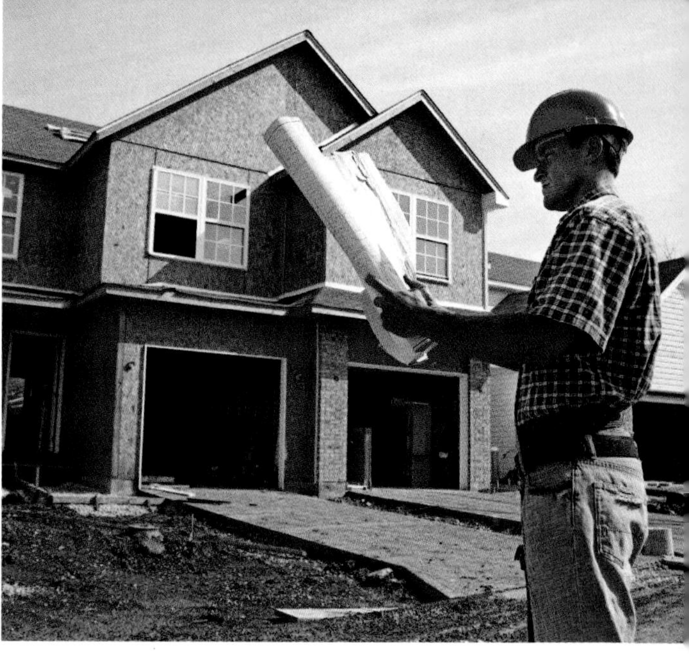

THINKING ABOUT CUSTOMIZING YOUR PLAN?

If you're like many customers, you may want to make changes to your home plan to make it the dream home you've always wanted. That's where our expert design and modification team comes in. You won't find a more efficient and economic way to get your changes done than by using our design services.

Whether it's enlarging a kitchen, adding a porch or converting a crawl space to a basement, we can customize any plan and make it perfect for your family. Simply create your wish list and let us go to work. Soon you'll have the blueprints for your new home and at a fraction of the cost of hiring an architect!

THE HDA MODIFICATION ADVANTAGE

- We can customize any of the thousands of plans
- FREE cost estimates for your home plan modifications within 48 hours (Monday-Friday, 8am-5pm CST).
- Average turn-around time to complete the modifications is 2-3 weeks.
- One-on-one design consultations.

Easy Steps For Fast Service

Visit any MENARDS® Building Materials Desk and request an HDA Custom Change Form.

Simply follow the instructions to receive your quote within two business days.

CUSTOMIZING FACTS

- The average cost for us to customize a house plan is typically less than 1 percent of the building costs — compare that to the national average of 7 percent of building costs.
- The average modification cost for a home is typically \$800 to \$1,500 (this does not include the cost of the reproducible blueprint, which is required to make plan changes).
- The average cost to modify a project plan is typically between \$200-\$500.

OTHER HELPFUL INFORMATION

- Feel free to include a sketch, or a specific list of changes you'd like to make.
- One of our designers will contact you within 24 hours with your free estimate.
- Upon accepting the estimate, you will need to purchase the reproducible set of plans.
- A contract, which includes a specific list of changes and fees will be sent to you for approval.
- Upon approving the contract, our designers will keep you up to date by emailing or faxing sketches throughout the project.
- Plan can be converted to metric.
- Barrier Free Conversion (accommodating a plan for special needs, transferring your living space for everyone).
- Customizing is also available for project plans, such as sheds, garages, apartment garages and more.

MENARDS

Ranch HOME PLANS

over 200 home plans

The following pages include a collection of best-selling home plans featuring the ever-popular ranch homes that are still the most widely desired home built today. This collection of one-story homes from some of the nation's leading designers and architects include open floor plans, abundant storage, and space for expansion. Whether you're interested in a cozy cottage or sprawling luxury home, these ranch homes will welcome you and create the perfect atmosphere for quality family living in a timeless setting. We are excited to present this collection designed for gracious ranch living. Whatever your tastes or needs, we invite you to discover the home of your dreams.

Plan #M06-055L-0748 can be found on page 14.

Plan #M06-022D-0026 can be found on page 27.

Plan #M06-065L-0041 can be found on page 12.

GRAY SUMMIT

MENARDS®

Plan #M06-051L-0187

Photo, above - Stainless steel appliances create a nice contrast against the rich, dark wood cabinets found throughout the kitchen.

Photo, left - The dramatic front entry with a tall ceiling and ornate window treatment offer an inviting feeling when guests arrive.

Photo, above - Step down into the cozy lower level recreation room encompassed by decorative wrought iron railings.

Photo, right - This stunning great room has a formal, yet friendly feel that can only be created when the design uses tall ceilings and open, airy spaces.

Plan #M06-051L-0187

TRADITIONAL RANCH

3,777 total square feet of living area

4 bedrooms, 3 1/2 baths

3-car garage

Walk-out basement foundation

SPECIAL FEATURES

Energy efficient home with 2" x 6" exterior walls

The master bedroom provides the ultimate relaxation with a deluxe bath and walk-in closet to keep everything organized

A walk-in pantry and snack bar island add efficiency to the kitchen that opens to the great room and cozy nook

The lower level is comprised of two secondary bedrooms, a recreation room and a wet bar

PRICE CODE G

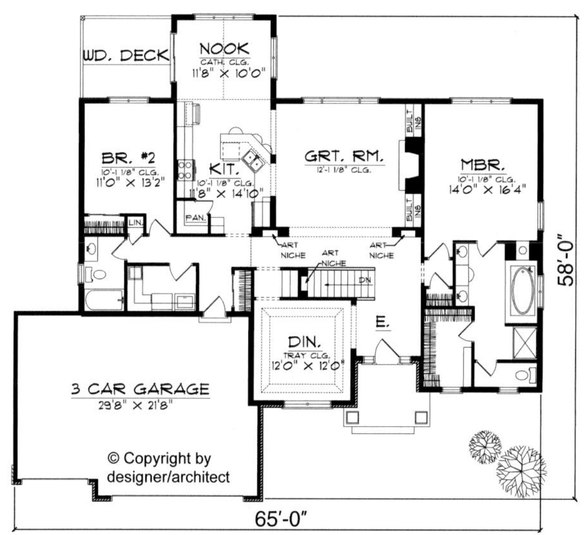
WD. DECK
NOOK
CATH. CLG.
11'8" X 10'0"
BR. #2
10'-1 1/8" CLG.
11'0" X 13'2"
KIT.
10'-1 1/8" CLG.
11'8" X 14'10"
PAN.
LIN.
GRT. RM.
12'-1 1/8" CLG.
MBR.
10'-1 1/8" CLG.
14'0" X 16'4"
ART NICHE
ART NICHE
ART NICHE
DN
E.
DIN.
TRAY CLG.
12'0" X 12'0"
3 CAR GARAGE
29'8" X 21'8"
© Copyright by designer/architect
58'-0"
65'-0"

First Floor
2,049 sq. ft.

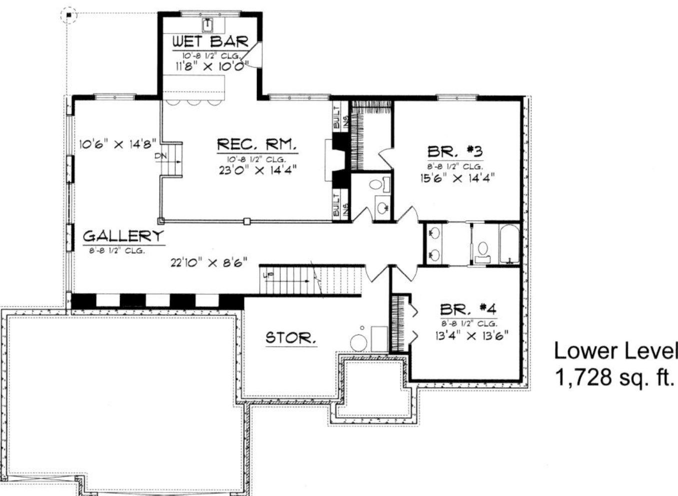
WET BAR
10'-8 1/2" CLG.
11'8" X 10'0"
10'6" X 14'8"
DN
REC. RM.
10'-8 1/2" CLG.
23'0" X 14'4"
BR. #3
8'-8 1/2" CLG.
15'6" X 14'4"
GALLERY
8'-8 1/2" CLG.
22'10" X 8'6"
UP
STOR.
BR. #4
8'-8 1/2" CLG.
13'4" X 13'6"

Lower Level
1,728 sq. ft.

To order plans, visit the Menards Building Materials Desk or visit www.Menards.com.

HUNGERFORD TRAIL

MENARDS

Plan #M06-065L-0041

Photo, above - Beautiful columns define the living space and create a lovely entryway from the foyer into the great room.

Photo, left - This expansive kitchen has a lengthy peninsula that serves as both prep and dining surfaces while providing a good view of the great room.

Photo, above - A magnificent site both back and front, this home's rear deck provides covered outdoor living space ideal for taking in some fresh air whether watching the sunset or enjoying a pleasant rain shower.

Photo, right - Dramatic carpentry offers an extraordinary focal point as seen in this close-up of the great room fireplace.

Plan #M06-065L-0041

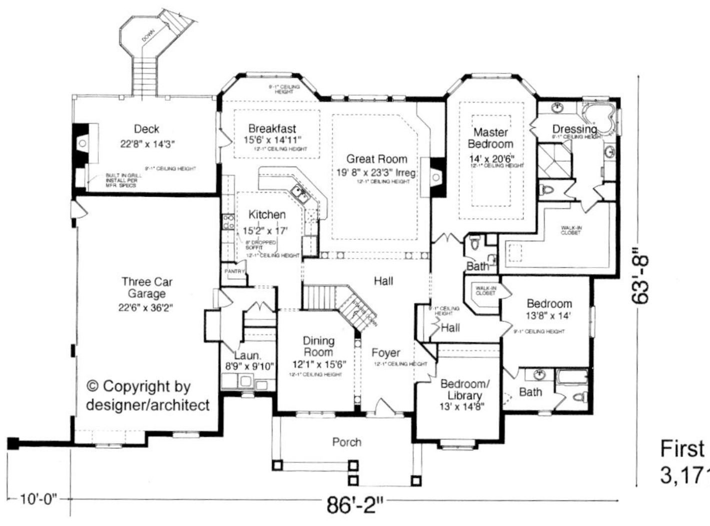
Deck
22'8" x 14'3"
Breakfast
15'6" x 14'11"
Great Room
19' 8" x 23'3" Irreg
Master
Bedroom
14' x 20'6"
Dressing
Kitchen
15'2" x 17'
Three Car
Garage
22'6" x 36'2"
Hall
Bath
Bedroom
13'8" x 14'
Hall
Laun.
8'9" x 9'10"
Dining
Room
12'1" x 15'6"
Foyer
Bedroom/
Library
13' x 14'8"
Bath
© Copyright by
designer/architect
Porch
63'-8"
10'-0"
86'-2"

First Floor
3,171 sq. ft.

Bar
Billiards
Bedroom
14'6" x 13'8"
Bedroom
11'8" x 16'1"
Rec Room
Unexcavated
Media Room
Basement
Unexcavated

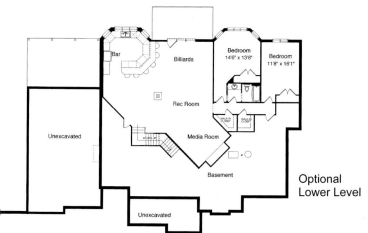

Optional
Lower Level

OUTDOOR COVERED DECK WARMED BY FIREPLACE

3,171 total square feet of living area

3 bedrooms, 2 1/2 baths

3-car side entry garage

Walk-out basement or basement foundation, please specify when ordering

SPECIAL FEATURES

An enormous walk-in closet is located in the master bath and dressing area

The great room, breakfast area and kitchen combine with 12' ceilings to create an open feel

The optional lower level has an additional 1,897 square feet of living area and is designed for entertaining featuring a wet bar with seating, a billiards room, large media room, two bedrooms and a full bath

PRICE CODE E

To order plans, visit the Menards Building Materials Desk or visit www.Menards.com.

Plan #M06-055L-0748

Photo, above - Unique contrasts add style and sophistication to the kitchen. With the dark colored stove, richly painted walls and light cabinetry, the feeling of this space is soothing and upscale.

Photo, left - Arched doorways access the bedrooms while built-ins attract attention in the great room.

Photo, above - The home theater/living room takes you to a whole new dimension of style and ambiance with its rich, chocolate brown walls and mood lighting. Relaxation will never take long as soon as you enter this space.

Photo, right - Full of luxury from end to end, the private master bath enjoys the beauty of inlaid mosaic tile and marble to decorate the tub and floor while stylish plumbing fixtures and lighting complete the space perfectly.

67'-2"
55'-10"
BEDROOM 2
14'-0" X 10'-8"
12" BRICK COLUMNS
GRILLING PORCH
30'-10" X 14'-0"
OUTDOOR FIREPLACE
MASTER SUITE
18'-8" X 14'-0"
10' BOXED CEILING
BATH
7'-0" X 5'-0"
BRKFST. ROOM
13'-4" X 11'-2"
10' CEILING
COMPUTER CENTER
SEAT
LIN
GLASS SHWR
M.BATH
15'-0" X 12'-6"
WHP TUB
GLASS BLOCKS
BEDROOM 3
14'-0" X 13'-10"
GREAT ROOM
18'-2" X 20'-0"
10' CEILING
DW
RG
KITCHEN
12'-0" X 14'-7"
10' CEILING
REF
W
D
LAU.
6'-0"X 11'-10"
STORAGE
15'-0" X 2'-8"
BUILT-INS
BATH
10'-2" X 5'-0"
PAN
© Copyright by designer/architect
8" COLUMNS
FOYER
8'-10" X 7'-6"
11' CEILING
BEDROOM 4
11'-4" X 13'-0"
HOME THEATER/ LIVING ROOM
12'-0" X 16'-10"
10' CEILING
ENTRY
8'-0" X 6'-8"
11' CEILING
DINING ROOM
11'-6" X 16'-3"
12' CEILING
GARAGE
21'-4" X 23'-4"

To order plans, visit the Menards Building Materials Desk or visit www.Menards.com.

Plan #M06-055L-0748

EXPANSIVE ONE-STORY DESIGN

2,525 total square feet of living area

4 bedrooms, 3 baths

2-car garage

Crawl space or slab foundation, please specify when ordering

SPECIAL FEATURES

Stunning columns frame the foyer that lead into the open great room with fireplace, as well as the home theater/living room

The formal dining room, casual breakfast room and grilling porch with fireplace provide an abundance of dining opportunities

Three bedrooms and two baths occupy one side of this home while the master suite is secluded on the other

PRICE CODE E

ALTAMONT

MENARDS

Plan #M06-007D-0007

RAMBLING RANCH HAS LUXURIOUS MASTER BEDROOM

2,523 total square feet of living area

3 bedrooms, 2 baths

3-car garage

Basement foundation, drawings also include crawl space and slab foundations

SPECIAL FEATURES

Entry with high ceiling leads to massive vaulted great room with wet bar, plant shelves, pillars and fireplace with a harmonious window trio

Elaborate kitchen with bay and breakfast bar adjoins the morning room with a fireplace-in-a-bay

Vaulted master bedroom features a fireplace, book and plant shelves, large walk-in closet and double baths

PRICE CODE D

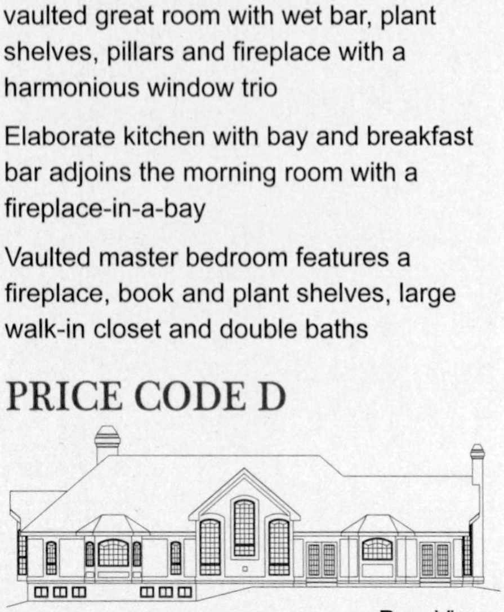

Rear View

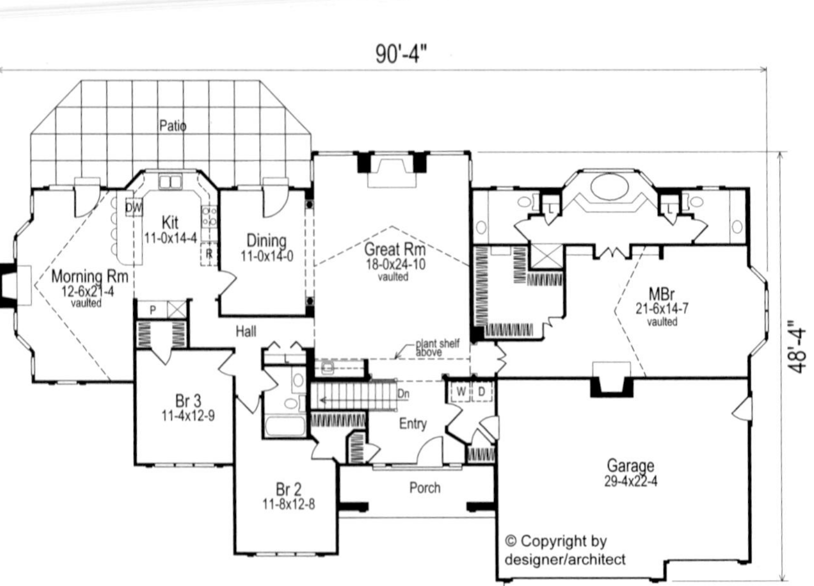

90'-4"
48'-4"
Patio
Kit
11-0x14-4
DW
Dining
11-0x14-0
Great Rm
18-0x24-10
vaulted
Morning Rm
12-6x21-4
vaulted
P
R
Hall
plant shelf above
MBr
21-6x14-7
vaulted
Br 3
11-4x12-9
Dn
W
D
Entry
Br 2
11-8x12-8
Porch
Garage
29-4x22-4
© Copyright by designer/architect

To order plans, visit the Menards Building Materials Desk or visit www.Menards.com.

MENARDS®

GREEN ORCHARD

Plan #M06-072L-1108

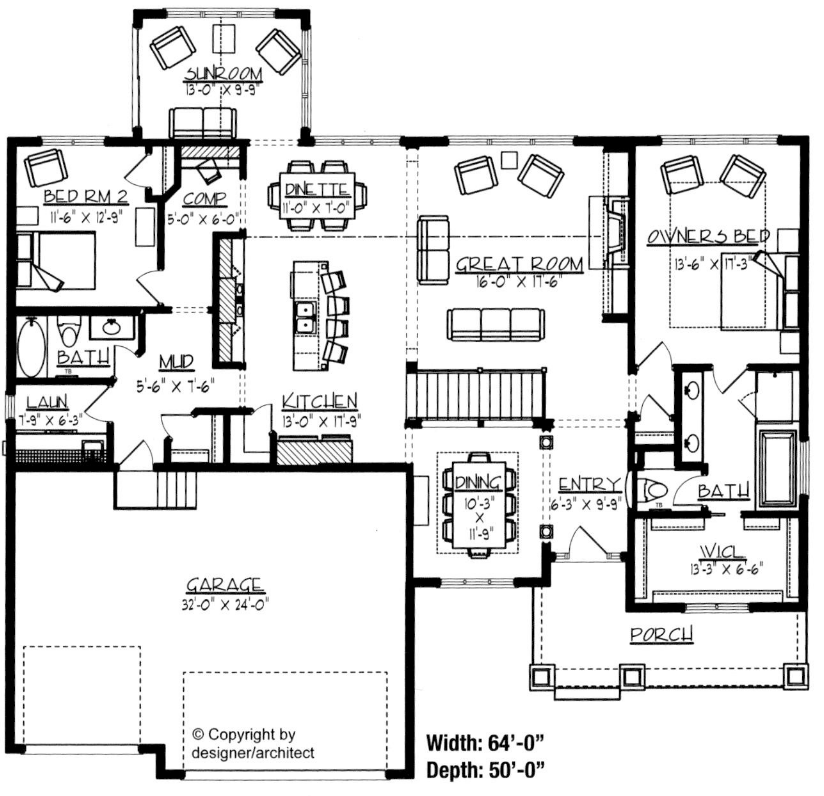
SUNROOM
13'-0" X 9'-9"
BED RM 2
11'-6" X 12'-9"
COMP
5'-0" X 6'-0"
DINETTE
11'-0" X 7'-0"
GREAT ROOM
16'-0" X 17'-6"
OWNER'S BED
13'-6" X 17'-3"
BATH
MUD
5'-6" X 7'-6"
LAUN
7'-9" X 6'-3"
KITCHEN
13'-0" X 17'-9"
DINING
10'-3" X 11'-9"
ENTRY
6'-3" X 9'-9"
BATH
WIC
13'-3" X 6'-6"
PORCH
GARAGE
32'-0" X 24'-0"
© Copyright by designer/architect
Width: 64'-0"
Depth: 50'-0"

INVITING FRONT PORCH

2,109 total square feet of living area

2 bedrooms, 2 baths

3-car garage

Walk-out basement foundation

SPECIAL FEATURES

Enjoy the spacious great room featuring a beautiful fireplace that creates a dramatic ambiance adding character and flair to this home

The efficient kitchen is quite charming and contains a breakfast island and generous pantry

The attractive sunroom provides a lovely space for relaxing and reading a good book

The optional lower level features an additional 336 square feet of living area

PRICE CODE B

To order plans, visit the Menards Building Materials Desk or visit www.Menards.com.

KINGS CROSSING

MENARDS®

Plan #M06-065L-0103

DELIGHTFUL ONE LEVEL HOME

1,860 total square feet of living area

3 bedrooms, 2 baths

2-car garage

Basement or walk-out basement foundation, please specify when ordering

SPECIAL FEATURES

Extended counter in the kitchen offers extra dining space

A bayed breakfast area is open to the great room and kitchen creating a spacious atmosphere

A beautiful corner fireplace in the great room is angled perfectly so it can also be enjoyed from the formal dining room

PRICE CODE C

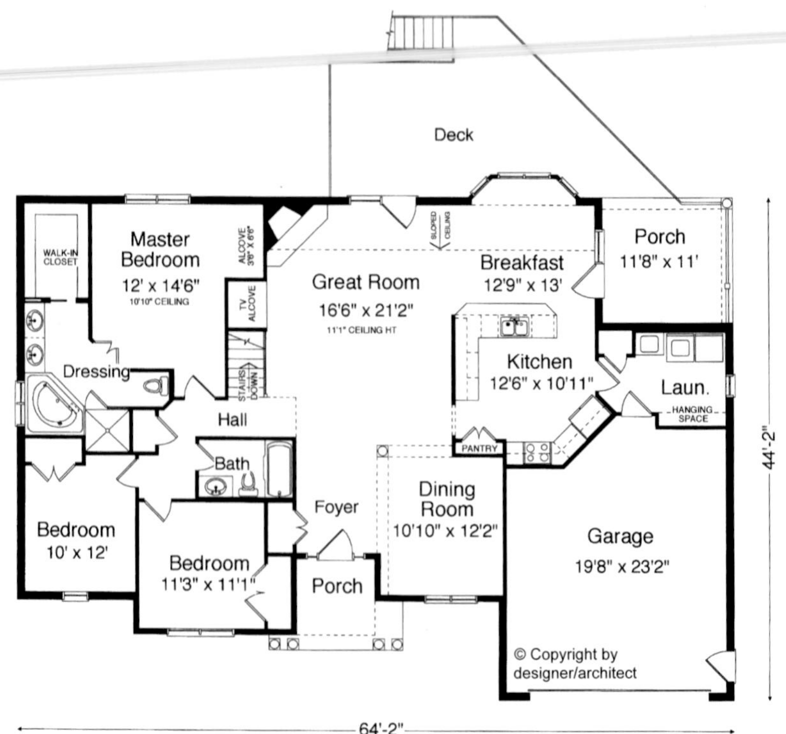
Deck
WALK-IN CLOSET
Master Bedroom
12' x 14'6"
10'10" CEILING
ALCOVE 3'6" X 6'6"
TV ALCOVE
Great Room
16'6" x 21'2"
11'1" CEILING HT
SLOPED CEILING
Breakfast
12'9" x 13'
Porch
11'8" x 11'
Kitchen
12'6" x 10'11"
Laun.
HANGING SPACE
Dressing
STAIRS DOWN
Hall
Bath
PANTRY
Dining Room
10'10" x 12'2"
Foyer
Bedroom
10' x 12'
Bedroom
11'3" x 11'1"
Porch
Garage
19'8" x 23'2"
© Copyright by designer/architect
64'-2"
44'-2"

To order plans, visit the Menards Building Materials Desk or visit www.Menards.com.

MENARDS®

ELLISPORT

Plan #M06-013L-0015

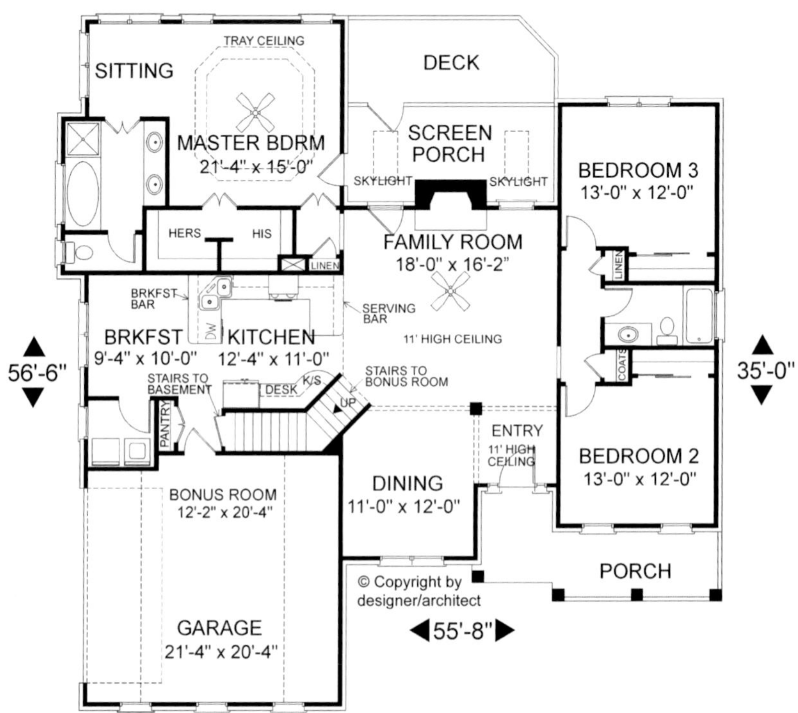

TRAY CEILING
SITTING
DECK
MASTER BDRM
21'-4" x 15'-0"
SCREEN PORCH
SKYLIGHT
SKYLIGHT
BEDROOM 3
13'-0" x 12'-0"
HERS
HIS
LINEN
FAMILY ROOM
18'-0" x 16'-2"
LINEN
BRKFST BAR
SERVING BAR
BRKFST
9'-4" x 10'-0"
DW
KITCHEN
12'-4" x 11'-0"
11' HIGH CEILING
56'-6"
35'-0"
STAIRS TO BASEMENT
DESK
K/S
STAIRS TO BONUS ROOM
UP
COATS
PANTRY
ENTRY
11' HIGH CEILING
BEDROOM 2
13'-0" x 12'-0"
BONUS ROOM
12'-2" x 20'-4"
DINING
11'-0" x 12'-0"
PORCH
© Copyright by designer/architect
55'-8"
GARAGE
21'-4" x 20'-4"

To order plans, visit the Menards Building Materials Desk or visit www.Menards.com.

UNCOMMONLY STYLED RANCH

1,787 total square feet of living area

3 bedrooms, 2 baths

2-car side entry garage

Basement, crawl space or slab foundation, please specify when ordering

SPECIAL FEATURES

Skylights brighten the screen porch that connects to the family room and deck outdoors

The master bedroom features a comfortable sitting area, large private bath and direct access to the screen porch

The kitchen has a serving bar that extends dining into the family room

Bonus room above the garage has an additional 263 square feet of living area

PRICE CODE B

MORTLAND

MENARDS

Plan #M06-021D-0002

CENTRAL FIREPLACE WARMS THIS COZY CONTEMPORARY

1,442 total square feet of living area

3 bedrooms, 2 baths

2-car garage

Slab foundation, drawings also include crawl space foundation

SPECIAL FEATURES

Centrally located living room has a recessed fireplace and 10' ceiling

Large U-shaped kitchen offers an eating bar and pantry

Expanded garage provides extra storage

Spacious master bedroom features a sitting area and large walk-in closet

PRICE CODE B

Rear View

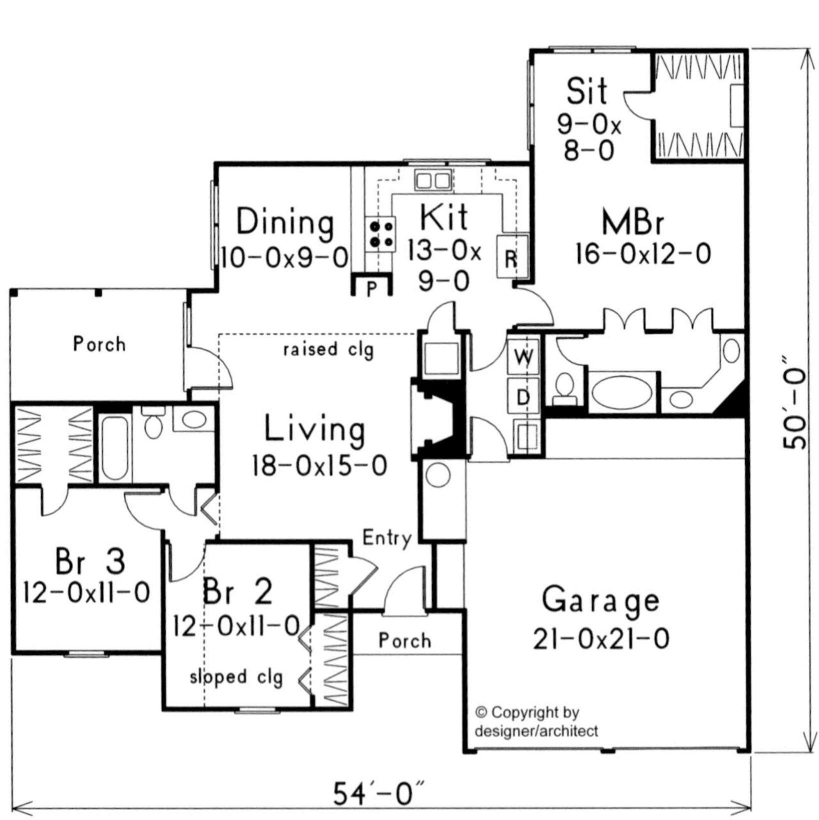
Sit
9-0x
8-0
Dining
10-0x9-0
Kit
13-0x
9-0
R
P
MBr
16-0x12-0
Porch
raised clg
W
D
Living
18-0x15-0
Entry
Br 3
12-0x11-0
Br 2
12-0x11-0
sloped clg
Porch
Garage
21-0x21-0
© Copyright by
designer/architect
50'-0"
54'-0"

To order plans, visit the Menards Building Materials Desk or visit www.Menards.com.

FOXBURY

Plan #M06-007D-0010

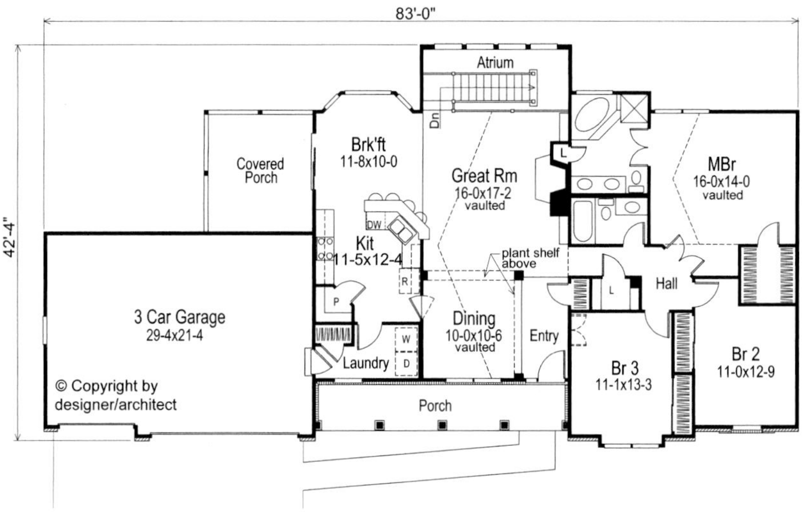

ATRIUM HAS DRAMATIC AMBIANCE

1,845 total square feet of living area

3 bedrooms, 2 baths

3-car garage

Walk-out basement foundation, drawings also include crawl space and slab foundations

SPECIAL FEATURES

Vaulted dining and great rooms are immersed in light from the atrium window wall

Breakfast area opens onto the covered porch

2" x 6" exterior walls available, please order plan #M06-007E-0010

The lower level has an additional 889 square feet of optional living area

PRICE CODE C

First Floor
1,845 sq. ft.

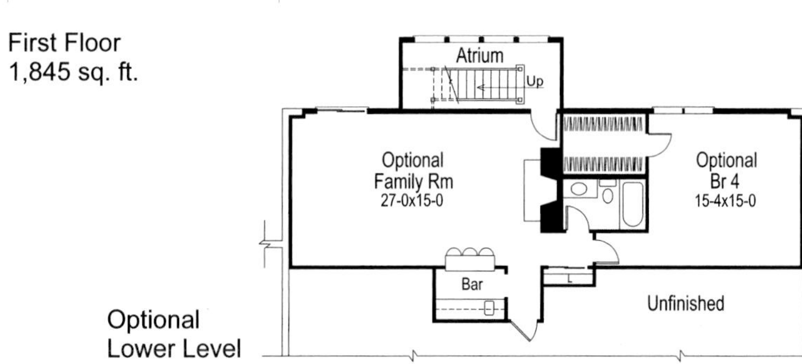
Atrium
Up
Optional
Family Rm
27-0x15-0
Optional
Br 4
15-4x15-0
Bar
Unfinished

Optional Lower Level

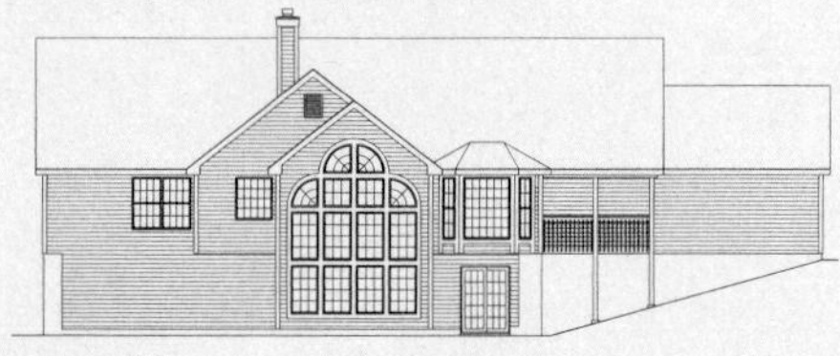

Rear View

To order plans, visit the Menards Building Materials Desk or visit www.Menards.com.

HOLLAND

MENARDS

Plan #M06-022D-0018

GREAT ROOM WINDOW ADDS CHARACTER INSIDE AND OUT

1,368 total square feet of living area

3 bedrooms, 2 baths

2-car garage

Basement foundation

SPECIAL FEATURES

Entry foyer steps down to an open living area that combines the great room and informal dining area

Vaulted master bedroom includes a box-bay window and a bath with a large vanity, separate tub and shower

Cozy breakfast area features direct access to the patio and pass-through kitchen

Handy linen closet is located in the hall

PRICE CODE A

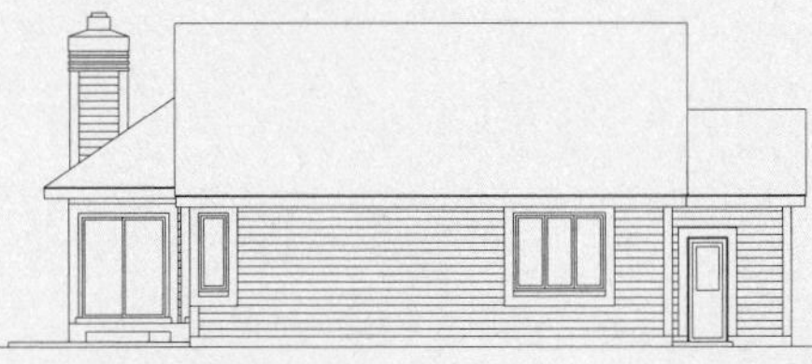

Rear View

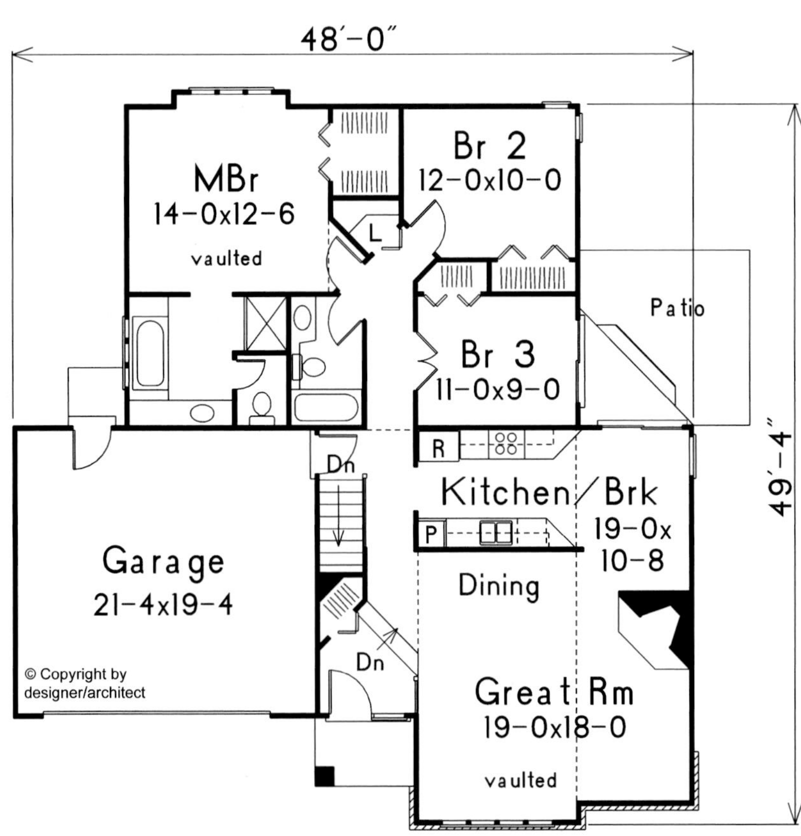
48′-0″
49′-4″
MBr
14-0x12-6
vaulted
Br 2
12-0x10-0
L
Br 3
11-0x9-0
Patio
R
Kitchen/Brk
19-0x
10-8
P
Dining
Dn
Garage
21-4x19-4
Dn
Great Rm
19-0x18-0
vaulted

To order plans, visit the Menards Building Materials Desk or visit www.Menards.com.

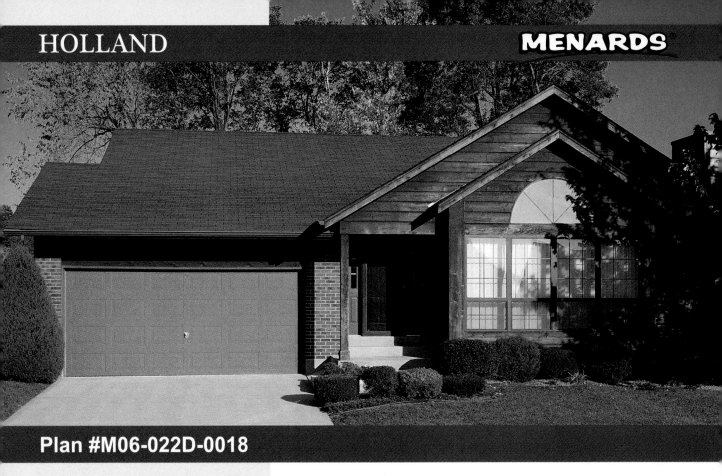

MENARDS
HUGES HILL
Plan #M06-065L-0170

DECORATIVE ENTRY WELCOMES GUESTS

1,537 total square feet of living area

3 bedrooms, 2 baths

2-car garage

Basement foundation

SPECIAL FEATURES

A corner fireplace in the great room is visible from the foyer offering a dramatic first impression

The kitchen island connects to the dining area that features a sloped ceiling and access to the rear porch

The private master bedroom enjoys its own bath, walk-in closet and access to the rear porch

PRICE CODE B

Porch
Master Bedroom 14' x 14'4"
Kitchen 9'1" x 14'7"
Laun
Dining Area 11'2" x 14'7"
slope ceiling
Great Room 16'4" x 17'2"
Bath
Hall
Two-car Garage 20' x 20'1"
wood rail
stairs dn
Foyer
Bath
Bedroom 10'4" x 10'6"
Porch
Bedroom 11' x 10'6"
slope ceiling

Width: 59'-8"
Depth: 42'-2"

To order plans, visit the Menards Building Materials Desk or visit www.Menards.com.

CEDARWOOD

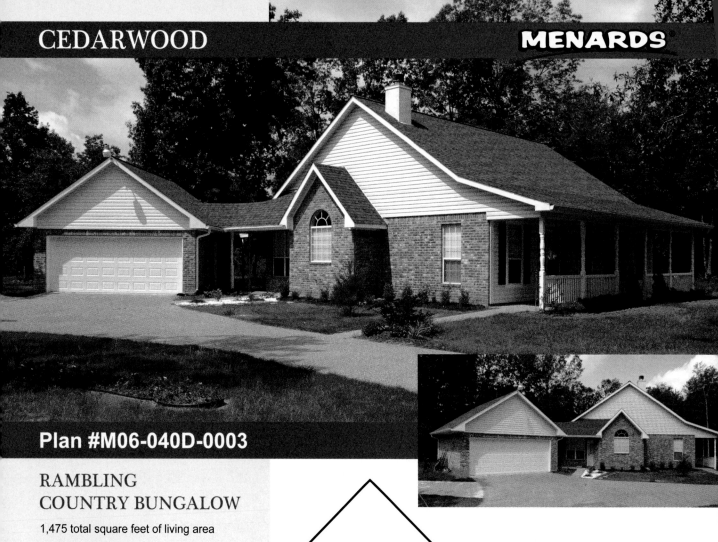

Plan #M06-040D-0003

RAMBLING COUNTRY BUNGALOW

1,475 total square feet of living area

3 bedrooms, 2 baths

2-car detached side entry garage

Slab foundation, drawings also include crawl space foundation

SPECIAL FEATURES

Family room features a 10' high ceiling and prominent corner fireplace

Kitchen with island counter and garden window makes a convenient connection between the family and dining rooms

Hallway leads to three bedrooms all with large walk-in closets

Covered breezeway joins the main house and garage

PRICE CODE B

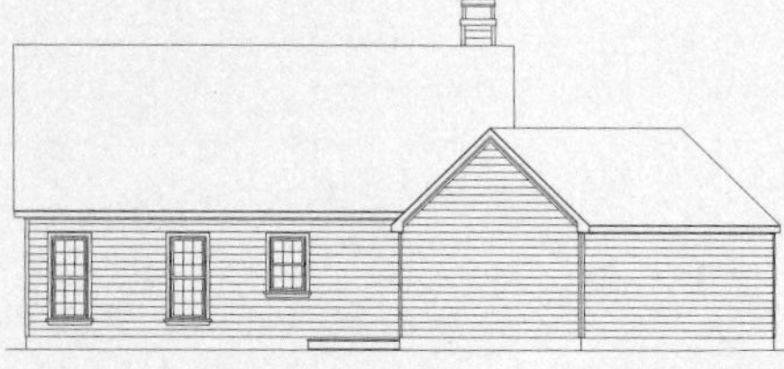

Rear View

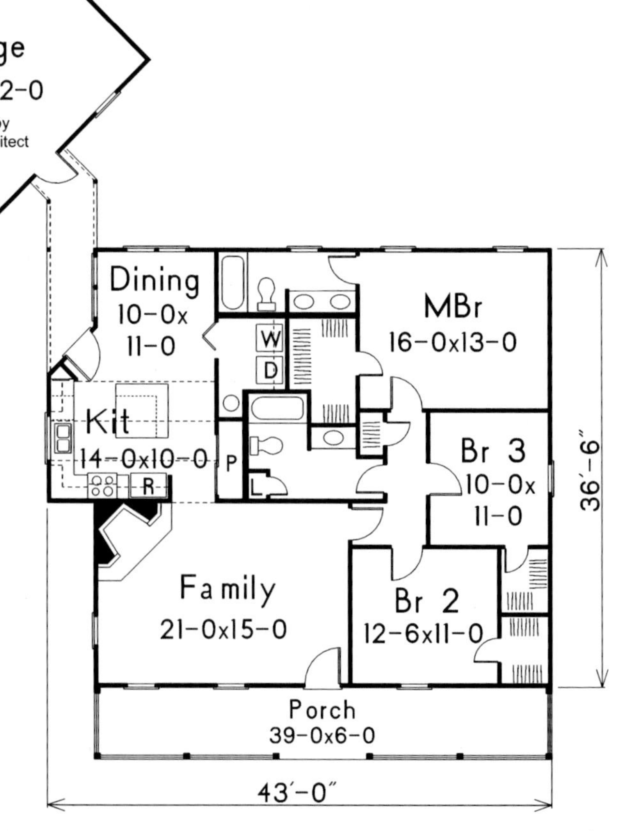
Garage
20-8x22-0
© Copyright by designer/architect
Dining
10-0x
11-0
MBr
16-0x13-0
W
D
Kit
14-0x10-0
P
L
R
Br 3
10-0x
11-0
36'-6"
Family
21-0x15-0
Br 2
12-6x11-0
Porch
39-0x6-0
43'-0"

To order plans, visit the Menards Building Materials Desk or visit www.Menards.com.

MENARDS

CARLSTON

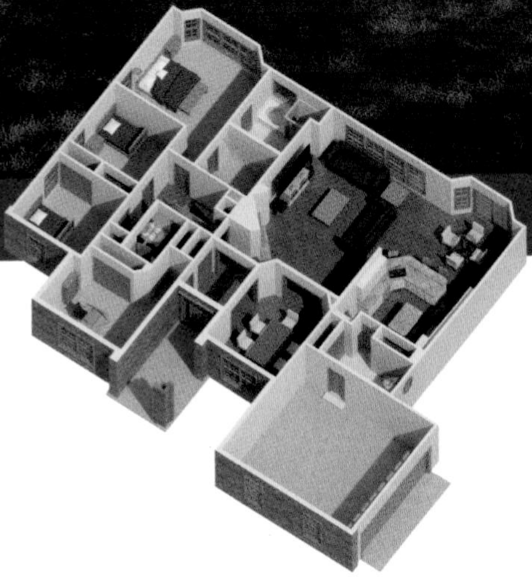

Plan #M06-007D-0062

CLASSIC ELEGANCE

2,483 total square feet of living area

3 bedrooms, 2 baths

2-car side entry garage

Basement foundation

SPECIAL FEATURES

A large entry porch with open brick arches and palladian door welcomes guests

The vaulted great room features an entertainment center alcove and the ideal layout for furniture placement

The dining room is extra large with a stylish tray ceiling

A convenient kitchen with wrap-around counter, menu desk and pantry opens to the cozy breakfast area

2" x 6" exterior walls available, please order plan #M06-007E-0062

PRICE CODE D

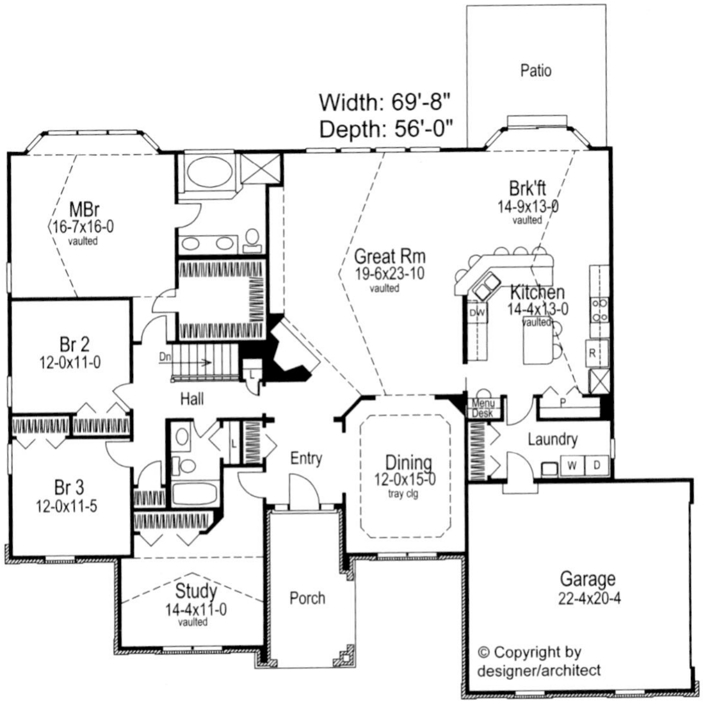

Width: 69'-8"
Depth: 56'-0"

Patio

MBr
16-7x16-0
vaulted

Brk'ft
14-9x13-0
vaulted

Great Rm
19-6x23-10
vaulted

Kitchen
14-4x13-0
vaulted

DW

R

Br 2
12-0x11-0

Dn

Hall

Menu Desk

P

Laundry

W D

Entry

Dining
12-0x15-0
tray clg

Br 3
12-0x11-5

Garage
22-4x20-4

Study
14-4x11-0
vaulted

Porch

© Copyright by designer/architect

To order plans, visit the Menards Building Materials Desk or visit www.Menards.com.

Rear View

SAVAGE HILL

MENARDS®

Plan #M06-051L-0060

DRAMATIC ROOF LINES CREATE A RANCH WITH STYLE

1,591 total square feet of living area

3 bedrooms, 2 baths

3-car garage

Basement foundation

SPECIAL FEATURES

Energy efficient home with 2" x 6" exterior walls

The fireplace in the great room is accented by windows on both sides

Practical kitchen is splendidly designed for organization

Large screen porch is ideal for three-season entertaining

PRICE CODE B

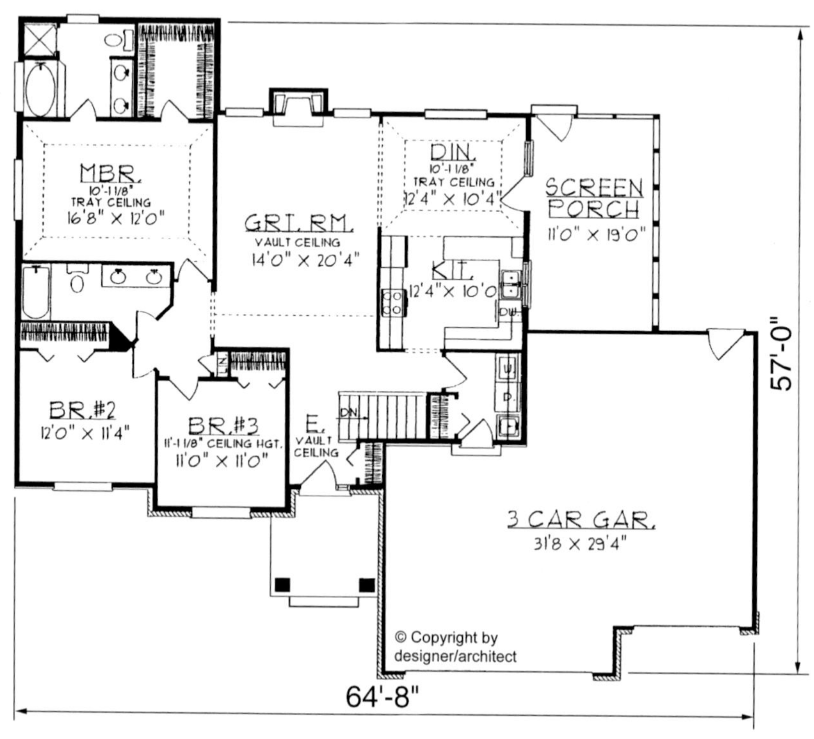

MBR.
10'-1 1/8" TRAY CEILING
16'8" x 12'0"
GRT. RM.
VAULT CEILING
14'0" x 20'4"
DIN.
10'-1 1/8" TRAY CEILING
12'4" x 10'4"
SCREEN PORCH
11'0" x 13'0"
KIT.
12'4" x 10'0"
BR.#2
12'0" x 11'4"
BR.#3
11'-1 1/8" CEILING HGT.
11'0" x 11'0"
E.
VAULT CEILING
DN
3 CAR GAR.
31'8 x 23'4"
© Copyright by designer/architect
64'-8"
57'-0"

To order plans, visit the Menards Building Materials Desk or visit www.Menards.com.

MENARDS

KENTLAND

Plan #M06-022D-0026

60′-0″

48′-0″

MBr 16-6x12-9

plant shelf

Living 14-0x21-6

vaulted

Dn

Dining 13-6x10-0

Deck

Country Kit 28-0x13-0

R P

D W

Dn

plant shelf

Br 2 10-0x11-0

Br 3 10-0x 10-6

Den 11-0x10-3

Garage 22-0x22-0

© Copyright by designer/architect

PROVIDES FAMILY LIVING AT ITS BEST

1,993 total square feet of living area

3 bedrooms, 2 baths

2-car garage

Basement foundation

SPECIAL FEATURES

Spacious country kitchen boasts a fireplace and plenty of natural light from windows

Formal dining room features a large bay window and steps down to the sunken living room

Master bedroom features corner windows, plant shelf and a deluxe private bath

Entry opens into the vaulted living room with windows flanking the fireplace

PRICE CODE D

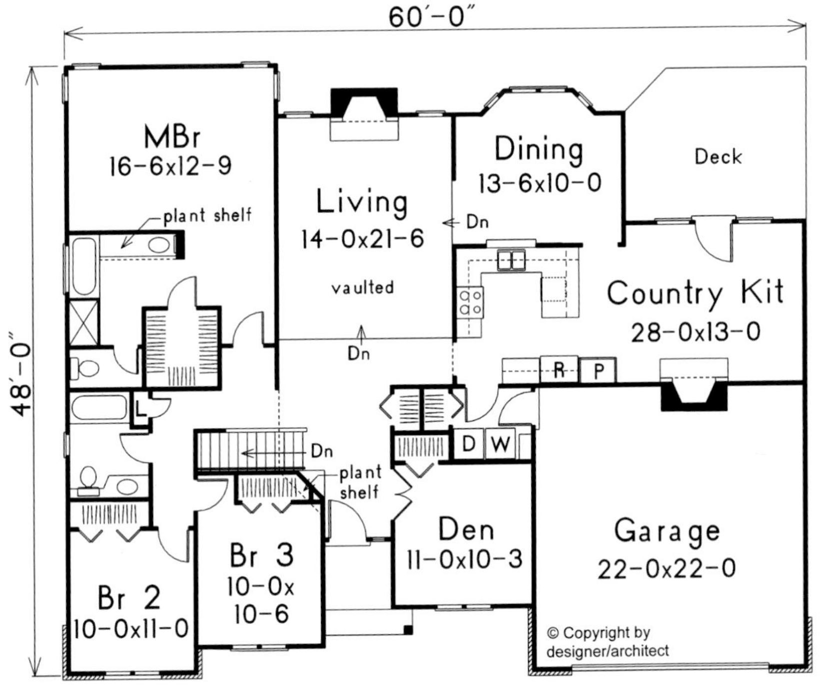

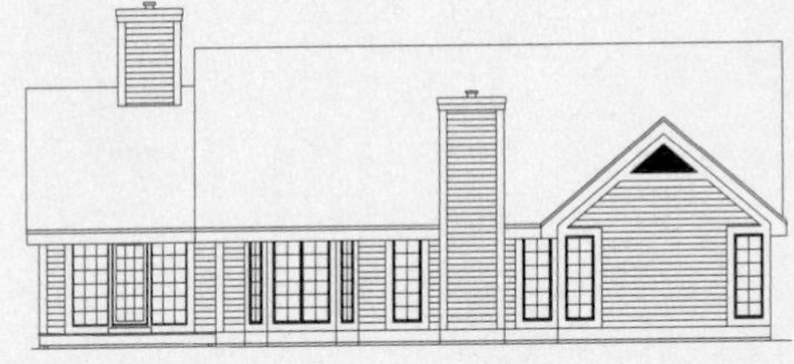

Rear View

To order plans, visit the Menards Building Materials Desk or visit www.Menards.com.

SPRINGLAKE

MENARDS

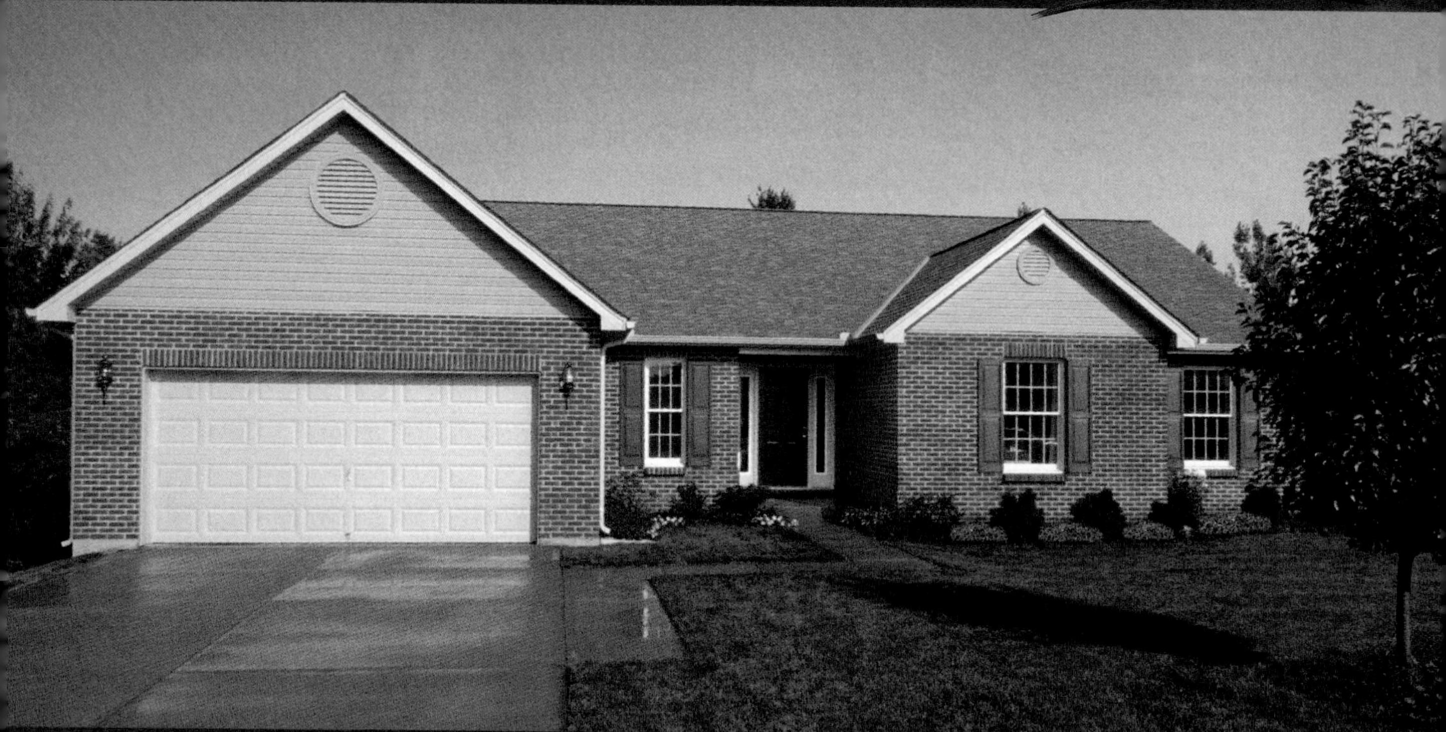

Plan #M06-065L-0066

CHARMING SIMPLICITY

1,598 total square feet of living area

3 bedrooms, 2 baths

2-car garage

Basement foundation

SPECIAL FEATURES

A spacious great room with fireplace and sloped ceiling opens generously to the dining area

Sliding glass doors lead to a covered porch, expanding enjoyment of this home to the outdoors

The spacious kitchen offers an abundance of cabinets and counterspace as well as a peninsula with seating

A master bedroom and two secondary bedrooms make this a great family sized home

PRICE CODE B

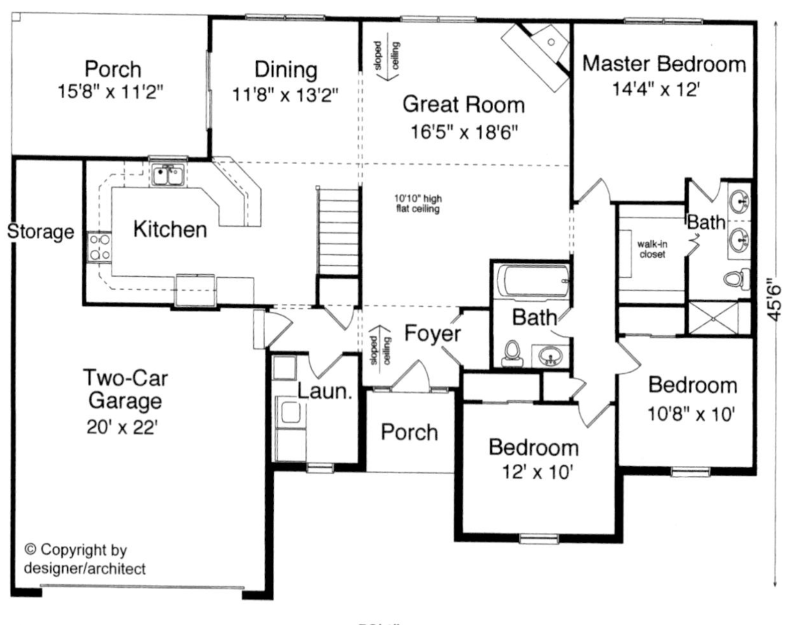

Porch
15'8" x 11'2"
Dining
11'8" x 13'2"
sloped ceiling
Great Room
16'5" x 18'6"
Master Bedroom
14'4" x 12'
Storage
Kitchen
10'10" high flat ceiling
walk-in closet
Bath
Bath
Foyer
sloped ceiling
Two-Car Garage
20' x 22'
Laun.
Porch
Bedroom
12' x 10'
Bedroom
10'8" x 10'
45'6"
59'4"

To order plans, visit the Menards Building Materials Desk or visit www.Menards.com.

MENARDS

SUNFIELD

Plan #M06-021D-0014

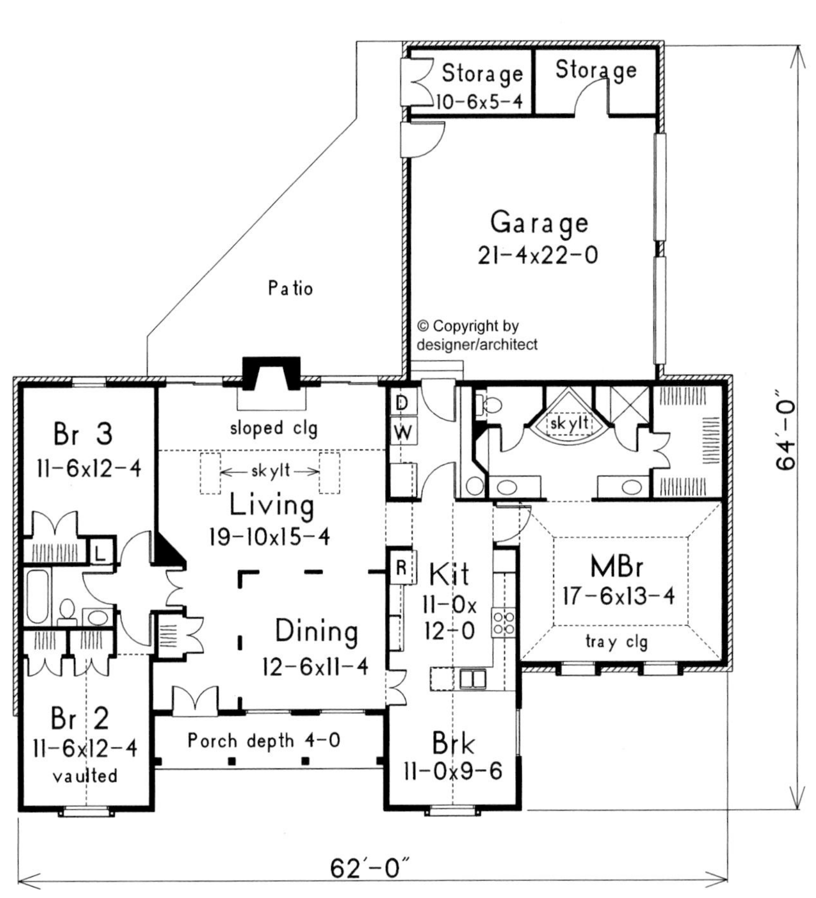
Storage
10-6x5-4
Storage
Garage
21-4x22-0
Patio
© Copyright by
designer/architect
Br 3
11-6x12-4
sloped clg
skylt
Living
19-10x15-4
D
W
skylt
MBr
17-6x13-4
tray clg
R
Kit
11-0x
12-0
L
Dining
12-6x11-4
Br 2
11-6x12-4
vaulted
Porch depth 4-0
Brk
11-0x9-6
64'-0"
62'-0"

To order plans, visit the Menards Building Materials Desk or visit www.Menards.com.

PRIVATE MASTER BEDROOM HAS A GRAND BATH

1,856 total square feet of living area

3 bedrooms, 2 baths

2-car side entry garage

Slab foundation, drawings also include crawl space foundation

SPECIAL FEATURES

Energy efficient home with 2" x 6" exterior walls

Living room features a fireplace, 12' ceiling and skylights

A vaulted ceiling creates an open space in the kitchen and breakfast room

Garage with storage areas conveniently accesses home through the utility room

PRICE CODE D

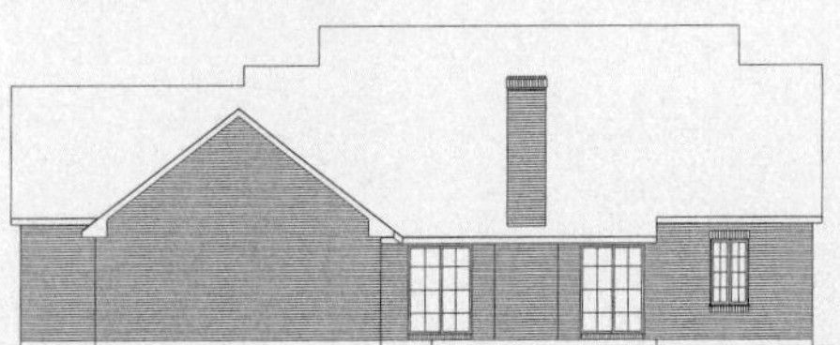

Rear View

CHELMSFORD TRAIL

MENARDS®

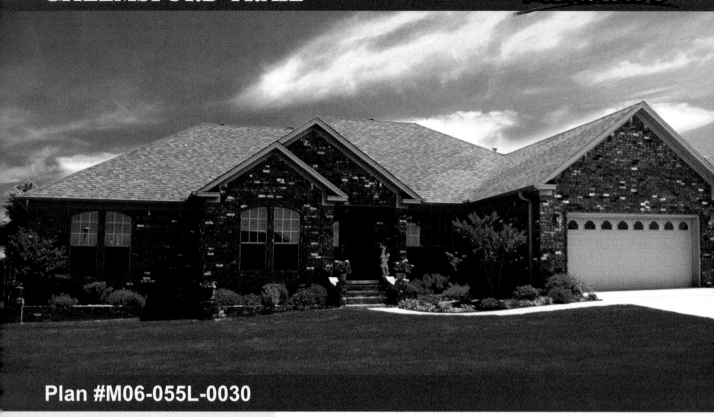

Plan #M06-055L-0030

ATTRACTIVE EXTERIOR

2,107 total square feet of living area

4 bedrooms, 2 1/2 baths

2-car garage

Slab or crawl space foundation, please specify when ordering; basement and walk-out basement foundations available for an additional fee

SPECIAL FEATURES

The master bedroom is separated from the other bedrooms for privacy

The spacious breakfast room and kitchen include a center island with eating space

The centralized great room has a fireplace and easy access to any area in the home

PRICE CODE D

Width: 64'-8"
Depth: 62'-1"
GLASS BLOCKS
WHP TUB
M. BATH
PATIO
COVERED PORCH
31'-8" X 9'-0"
M. BED RM.
16'-8" X 14'-0"
9' PAN CEILING
BED RM. 4
14'-4" X 11'-0"
BRKFST. RM.
12'-6" X 9'-6"
KITCHEN
12'-6" X 10'-0"
REF
PAN
LIN
BATH
LIN
GREAT RM.
19'-6" X 17'-0"
10' CEILING
1/2 B.
LAU.
W
D
HVAC
WH
STOR.
CT
OVEN
DW
BUILT-INS
(OPT. TO STUDY)
BED RM. 3
10'-6" X 12'-0"
OPT. DOOR
FOYER
10' CEILING
DINING RM.
11'-0" X 12'-0"
9' CEILING
8' CEILING
GARAGE
20'-4" X 21'-0"
BED RM. 2 / STUDY
11'-0" X 12'-0"
PORCH
PLANTER
© Copyright by designer/architect

To order plans, visit the Menards Building Materials Desk or visit www.Menards.com.

MENARDS

RYEGATE

Plan #M06-077L-0037

SPLIT-BEDROOM DESIGN

1,639 total square feet of living area

3 bedrooms, 2 baths

2-car side entry garage

Slab or crawl space foundation, please specify when ordering

SPECIAL FEATURES

The great room has a tray ceiling and a welcoming fireplace

The kitchen is designed for efficiency with plenty of counterspace and conveniently placed pantry and refrigerator

The eating area opens onto the back covered porch through beautiful French doors

PRICE CODE D

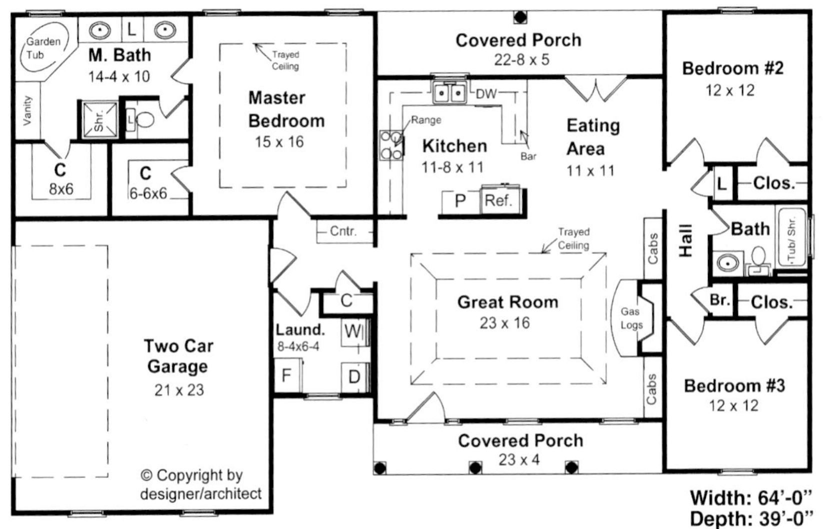
Garden Tub
M. Bath
14-4 x 10
L
Vanity
Shr.
C
8x6
C
6-6x6
Trayed Ceiling
Master Bedroom
15 x 16
Covered Porch
22-8 x 5
DW
Range
Kitchen
11-8 x 11
Bar
P
Ref.
Eating Area
11 x 11
Bedroom #2
12 x 12
L
Clos.
Bath
Tub/ Shr.
Hall
Cabs
Br.
Clos.
Cntr.
Trayed Ceiling
Great Room
23 x 16
Gas Logs
C
Laund.
8-4x6-4
W
F
D
Two Car Garage
21 x 23
Cabs
Bedroom #3
12 x 12
Covered Porch
23 x 4
© Copyright by designer/architect
Width: 64'-0"
Depth: 39'-0"

To order plans, visit the Menards Building Materials Desk or visit www.Menards.com.

SELKIRK

MENARDS

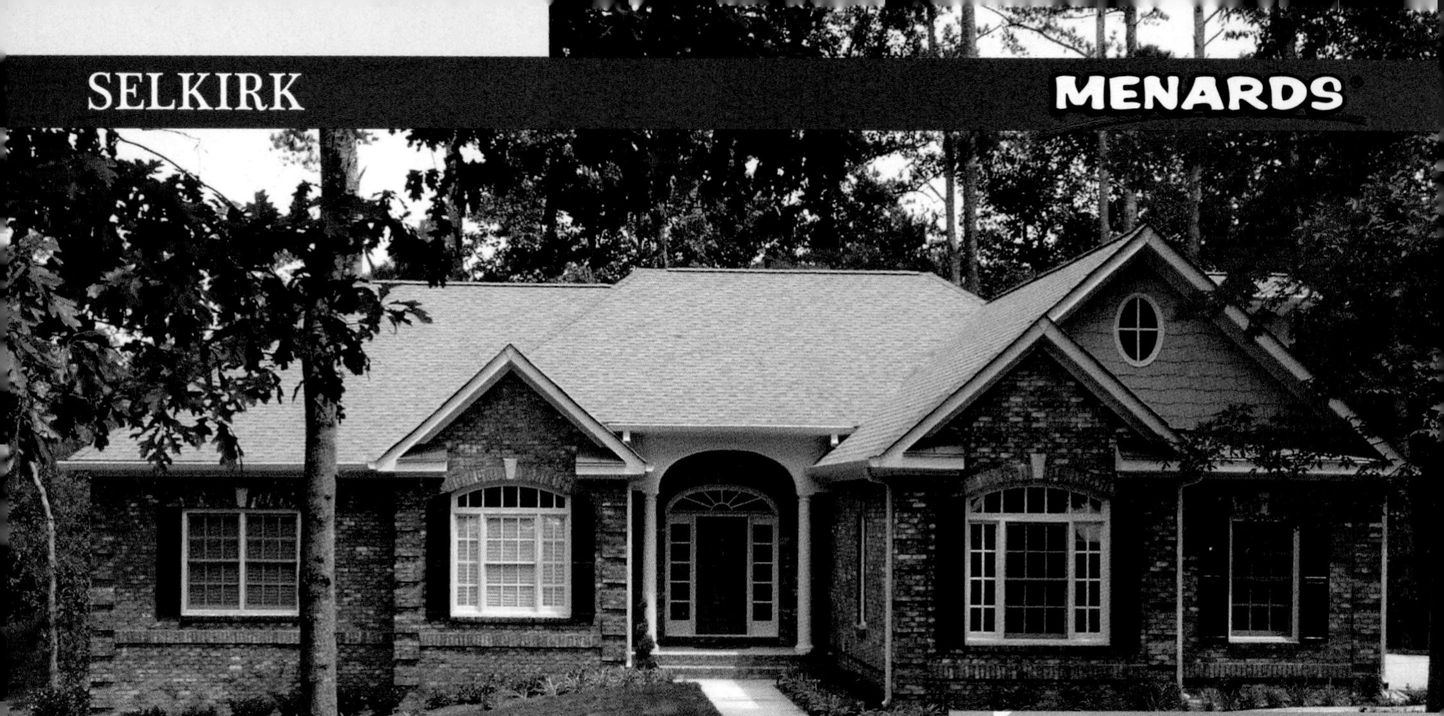

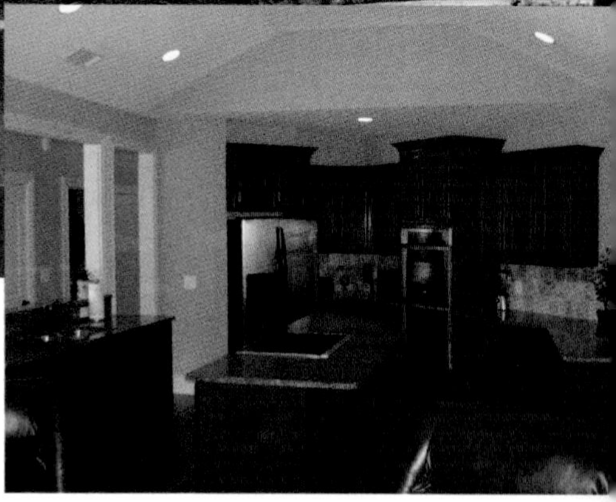

Plan #M06-013L-0053

BRIGHT, CHEERFUL WINDOWS

2,461 total square feet of living area

3 bedrooms, 3 1/2 baths

3-car side entry garage

Basement foundation

SPECIAL FEATURES

The cooktop island in the kitchen has ample counterspace for easy food preparation and connects to the cozy hearth room

Luxurious master suite has a large closet with conveniently separated hanging areas

The covered deck/screened porch with vaulted ceiling creates a great outdoor gathering area

The optional second floor has an additional 518 square feet of living area

PRICE CODE D

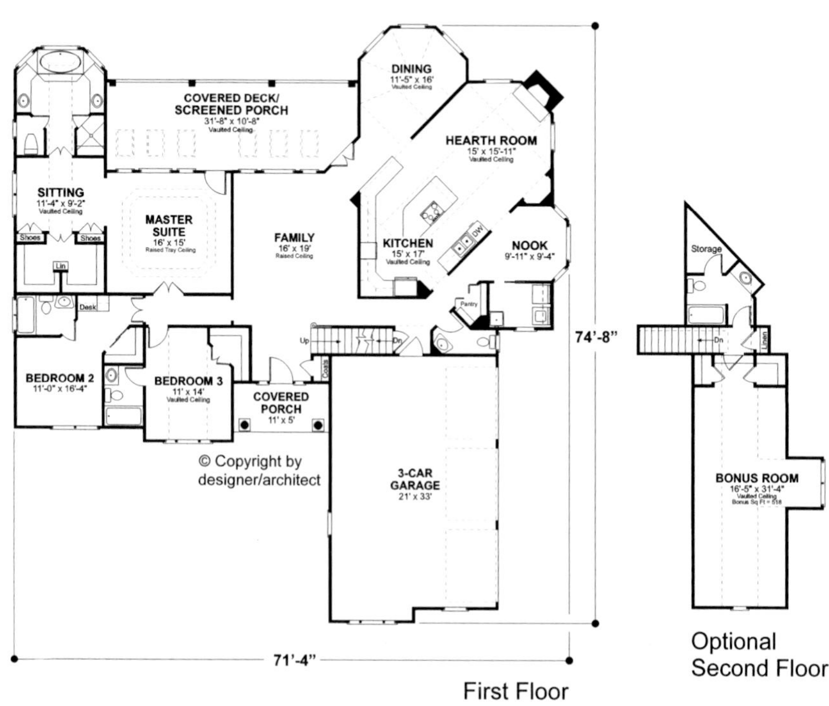

DINING
11'-5" x 16'
COVERED DECK/
SCREENED PORCH
31'-8" x 10'-8"
HEARTH ROOM
15' x 15'-11"
SITTING
11'-4" x 9'-2"
MASTER
SUITE
16' x 15'
FAMILY
16' x 19'
KITCHEN
15' x 17'
NOOK
9'-11" x 9'-4"
BEDROOM 2
11'-0" x 16'-4"
BEDROOM 3
11' x 14'
COVERED
PORCH
11' x 5'
3-CAR
GARAGE
21' x 33'
Storage
BONUS ROOM
16'-5" x 31'-4"
74'-8"
71'-4"

First Floor
2,461 sq. ft.

Optional
Second Floor

To order plans, visit the Menards Building Materials Desk or visit www.Menards.com.

CATALINA PLACE

Plan #M06-065L-0250

BEAUTIFUL ONE-LEVEL HOME

2,959 total square feet of living area

3 bedrooms, 2 1/2 baths

3-car side entry garage

Walk-out basement foundation

SPECIAL FEATURES

A beamed ceiling tops the great room and a fireplace with built-ins decorate one wall

A breakfast area, sitting area and stylish kitchen create a family center perfect for casual gatherings

A library with built-in shelving and angled walls provides an area dedicated for organized work at home

PRICE CODE E

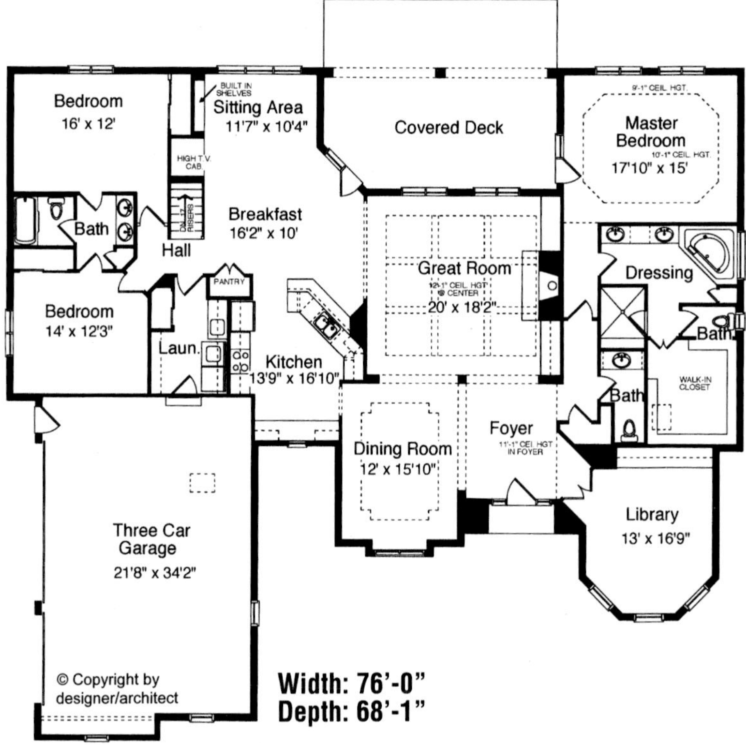
Bedroom
16' x 12'
Sitting Area
11'7" x 10'4"
Covered Deck
Master
Bedroom
17'10" x 15'
Bath
Breakfast
16'2" x 10'
Hall
Great Room
20' x 18'2"
Dressing
Bedroom
14' x 12'3"
PANTRY
Laun.
Kitchen
13'9" x 16'10"
Bath
Bath
WALK-IN CLOSET
Dining Room
12' x 15'10"
Foyer
Library
13' x 16'9"
Three Car
Garage
21'8" x 34'2"
© Copyright by
designer/architect
Width: 76'-0"
Depth: 68'-1"

To order plans, visit the Menards Building Materials Desk or visit www.Menards.com.

Plan #M06-077L-0002

FRONT AND REAR COVERED PORCHES ADD CHARM

1,855 total square feet of living area

3 bedrooms, 2 1/2 baths

2-car side entry garage

Basement, crawl space or slab foundation, please specify when ordering

SPECIAL FEATURES

The great room boasts a 12' ceiling and corner fireplace

Bayed breakfast area adjoins the kitchen that features a walk-in pantry

The relaxing master bedroom includes a private bath with walk-in closet and garden tub

Optional second floor has an additional 352 square feet of living area

PRICE CODE D

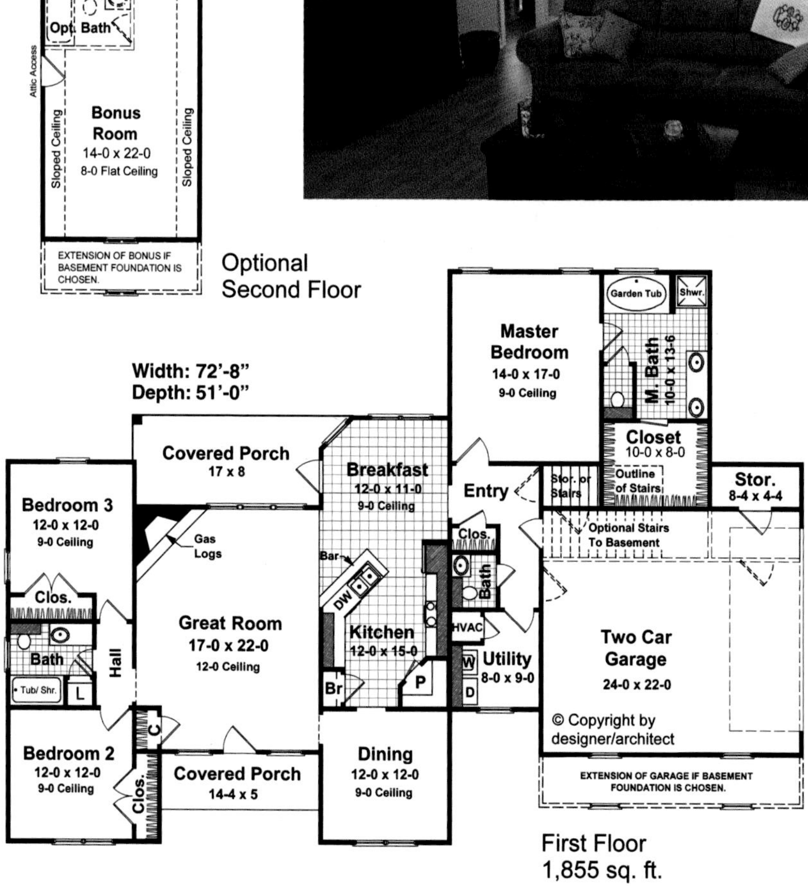
Down
Clos.
Opt. Bath
Attic Access
Sloped Ceiling
Bonus Room
14-0 x 22-0
8-0 Flat Ceiling
Sloped Ceiling
EXTENSION OF BONUS IF BASEMENT FOUNDATION IS CHOSEN.
Optional Second Floor
Width: 72'-8"
Depth: 51'-0"
Master Bedroom
14-0 x 17-0
9-0 Ceiling
Garden Tub
Shwr.
M. Bath
10-0 x 13-6
Closet
10-0 x 8-0
Covered Porch
17 x 8
Breakfast
12-0 x 11-0
9-0 Ceiling
Entry
Stor. or Stairs
Outline of Stairs
Stor.
8-4 x 4-4
Bedroom 3
12-0 x 12-0
9-0 Ceiling
Gas Logs
Clos.
Optional Stairs To Basement
Bar
DW
Bath
Clos.
Great Room
17-0 x 22-0
12-0 Ceiling
Kitchen
12-0 x 15-0
HVAC
Two Car Garage
24-0 x 22-0
Bath
Hall
W
Utility
8-0 x 9-0
Tub/ Shr.
L
Br
P
D
© Copyright by designer/architect
C
Bedroom 2
12-0 x 12-0
9-0 Ceiling
Clos.
Covered Porch
14-4 x 5
Dining
12-0 x 12-0
9-0 Ceiling
EXTENSION OF GARAGE IF BASEMENT FOUNDATION IS CHOSEN.

First Floor
1,855 sq. ft.

To order plans, visit the Menards Building Materials Desk or visit www.Menards.com.

MENARDS

EVERGREEN

Plan #M06-027D-0006

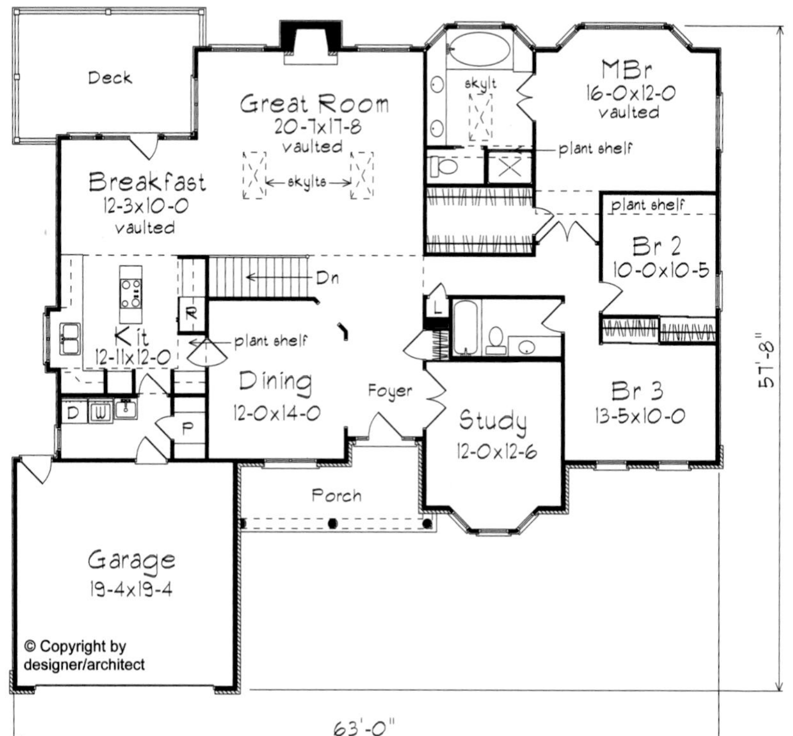
Deck
Great Room
20-7x17-8
vaulted
skylts
Breakfast
12-3x10-0
vaulted
MBr
16-0x12-0
vaulted
skylt
plant shelf
plant shelf
Br 2
10-0x10-5
Dn
Kit
12-11x12-0
plant shelf
Dining
12-0x14-0
Foyer
Study
12-0x12-6
Br 3
13-5x10-0
57'-8"
Porch
Garage
19-4x19-4
© Copyright by
designer/architect
63'-0"

To order plans, visit the Menards Building Materials Desk or visit www.Menards.com.

GREAT ROOM FORMS CORE OF THIS HOME

2,076 total square feet of living area

3 bedrooms, 2 baths

2-car garage

Basement foundation, drawings also include walk-out basement foundation

SPECIAL FEATURES

Vaulted great room has a fireplace flanked by windows and skylights that welcome the sun

Kitchen leads to the vaulted breakfast room and rear deck

Study located off the foyer provides a great location for a home office

Large bay windows grace the master bedroom and bath

PRICE CODE C

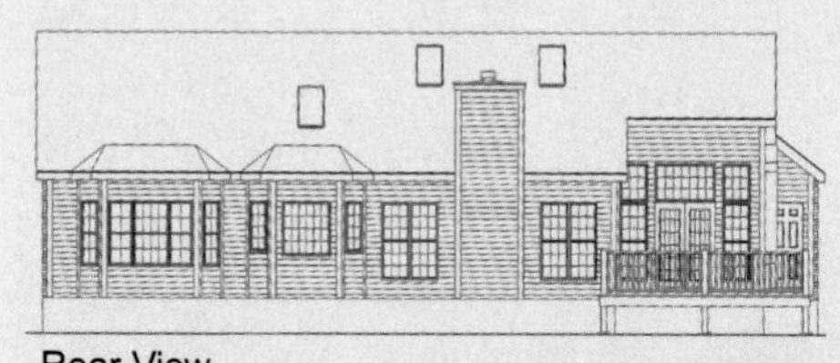

Rear View

WILLOWHILL

MENARDS

Plan #M06-007D-0157

INVITING RANCH

1,599 total square feet of living area

4 bedrooms, 2 1/2 baths

2-car garage

Basement foundation

SPECIAL FEATURES

Spacious entry leads to the great room featuring a vaulted ceiling, fireplace and an octagon-shaped dining area with views to the covered patio

The kitchen enjoys a snack counter open to the dining area, a breakfast area with bay window and a built-in pantry

Master bedroom has a sitting area, large walk-in closet and a luxury bath

The laundry room has a convenient half bath and access to the garage with storage area

PRICE CODE B

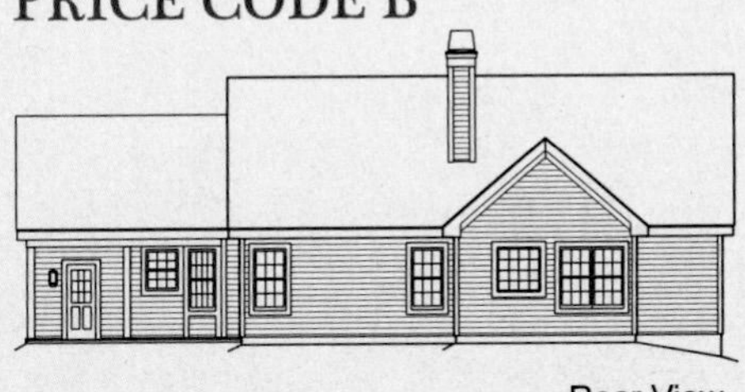

Rear View

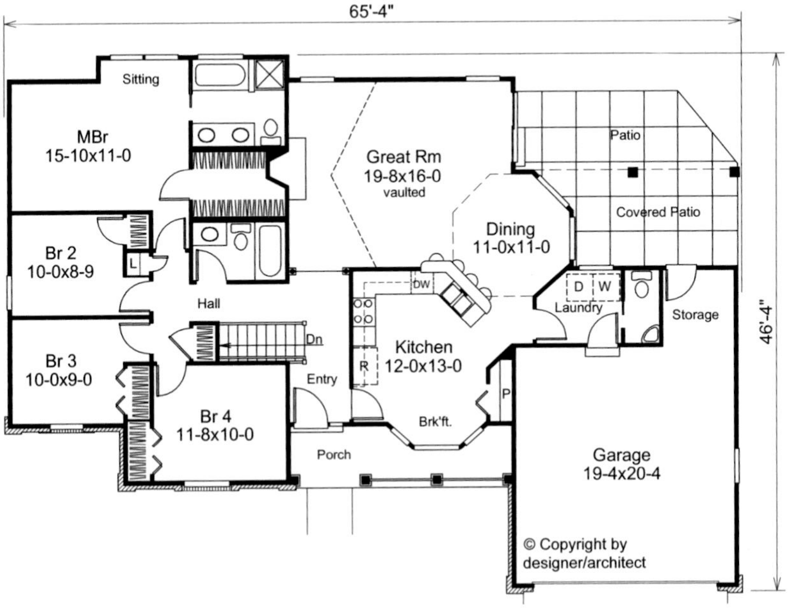

To order plans, visit the Menards Building Materials Desk or visit www.Menards.com.

SUNRIDGE

Plan #M06-048D-0011

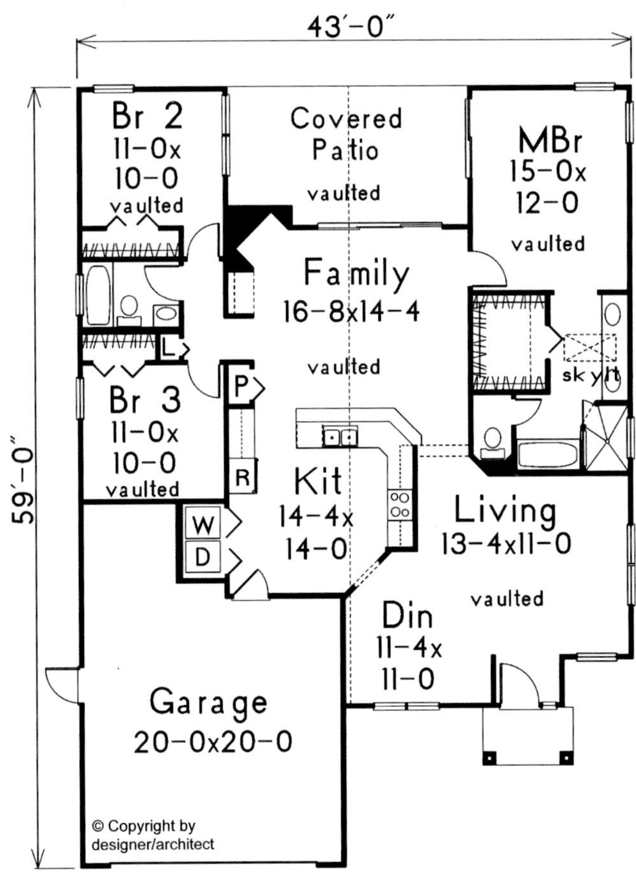
43'-0"
59'-0"
Br 2
11-0x
10-0
vaulted
Covered
Patio
vaulted
MBr
15-0x
12-0
vaulted
Family
16-8x14-4
vaulted
sky lt
Br 3
11-0x
10-0
vaulted
P
R
Kit
14-4x
14-0
W
D
Living
13-4x11-0
vaulted
Din
11-4x
11-0
Garage
20-0x20-0
© Copyright by
designer/architect

VAULTED CEILINGS ADD SPACIOUSNESS

1,550 total square feet of living area

3 bedrooms, 2 baths

2-car garage

Slab foundation

SPECIAL FEATURES

Alcove in the family room can be used as a cozy corner fireplace or as a media center

Master bedroom features a large walk-in closet, bath with a skylight and separate tub and shower

Kitchen with pantry and breakfast bar connects to the family room

Family room and master bedroom access the covered patio

PRICE CODE B

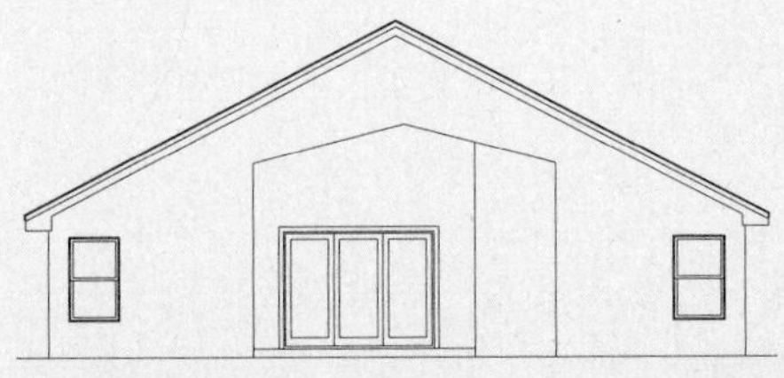
Rear View

To order plans, visit the Menards Building Materials Desk or visit www.Menards.com.

ROBERTA

MENARDS

Plan #M06-065L-0022

SPACIOUS FOYER WELCOMES GUESTS

1,593 total square feet of living area

3 bedrooms, 2 baths

2-car garage

Basement foundation

SPECIAL FEATURES

This home is designed with an insulated foundation system featuring pre-mounted insulation on concrete walls providing a drier, warmer and smarter structure

The rear covered porch is a pleasant surprise and perfect for enjoying the outdoors

Great room is filled with extras such as a corner fireplace, sloping ceiling and view to the outdoors

A large island with seating separates the kitchen from the dining area

PRICE CODE B

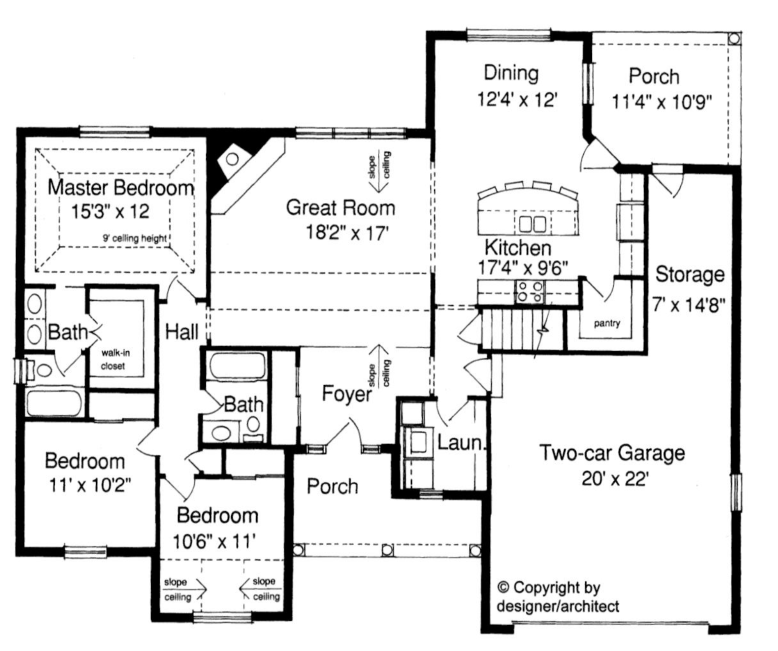

Dining
12'4' x 12'
Porch
11'4" x 10'9"
Master Bedroom
15'3" x 12
9' ceiling height
Great Room
18'2" x 17'
slope ceiling
Kitchen
17'4" x 9'6"
Storage
7' x 14'8"
pantry
Bath
walk-in closet
Hall
Bath
Foyer
Laun.
Two-car Garage
20' x 22'
Bedroom
11' x 10'2"
Porch
Bedroom
10'6" x 11'
slope ceiling
slope ceiling
© Copyright by designer/architect
48'10"
60'

To order plans, visit the Menards Building Materials Desk or visit www.Menards.com.

PRINCETON RIDGE

Plan #M06-055L-0211

FIREPLACES WARM CHARMING RANCH

2,405 total square feet of living area

4 bedrooms, 3 baths

3-car side entry garage

Slab or crawl space foundation, please specify when ordering

SPECIAL FEATURES

The grilling and covered porches combine for a relaxing outdoor living area

The master suite enjoys a bayed sitting area and luxurious bath with large walk-in closet

Kitchen, breakfast and hearth rooms combine for a cozy family living area

The optional second floor has an additional 358 square feet of living area

PRICE CODE E

66'-4"

67'-2"

BREAKFAST ROOM 11'-0" X 9'-0"

GRILLING PORCH 10'-4" X 7'-8"

COVERED PORCH 18'-0" X 11'-8"

WHP TUB

GLASS SHWR

SITTING ROOM 9'-4" X 9'-4"

MASTER SUITE 13'-6" X 15'-3"

M.BATH 11'-8" X 22'-0"

LIN.

DW.

GAS FIREPLACE

C.T.

HEARTH ROOM 11'-0" X 14'-0"

OVEN

REF

KITCHEN 10'-4" X 15'-0"

COMPUTER CENTER

FRENCH DOORS

MEDIA CENTER

GREAT ROOM 10' CEILING 18'-0" X 17'-4"

BEDROOM 4 11'-4" X 10'-8"

LAU. 8'-4" X 6'-6"

PANTRY

UP

8" COLUMNS

DINING ROOM 10' CEILING 11'-0" X 12'-6"

FOYER 10' CEILING 7'-0" X 12'-6"

LIN.

BEDROOM 3 11'-4" X 10'-11"

OPT. DOOR

BEDROOM 2/ STUDY 14'-0" X 12'-0"

BATH

GARAGE 21'-4" X 34'-4"

PORCH 11' CEILING 18'-0" X 5'-0"

8" COLUMNS

BOOK SHELVES

First Floor
2,405 sq. ft.

Optional Second Floor

DN.

BONUS ROOM 11'-8" X 29'-0"

6' 8" LINE

6' 8" LINE

3' WALLS

3' WALLS

To order plans, visit the Menards Building Materials Desk or visit www.Menards.com.

MOYLAN

MENARDS

Plan #M06-055L-0105

WELCOMING COVERED PORCH

1,023 total square feet of living area

3 bedrooms, 2 baths

2-car garage

Crawl space or slab foundation, please specify when ordering

SPECIAL FEATURES

Kitchen includes a snack bar and is open to the great room and breakfast room

Master suite features a private bath

Centrally located laundry area

PRICE CODE A

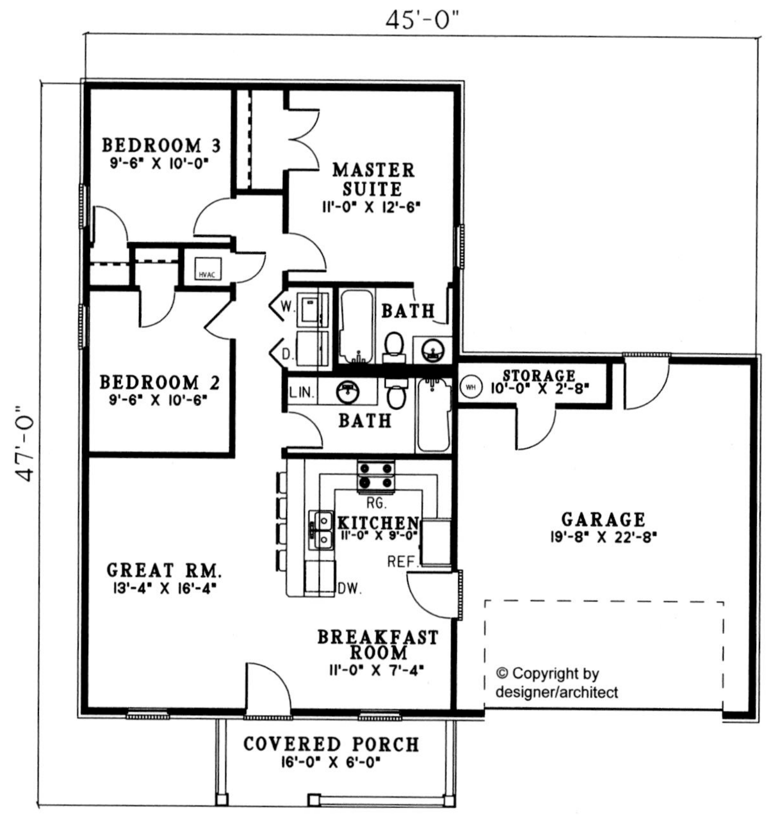

45'-0"
47'-0"
BEDROOM 3
9'-6" X 10'-0"
MASTER SUITE
11'-0" X 12'-6"
HVAC
W.
D.
BATH
LIN.
BATH
BEDROOM 2
9'-6" X 10'-6"
STORAGE
10'-0" X 2'-8"
WH
RG.
KITCHEN
11'-0" X 9'-0"
REF.
DW.
GARAGE
19'-8" X 22'-8"
GREAT RM.
13'-4" X 16'-4"
BREAKFAST ROOM
11'-0" X 7'-4"
© Copyright by designer/architect
COVERED PORCH
16'-0" X 6'-0"

To order plans, visit the Menards Building Materials Desk or visit www.Menards.com.

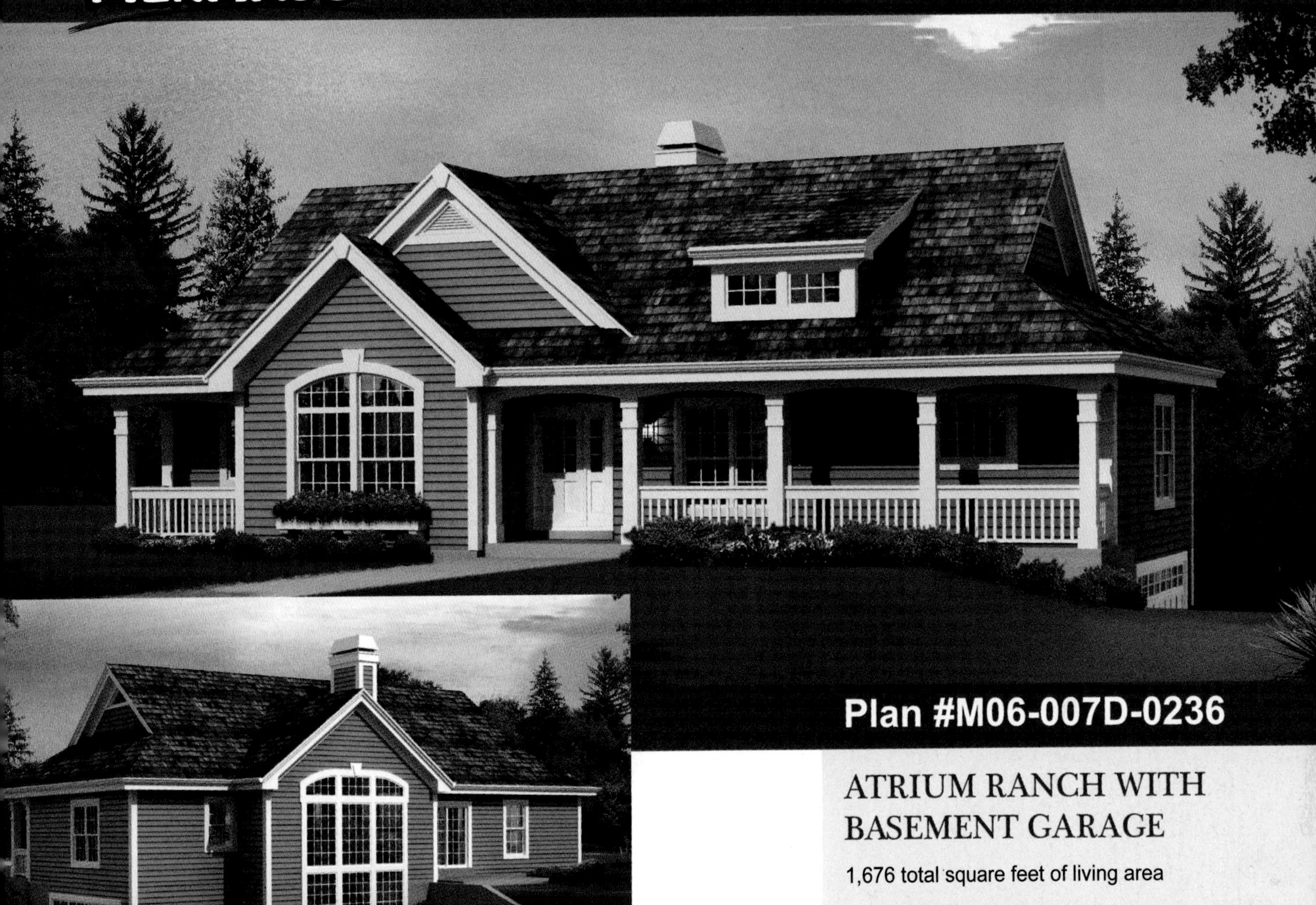
MENARDS
ROYALVIEW
Plan #M06-007D-0236

59'-0"

36'-0"

Patio
Atrium
Dn
Laun
W
D
P
Br 2
12-4x11-0
Br 3/Study
11-8x10-0
Great Rm
20-x13-11
Vaulted
Brkfst
11-1x8-6
Garage Below
Hall
L
R
Dining
11-8x9-8
Kitchen
14-0x10-5
DW
Foyer
MBr
15-4x12-0
Vaulted
Porch
Porch
Planter

ATRIUM RANCH WITH BASEMENT GARAGE

1,676 total square feet of living area

3 bedrooms, 2 baths

2-car drive under side entry garage

Basement foundation

SPECIAL FEATURES

The vaulted great room features a fireplace and an atrium staircase with arched window wall

A walk-in pantry, laundry room and breakfast area are featured in the well-planned kitchen with center island

The vaulted master bedroom has arched windows with planter boxes, two walk-in closets and a luxury bath

The lower level atrium has 85 square feet of living area which is included in the total square footage

PRICE CODE B

To order plans, visit the Menards Building Materials Desk or visit www.Menards.com.

FRUITLAND

MENARDS

Plan #M06-013L-0025

INVITING VAULTED ENTRY

2,097 total square feet of living area

3 bedrooms, 3 baths

3-car side entry garage

Basement, crawl space or slab foundation, please specify when ordering

SPECIAL FEATURES

Country kitchen, family room and dining area add interest to this home

Family room includes a TV niche making this a cozy place to relax

Sumptuous master bedroom includes a sitting area, walk-in closet and a full bath with double vanities

Bonus room above garage has an additional 452 square feet of living space

PRICE CODE D

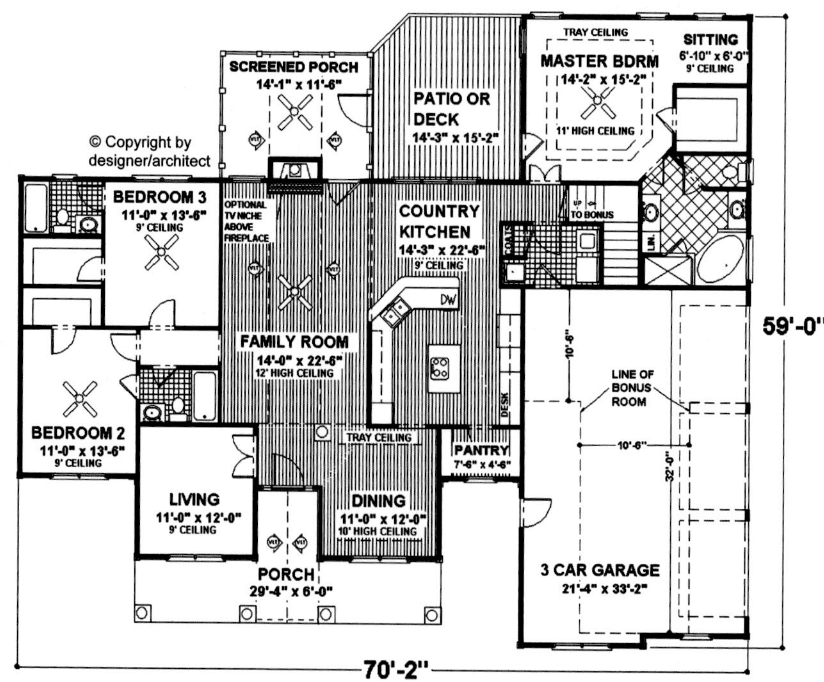

SCREENED PORCH
14'-1" x 11'-6"
PATIO OR DECK
14'-3" x 15'-2"
TRAY CEILING
MASTER BDRM
14'-2" x 15'-2"
11' HIGH CEILING
SITTING
6'-10" x 6'-0"
9' CEILING
© Copyright by designer/architect
BEDROOM 3
11'-0" x 13'-6"
9' CEILING
OPTIONAL TV NICHE ABOVE FIREPLACE
COUNTRY KITCHEN
14'-3" x 22'-6"
9' CEILING
UP TO BONUS
COATS
LIN.
DW
FAMILY ROOM
14'-0" x 22'-6"
12' HIGH CEILING
10'-6"
LINE OF BONUS ROOM
59'-0"
BEDROOM 2
11'-0" x 13'-6"
9' CEILING
TRAY CEILING
DESK
PANTRY
7'-6" x 4'-6"
10'-6"
32'-0"
LIVING
11'-0" x 12'-0"
9' CEILING
DINING
11'-0" x 12'-0"
10' HIGH CEILING
PORCH
29'-4" x 6'-0"
3 CAR GARAGE
21'-4" x 33'-2"
70'-2"

To order plans, visit the Menards Building Materials Desk or visit www.Menards.com.

MENARDS

SHARITA

Plan #M06-077L-0007

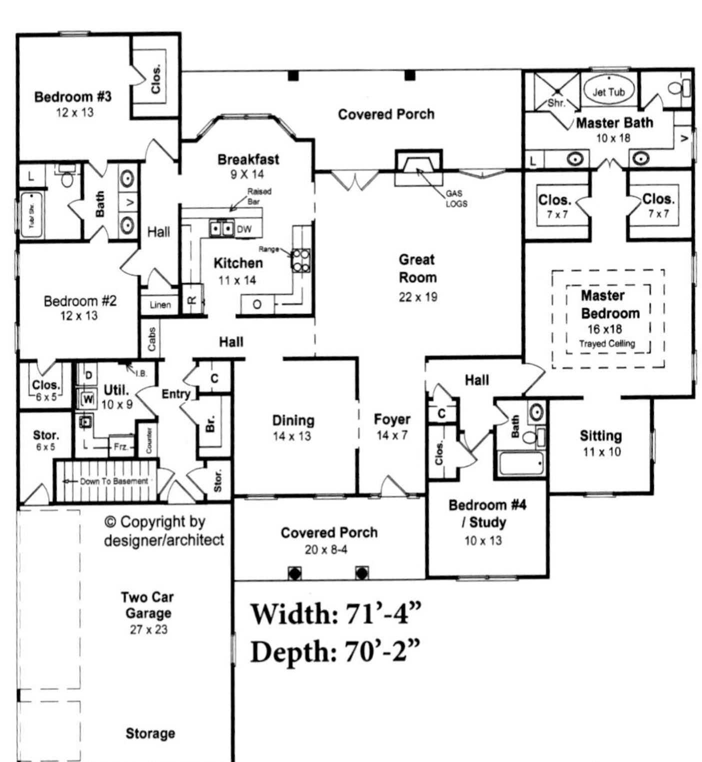

Bedroom #3
12 x 13
Clos.
Covered Porch
Breakfast
9 X 14
Raised Bar
Bath
Hall
DW
Range
Kitchen
11 x 14
GAS LOGS
Great Room
22 x 19
Jet Tub
Shr.
Master Bath
10 x 18
Clos.
7 x 7
Clos.
7 x 7
Master Bedroom
16 x18
Trayed Ceiling
Bedroom #2
12 x 13
Linen
Cabs
Hall
Clos.
6 x 5
Util.
10 x 9
Entry
C
Br.
Stor.
6 x 5
Frz.
Counter
Down To Basement
Stor.
Dining
14 x 13
Foyer
14 x 7
Hall
C
Clos.
Bath
Sitting
11 x 10
Bedroom #4 / Study
10 x 13
Covered Porch
20 x 8-4
© Copyright by designer/architect
Two Car Garage
27 x 23
Storage
Width: 71'-4"
Depth: 70'-2"

LUXURIOUS MASTER BEDROOM

2,805 total square feet of living area

4 bedrooms, 3 baths

2-car side entry garage

Basement, crawl space or slab foundation, please specify when ordering

SPECIAL FEATURES

The wrap-around counter in the kitchen opens to a bayed breakfast area

The great room features a grand fireplace flanked by doors that access the rear covered porch

Bedrooms #2 and #3 enjoy walk-in closets

The extra-large utility room offers an abundance of workspace

PRICE CODE F

To order plans, visit the Menards Building Materials Desk or visit www.Menards.com.

TAMPA SPRINGS

MENARDS

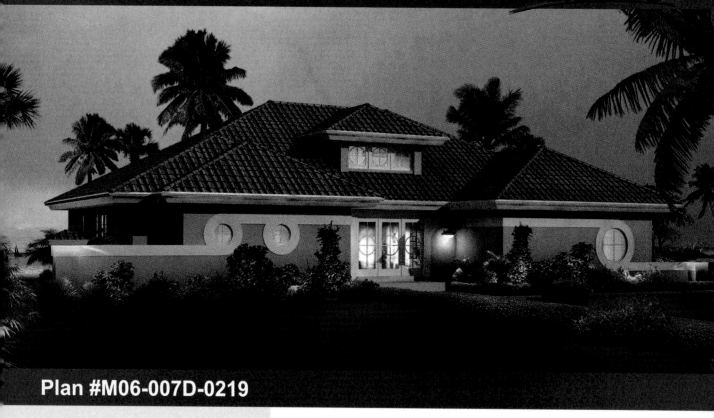

Plan #M06-007D-0219

IDEAL SUNBELT DESIGN

1,939 total square feet of living area

2 bedrooms, 2 baths

2-car side entry garage

Crawl space foundation

SPECIAL FEATURES

A grand entry has unique curved walls and flanking coat closets leading down a few steps into an enormous sunken great room

The spacious kitchen with cabinets galore has a built-in pantry, functional island/snack bar and dining area with views of the covered patio nearby

A laundry room, mechanical and coat closets are conveniently situated between the kitchen and garage

The huge master bedroom features a luxury bath with separate shower, large walk-in closet and private covered patio

PRICE CODE B

Rear View

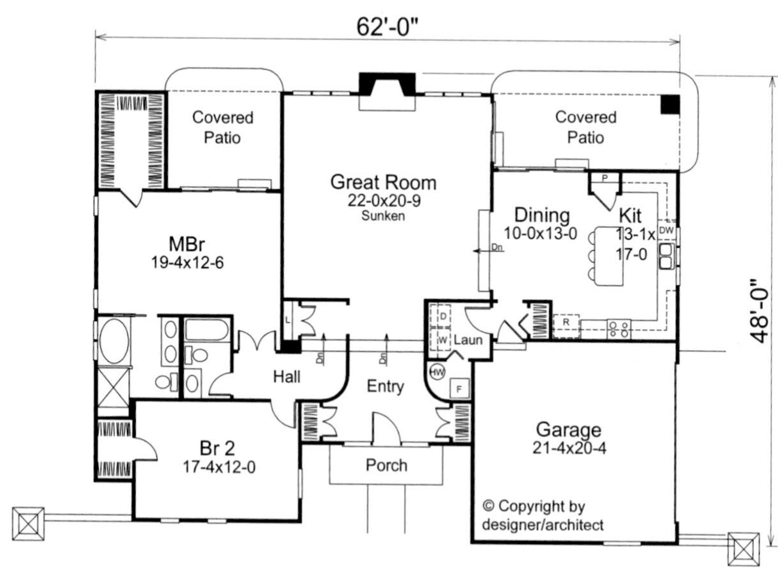

62'-0"
Covered Patio
Great Room
22-0x20-9
Sunken
Covered Patio
Dining
10-0x13-0
Kit
13-1x
17-0
MBr
19-4x12-6
Laun
Hall
Entry
Br 2
17-4x12-0
Porch
Garage
21-4x20-4
© Copyright by designer/architect
48'-0"

To order plans, visit the Menards Building Materials Desk or visit www.Menards.com.

MENARDS

ELMSDALE

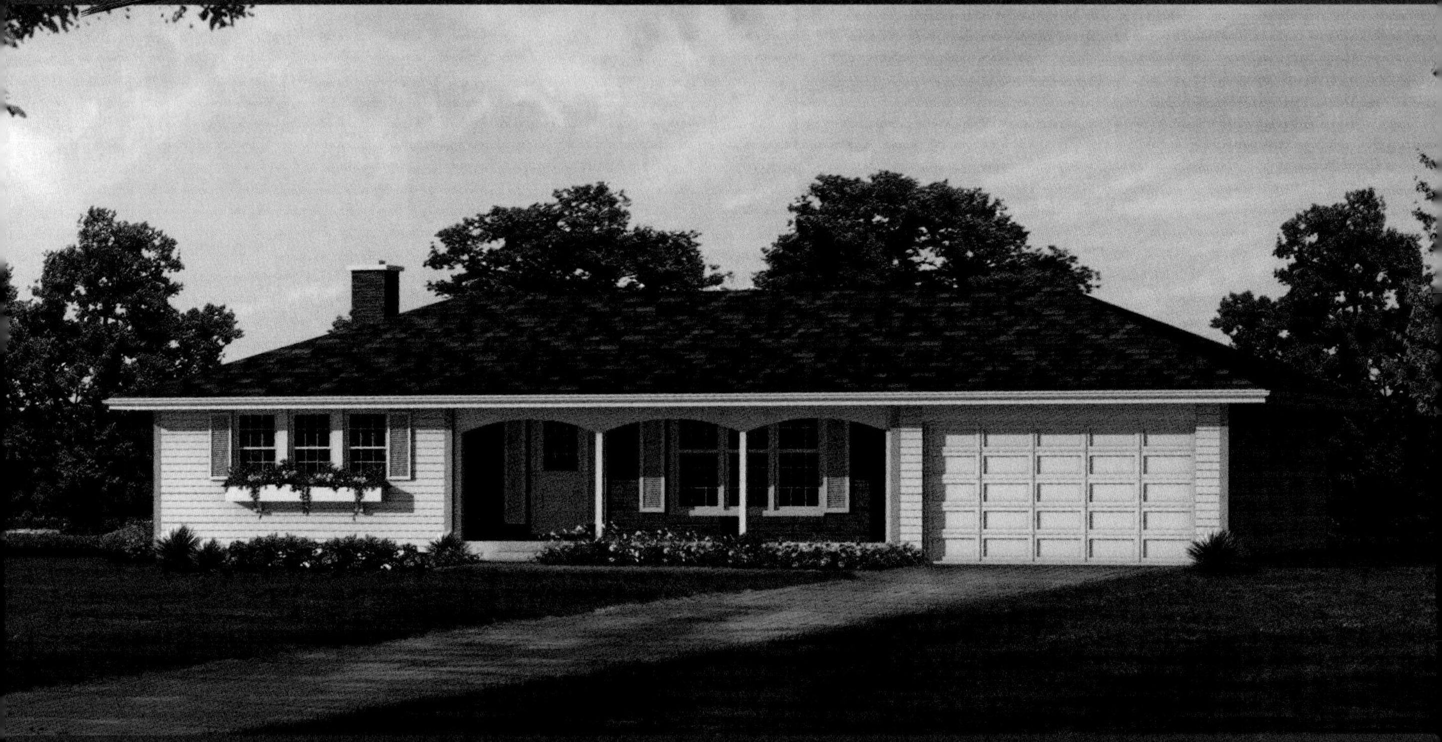

Plan #M06-017D-0004

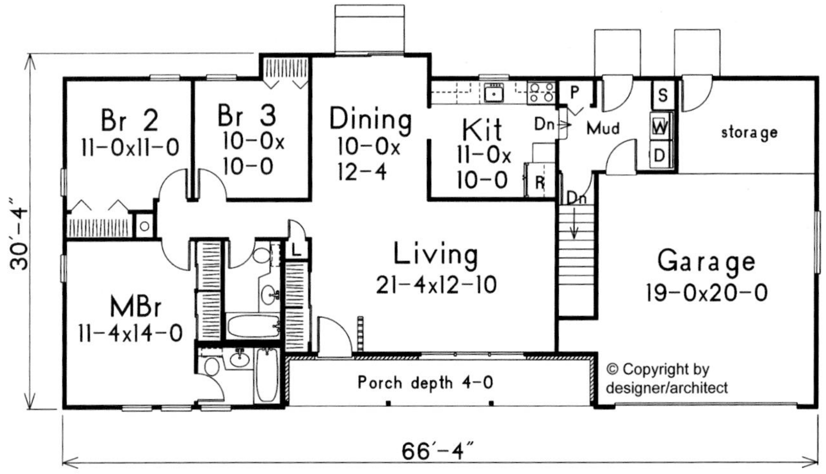

Br 2
11-0x11-0
Br 3
10-0x
10-0
Dining
10-0x
12-4
Kit
11-0x
10-0
Mud
storage
Living
21-4x12-10
Garage
19-0x20-0
MBr
11-4x14-0
Porch depth 4-0
30'-4"
66'-4"

To order plans, visit the Menards Building Materials Desk or visit www.Menards.com.

SWEEPING RANCH WITH HIP ROOF

1,315 total square feet of living area

3 bedrooms, 2 baths

2-car garage

Basement foundation, drawings also include slab foundation

SPECIAL FEATURES

Dining room has sliding glass doors to the rear patio

Large storage space in garage

Cozy eating area in the kitchen

Kitchen has easy access to the mud room

Large living room has double closets for storage and coats

PRICE CODE B

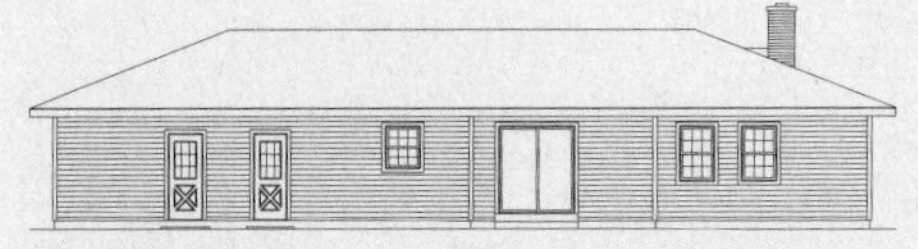

Rear View

RYLAND

MENARDS

Plan #M06-005D-0001

CLASSIC RANCH HAS GRAND APPEAL WITH EXPANSIVE PORCH

1,400 total square feet of living area

3 bedrooms, 2 baths

2-car garage

Basement foundation, drawings also include crawl space foundation

SPECIAL FEATURES

Master bedroom is secluded for privacy

The large utility room has additional cabinet space

The covered porch provides an outdoor seating area

The living room and master bedroom feature vaulted ceilings

The oversized two-car garage has storage space

PRICE CODE B

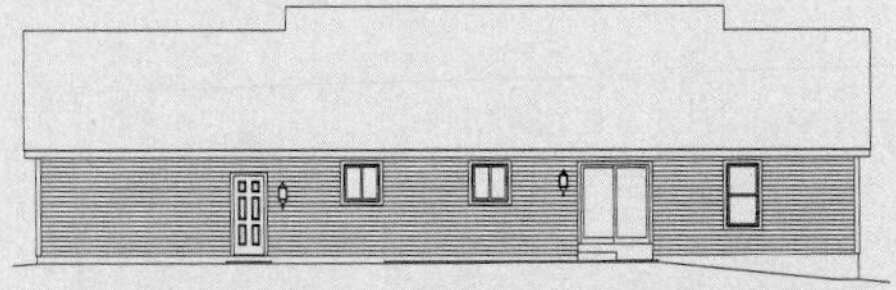

Rear View

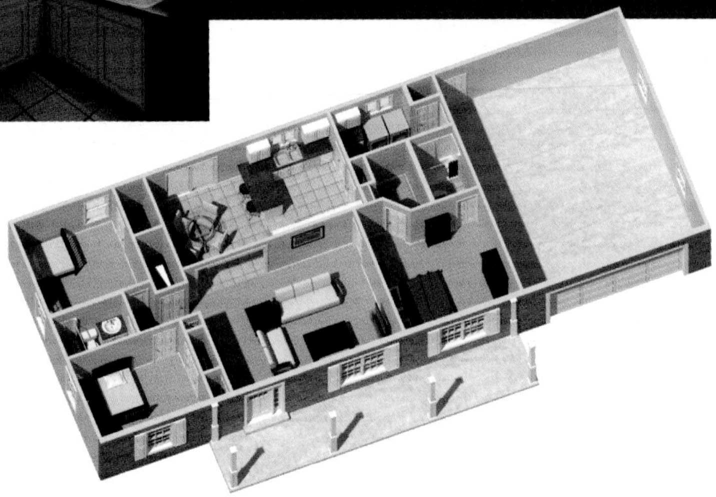

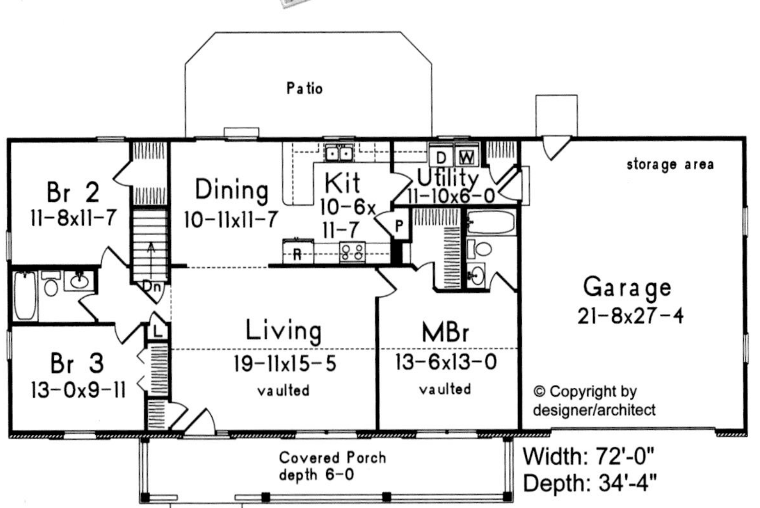
Patio
Br 2
11-8x11-7
Dining
10-11x11-7
Kit
10-6x
11-7
D W
Utility
11-10x6-0
P
R
Dn
L
storage area
Garage
21-8x27-4
Living
19-11x15-5
vaulted
MBr
13-6x13-0
vaulted
Br 3
13-0x9-11
© Copyright by
designer/architect
Covered Porch
depth 6-0

Width: 72'-0"
Depth: 34'-4"

To order plans, visit the Menards Building Materials Desk or visit www.Menards.com.

ROCHELLE BAY

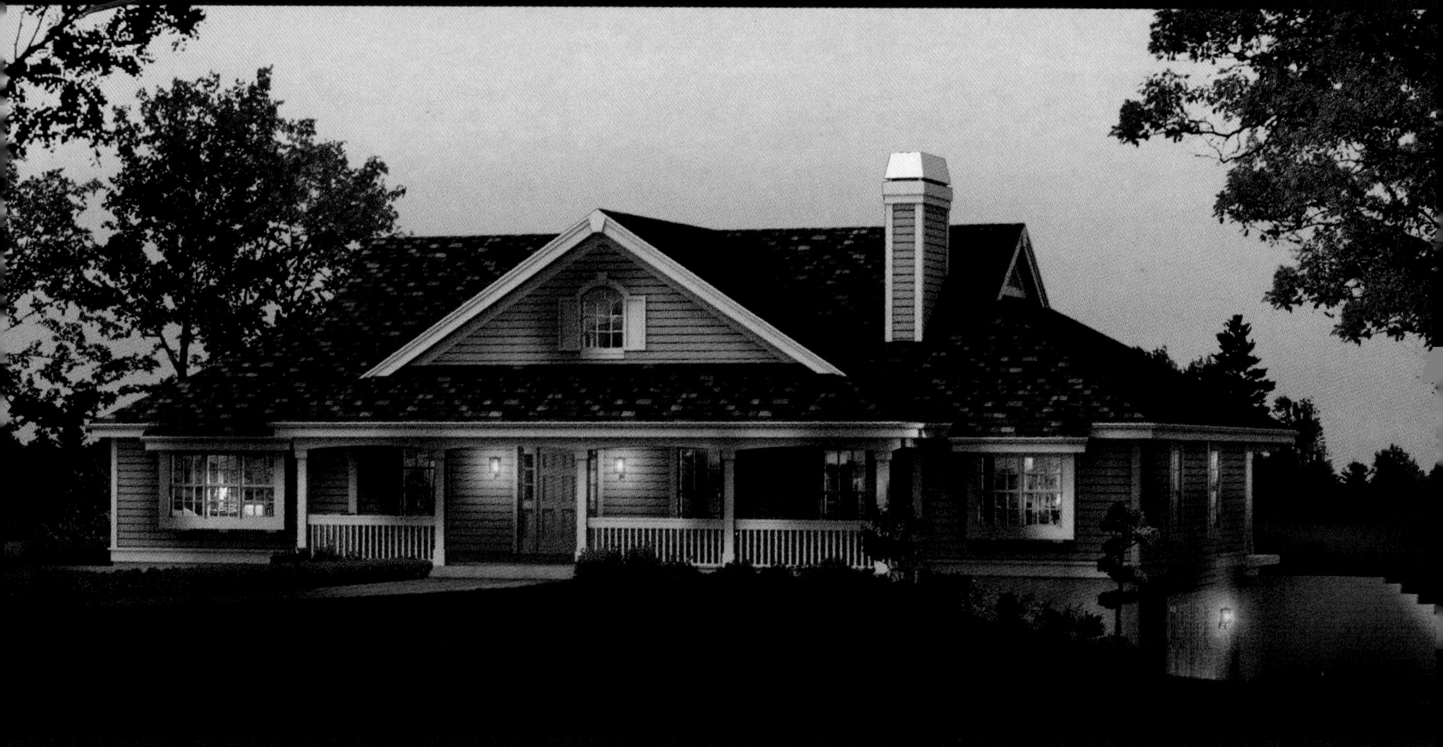

Plan #M06-007D-0204

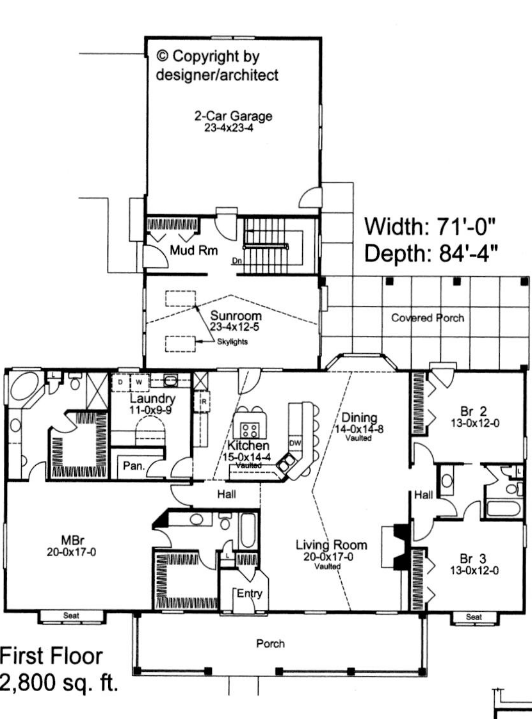
© Copyright by designer/architect
2-Car Garage
23-4x23-4
Width: 71'-0"
Depth: 84'-4"
Mud Rm
Sunroom
23-4x12-5
Skylights
Covered Porch
Laundry
11-0x9-9
Pan.
Kitchen
15-0x14-4
Vaulted
Dining
14-0x14-8
Vaulted
Br 2
13-0x12-0
Hall
MBr
20-0x17-0
Living Room
20-0x17-0
Vaulted
Br 3
13-0x12-0
Entry
Seat
Porch
First Floor
2,800 sq. ft.

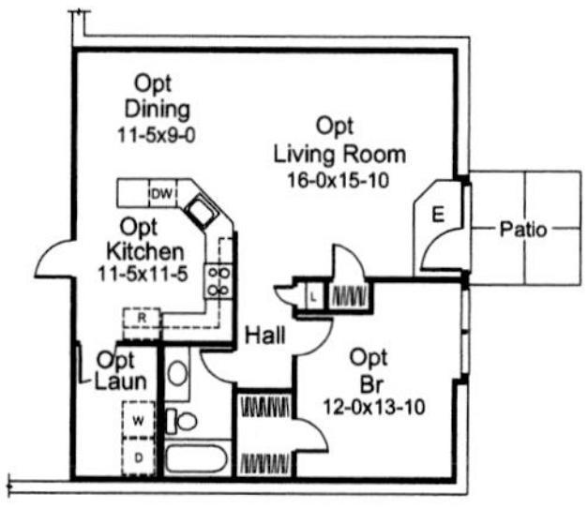

Optional
Lower Level

To order plans, visit the Menards Building Materials Desk or visit www.Menards.com.

SUNROOM AND TWO COVERED PORCHES

2,800 total square feet of living area

3 bedrooms, 3 baths

2-car side entry garage

Walk-out basement foundation

SPECIAL FEATURES

The vaulted living and dining rooms have a fireplace, bay window with views of the rear porch and are open to the kitchen

The spacious master bedroom with coffered ceiling has both his and hers baths with walk-in closets

A sunroom, perfect for informal gatherings, is adjacent to the rear covered porch

The optional lower level basement apartment has an additional 932 square feet of living area

PRICE CODE D

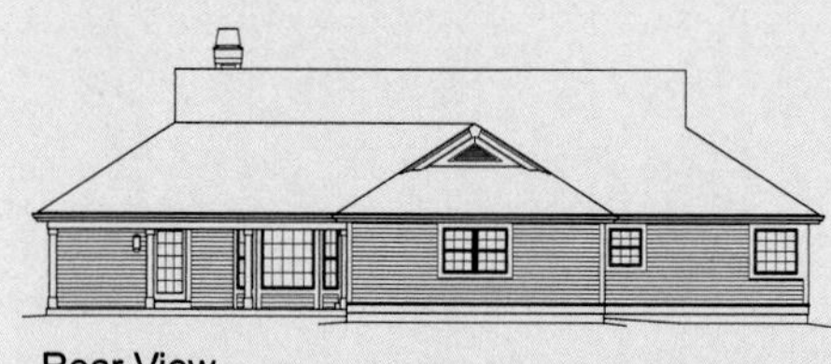

Rear View

ROCKWOOD

MENARDS

Plan #M06-006D-0003

SCULPTURED ROOF LINE AND FACADE ADD CHARM

1,674 total square feet of living area

3 bedrooms, 2 baths

2-car garage

Basement foundation, drawings also include crawl space and slab foundations

SPECIAL FEATURES

Vaulted great room, dining area and kitchen all enjoy a central fireplace

Convenient laundry/mud room is located between the garage and the rest of the home with handy stairs to the basement

Easily expandable screened porch and adjacent patio access the dining area

Master bedroom features a full bath with tub, separate shower and walk-in closet

PRICE CODE B

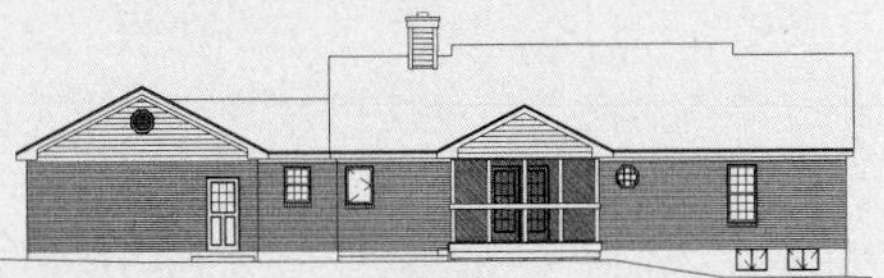

Rear View

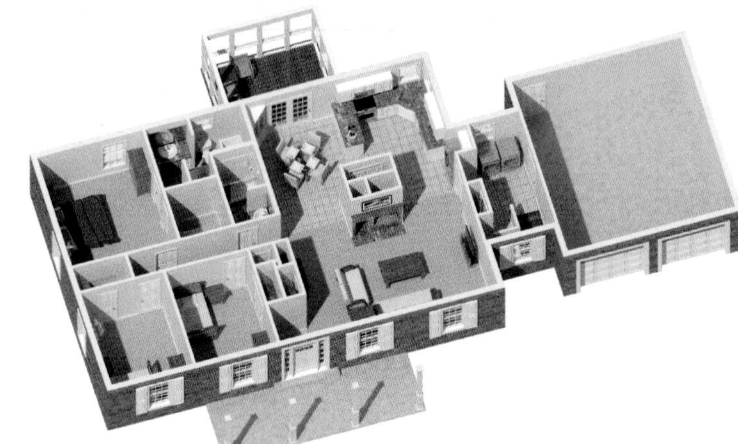

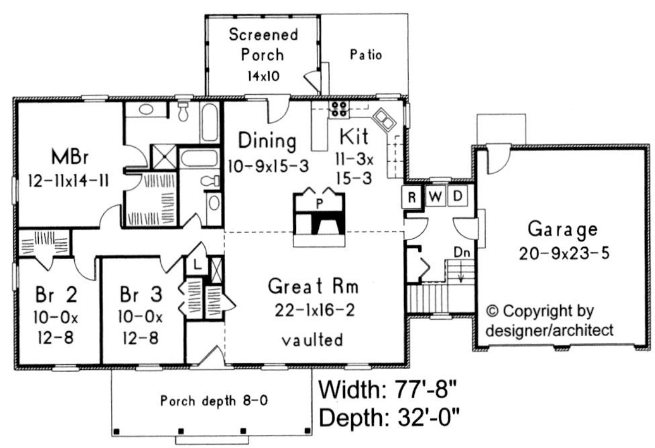

Screened Porch 14x10
Patio
MBr 12-11x14-11
Dining 10-9x15-3
Kit 11-3x 15-3
R W D
P
Dn
L
Garage 20-9x23-5
Br 2 10-0x 12-8
Br 3 10-0x 12-8
Great Rm 22-1x16-2 vaulted
© Copyright by designer/architect
Porch depth 8-0
Width: 77'-8"
Depth: 32'-0"

To order plans, visit the Menards Building Materials Desk or visit www.Menards.com.

MENARDS

YATES

Plan #M06-013L-0051

POOL

3-CAR GARAGE 22'-4" x 30'-0"

© Copyright by designer/architect

Arched Transom

MASTER SUITE 22'-4" x 21'-10" 13'-6" Ceiling

SITTING

COVERED PORCH 15'-4" x 7'-8"

WORKSHOP 10'-4" x 5'-6"

Arched Transom

NOOK 11' x 9'-8"

FAMILY ROOM 16' x 25' 13'-2" Ceiling

Entertainment Center

KITCHEN 11' x 14'-6"

Table

Pantry

DW

MEDIA ROOM 11' x 13'

Tray Ceiling

DINING 11' x 14'

BEDROOM 2 11' x 13'

BEDROOM 3 11' x 13'

PORCH 15'-4" x 5'-11"

69'-2"

62'-0"

First Floor
2,260 sq. ft.

BONUS ROOM 10'-6" x 30'-10" 404 Sq. Ft.

Optional
Second Floor

BEAUTIFUL BRICK EXTERIOR

2,260 total square feet of living area

3 bedrooms, 3 baths

3-car side entry garage

Basement or crawl space foundation, please specify when ordering

SPECIAL FEATURES

The master suite has a bayed window wall with a view of the backyard and pool

Large kitchen includes a useful table in the middle

The entertainment center and fireplace create a focal point for the family room

The optional second floor has an additional 404 square feet of living space

PRICE CODE D

To order plans, visit the Menards Building Materials Desk or visit www.Menards.com.

TRISTA

MENARDS

Plan #M06-051L-0174

IMPRESSIVE ENTRY SETS TONE OF HOME

1,817 total square feet of living area

3 bedrooms, 2 baths

2-car garage

Basement foundation

SPECIAL FEATURES

Energy efficient home with 2" x 6" exterior walls

12' ceilings grace the entry and great room

The formal dining room boasts a 12' ceiling and a wall of windows bringing in warm natural light

The bayed nook accesses the outdoors through sliding glass doors

The secluded master bedroom features two closets and a private bath with whirlpool tub and double-bowl vanity

PRICE CODE D

Rear View

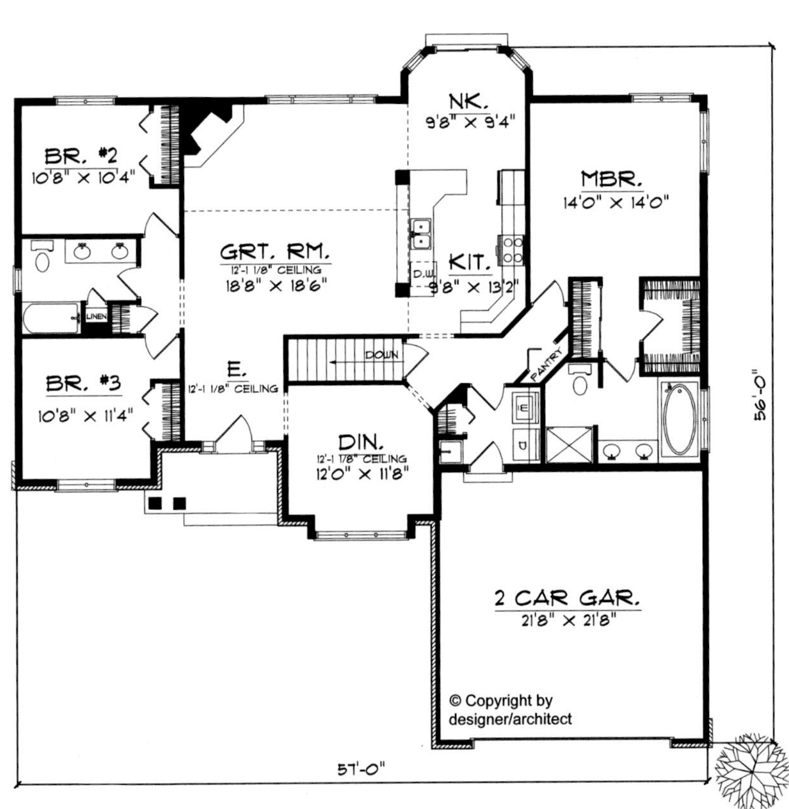

NK.
9'8" X 9'4"
BR. #2
10'8" X 10'4"
MBR.
14'0" X 14'0"
GRT. RM.
12'-1 1/8" CEILING
18'8" X 18'6"
KIT.
9'8" X 13'2"
D.W.
LINEN
DOWN
PANTRY
E.
12'-1 1/8" CEILING
BR. #3
10'8" X 11'4"
DIN.
12'-1 1/8" CEILING
12'0" X 11'8"
2 CAR GAR.
21'8" X 21'8"
© Copyright by designer/architect
57'-0"
56'-0"

To order plans, visit the Menards Building Materials Desk or visit www.Menards.com.

MENARDS

BAKERSPORT

Plan #M06-058D-0060

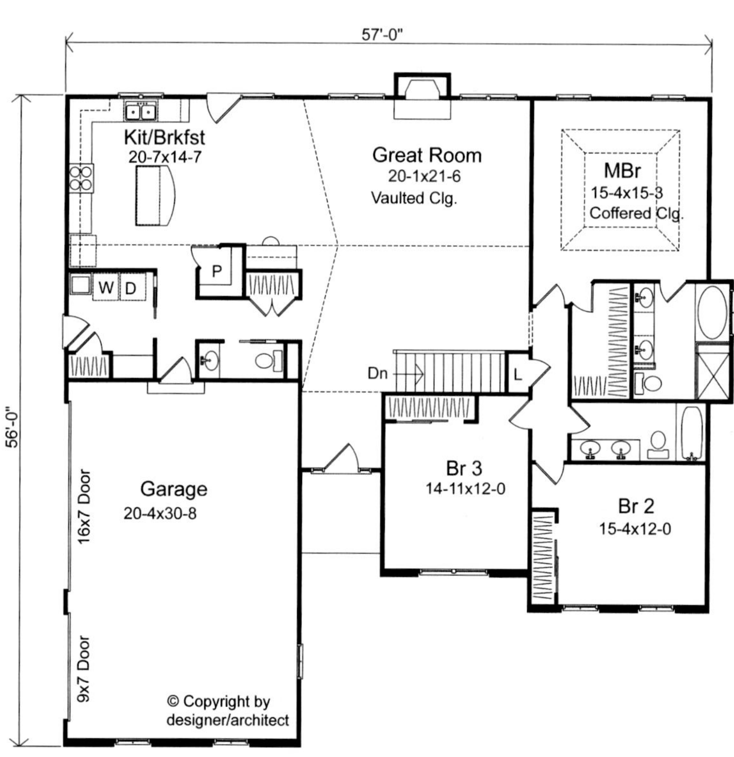

57'-0"
56'-0"
Kit/Brkfst
20-7x14-7
Great Room
20-1x21-6
Vaulted Clg.
MBr
15-4x15-3
Coffered Clg.
P
W
D
Dn
L
Br 3
14-11x12-0
Br 2
15-4x12-0
Garage
20-4x30-8
16x7 Door
9x7 Door
© Copyright by
designer/architect

TRADITIONAL RANCH HOME

2,015 total square feet of living area

3 bedrooms, 2 1/2 baths

3-car side entry garage

Basement foundation

SPECIAL FEATURES

The foyer opens into the spacious vaulted great room

The open kitchen/breakfast area includes an island with seating, a pantry and built-in desk

The bedrooms remain private from the living areas

PRICE CODE C

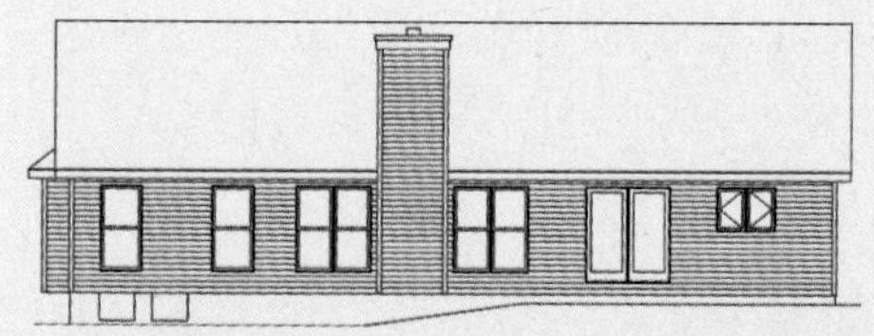
Rear View

To order plans, visit the Menards Building Materials Desk or visit www.Menards.com.

HILLSHIRE

MENARDS

Plan #M06-057D-0010

SPLIT-BEDROOM FLOOR PLAN

1,242 total square feet of living area

3 bedrooms, 2 baths

2-car garage

Basement foundation

SPECIAL FEATURES

Energy efficient home with 2" x 6" exterior walls

The wide foyer opens to the living room for a spacious atmosphere and grand first impression

The centrally located kitchen easily serves the large dining and living rooms

The split-bedroom design allows privacy for the homeowners who will love spending time in their master bedroom retreat

PRICE CODE A

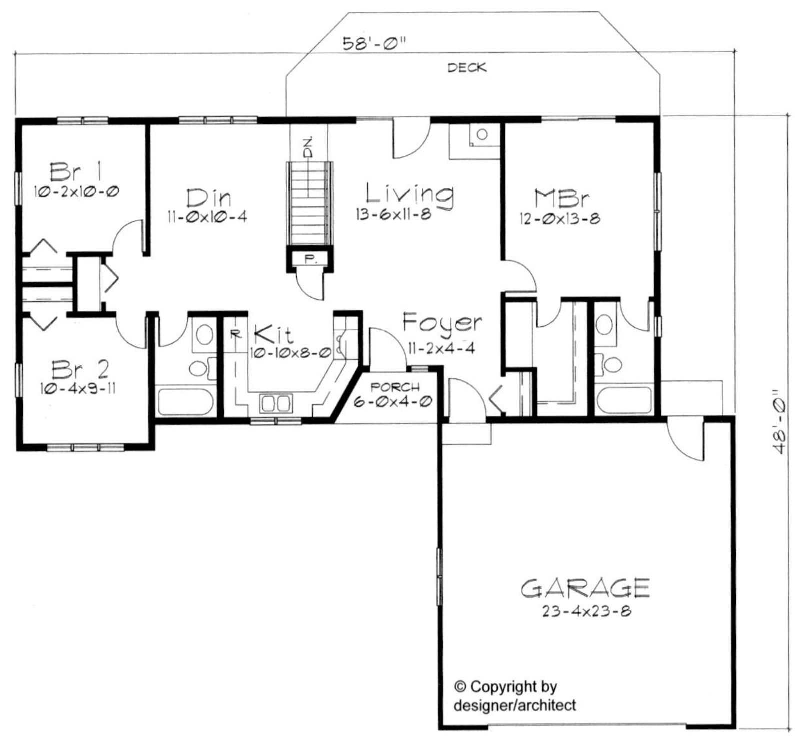
58'-0"
DECK
Br 1
10-2x10-0
Din
11-0x10-4
DN
Living
13-6x11-8
MBr
12-0x13-8
P.
R
Kit
10-10x8-0
Foyer
11-2x4-4
Br 2
10-4x9-11
PORCH
6-0x4-0
48'-0"
GARAGE
23-4x23-8
© Copyright by
designer/architect

To order plans, visit the Menards Building Materials Desk or visit www.Menards.com.

MENARDS

SHADYVIEW

Plan #M06-007D-0124

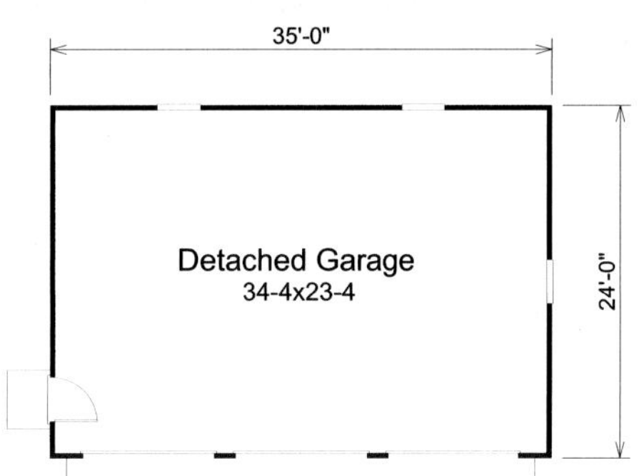

35'-0"
Detached Garage
34-4x23-4
24'-0"

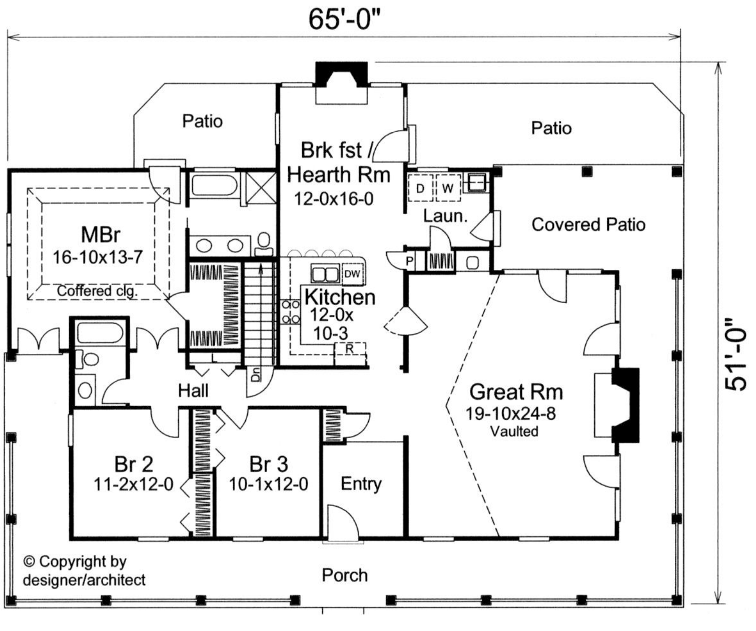

65'-0"
51'-0"
Patio
Brk fst /
Hearth Rm
12-0x16-0
Patio
D
W
Laun.
Covered Patio
MBr
16-10x13-7
Coffered clg.
DW
Kitchen
12-0x
10-3
R
P
Dn
Hall
Great Rm
19-10x24-8
Vaulted
Br 2
11-2x12-0
Br 3
10-1x12-0
Entry
© Copyright by
designer/architect
Porch

To order plans, visit the Menards Building Materials Desk or visit www.Menards.com.

COUNTRY RANCH HOME

1,944 total square feet of living area

3 bedrooms, 2 baths

3-car detached garage

Basement foundation

SPECIAL FEATURES

The large entry leads to a grand-sized great room featuring a vaulted ceiling, fireplace, wet bar and access to the porch through three patio doors

The U-shaped kitchen is open to the breakfast/hearth room and enjoys a snack bar, fireplace and patio access

A luxury bath, walk-in closet and doors to the porch are a few of the amenities of the master bedroom

PRICE CODE C

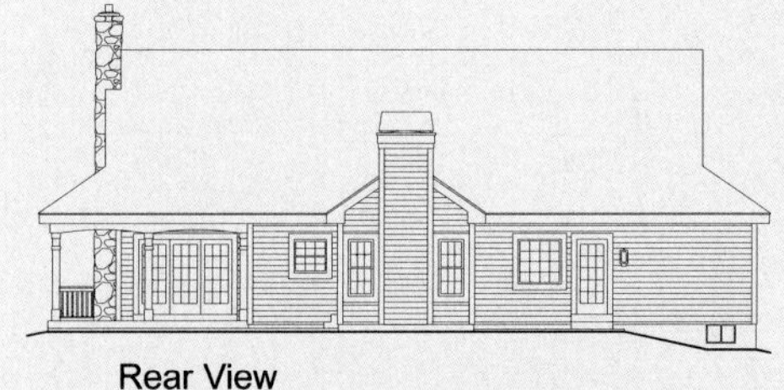

Rear View

SUNDERLAND MANOR

MENARDS

Plan #M06-077L-0184

LUXURY INSIDE AND OUT

2,400 total square feet of living area

4 bedrooms, 2 1/2 baths

2-car side entry garage

Slab or crawl space foundation, please specify when ordering

SPECIAL FEATURES

All the bedrooms feature walk-in closets for extra organization

The master bedroom with private bath and two walk-in closets is separated from the other bedrooms for privacy

The flex space is a versatile room that can adapt to your needs whether it be an office or formal dining room

The unfinished bonus room has an additional 452 square feet of living area

PRICE CODE E

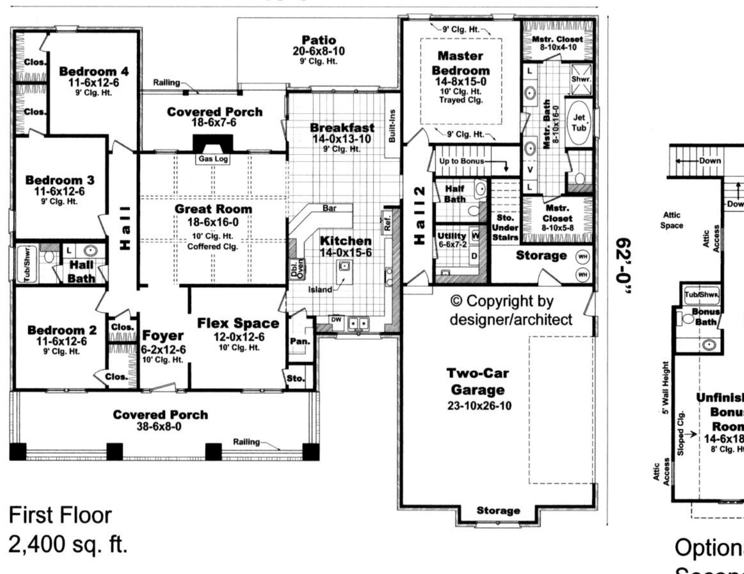

73'-6"
62'-0"
Patio
20-6x8-10
Bedroom 4
11-6x12-6
Covered Porch
18-6x7-6
Breakfast
14-0x13-10
Master Bedroom
14-8x15-0
Mstr. Closet
8-10x4-10
Mstr. Bath
8-10x16-0
Jet Tub
Bedroom 3
11-6x12-6
Hall
Great Room
18-6x16-0
Kitchen
14-0x15-6
Hall 2
Half Bath
Utility
6-6x7-2
Mstr. Closet
8-10x5-8
Storage
Hall Bath
Bedroom 2
11-6x12-6
Foyer
6-2x12-6
Flex Space
12-0x12-6
© Copyright by designer/architect
Two-Car Garage
23-10x26-10
Covered Porch
38-6x8-0
Storage
Unfinished Bonus Room
14-6x18-0
Bonus Bath
Closet

First Floor
2,400 sq. ft.

Optional
Second Floor

To order plans, visit the Menards Building Materials Desk or visit www.Menards.com.

SAXONY II

Plan #M06-001D-0108

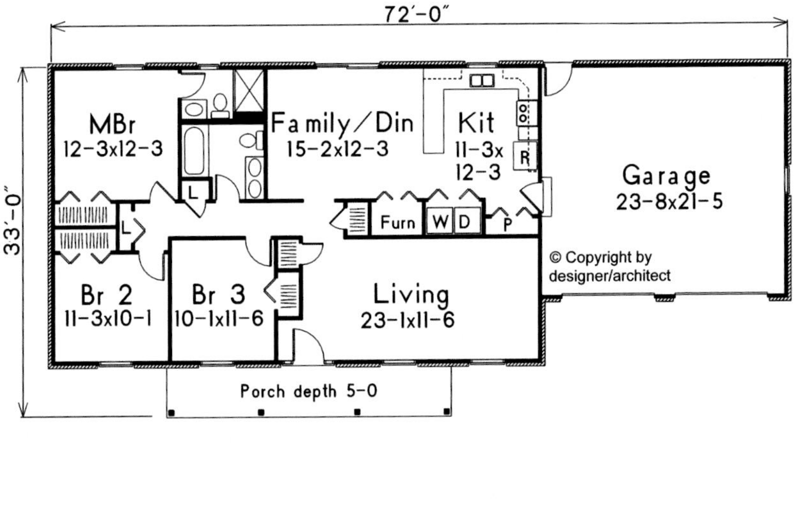

72'-0"

33'-0"

MBr
12-3x12-3

Family/Din
15-2x12-3

Kit
11-3x
12-3

R

L

Furn W D P

Garage
23-8x21-5

© Copyright by
designer/architect

Br 2
11-3x10-1

Br 3
10-1x11-6

Living
23-1x11-6

Porch depth 5-0

STYLISH RANCH WITH RUSTIC CHARM

1,344 total square feet of living area

3 bedrooms, 2 baths

2-car garage

Crawl space foundation, drawings also include basement and slab foundations

SPECIAL FEATURES

Energy efficient home with 2" x 6" exterior walls

The front door opens into a large living space perfect for entertaining guests

The U-shaped kitchen is easily accessed by the family/dining area for convenience

There is ample closet storage space throughout this home

PRICE CODE A

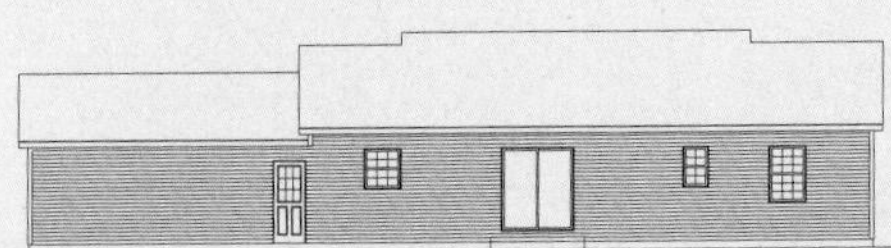

Rear View

To order plans, visit the Menards Building Materials Desk or visit www.Menards.com.

ALYSSA

MENARDS

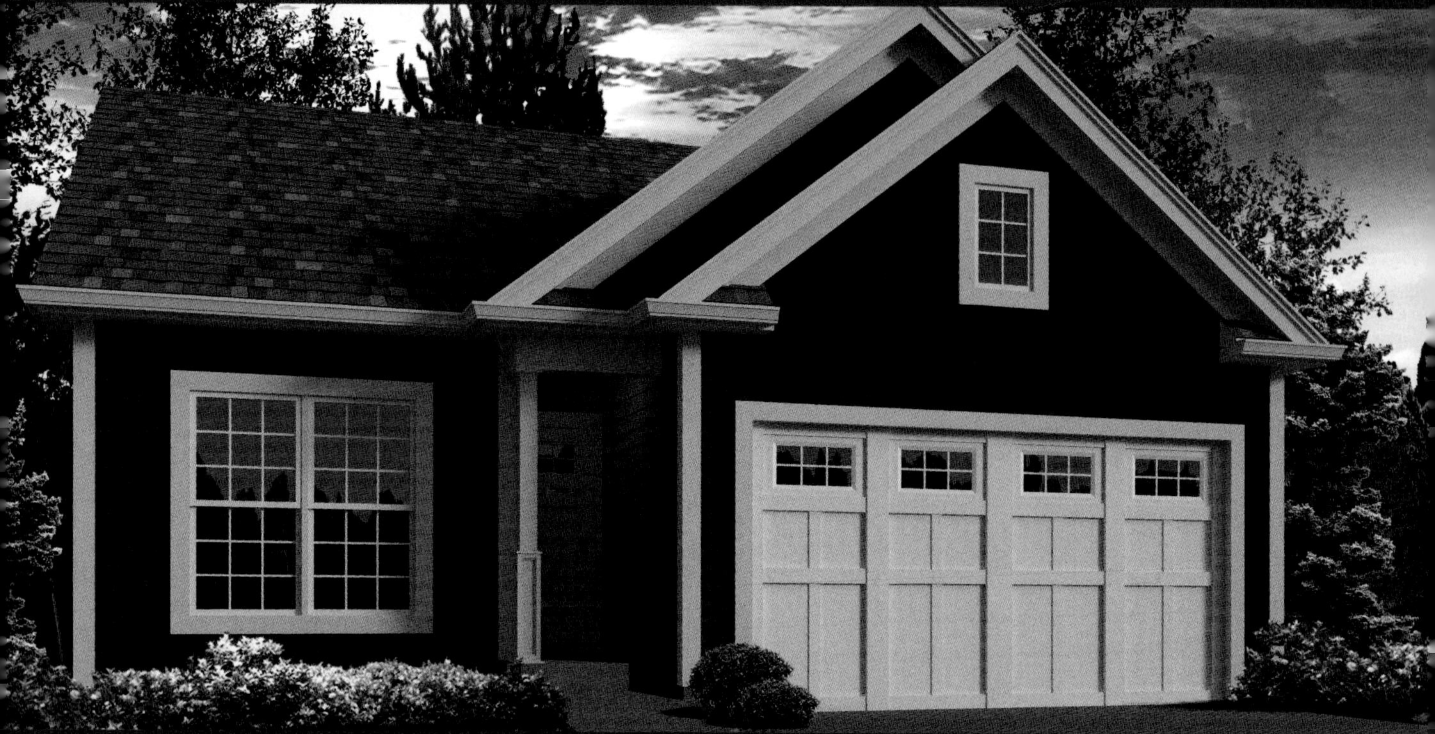

Plan #M06-121D-0028

COUNTRY-STYLE COTTAGE

1,433 total square feet of living area

2 bedrooms, 2 baths, 2-car garage

Basement foundation

SPECIAL FEATURES

The vaulted dining area enjoys access to the rear patio

The kitchen boasts a corner island and flows into the vaulted great room

There are many amenities of the master bedroom including a private bath and walk-in closet

PRICE CODE AA

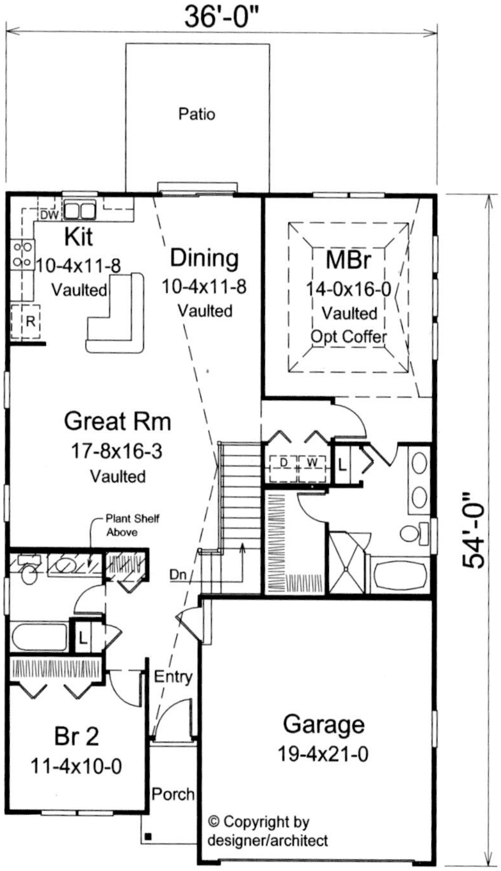

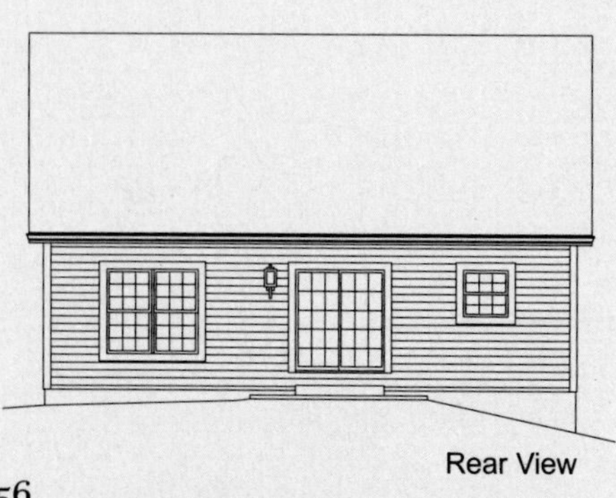

Rear View

36'-0"
Patio
DW
Kit
10-4x11-8
Vaulted
R
Dining
10-4x11-8
Vaulted
MBr
14-0x16-0
Vaulted
Opt Coffer
Great Rm
17-8x16-3
Vaulted
D W
L
Plant Shelf Above
Dn
L
Entry
Br 2
11-4x10-0
Porch
Garage
19-4x21-0
54'-0"

To order plans, visit the Menards Building Materials Desk or visit www.Menards.com.

MENARDS

DAYTON

Plan #M06-041D-0004

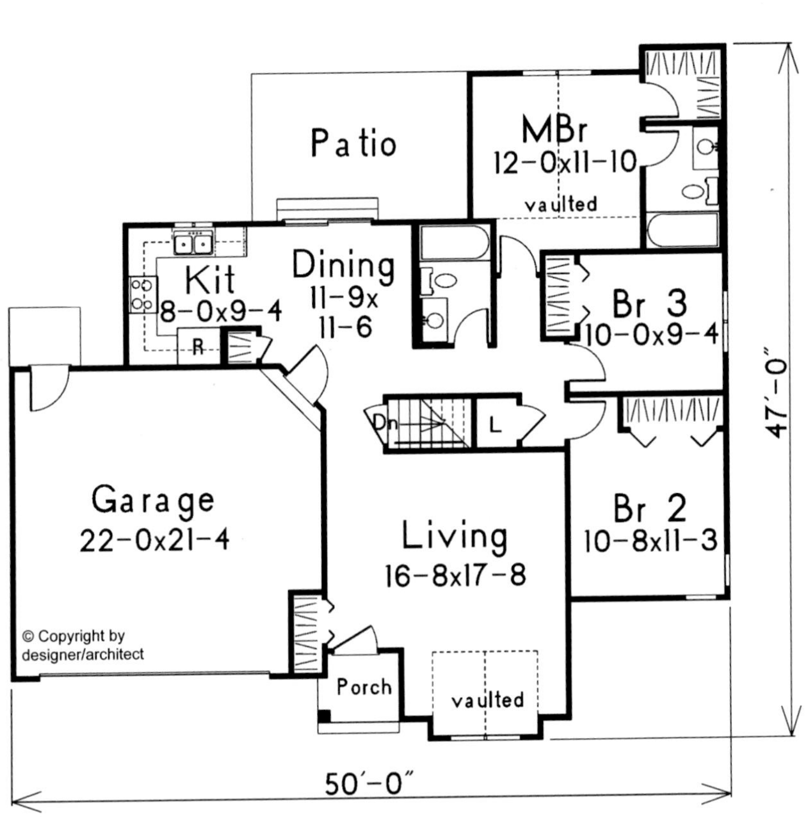
Patio
MBr
12-0x11-10
vaulted
Kit
8-0x9-4
Dining
11-9x
11-6
R
Br 3
10-0x9-4
Dn
L
Garage
22-0x21-4
Living
16-8x17-8
Br 2
10-8x11-3
47'-0"
© Copyright by
designer/architect
Porch
vaulted
50'-0"

VAULTED CEILING FRAMES CIRCLE-TOP WINDOW

1,195 total square feet of living area

3 bedrooms, 2 baths

2-car garage

Basement foundation

SPECIAL FEATURES

The dining room opens onto the patio

The master bedroom features a vaulted ceiling, private bath and walk-in closet

The coat closets are located by both the entrances

Convenient secondary entrance is located at the back of the garage

PRICE CODE AA

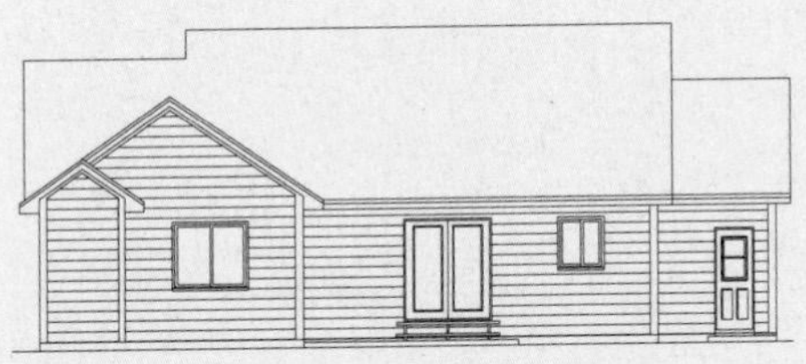
Rear View

To order plans, visit the Menards Building Materials Desk or visit www.Menards.com.

ST. TROPEZ

MENARDS

Plan #M06-007D-0230

INNOVATIVE DESIGN

1,923 total square feet of living area

3 bedrooms, 2 baths

2-car side entry garage

Slab foundation

SPECIAL FEATURES

A spacious entrance with double coat closets invites you into the grand-sized great room with fireplace, bar area open to the kitchen with glass sliding doors to the rear patio and adjacent dining room

The large and smartly designed bay-shaped kitchen features cabinet and counter space galore with a 7' wide window above the sink for taking in the views

A luxury bath with double entry doors, a walk-in closet and 9' wide glass sliding doors to the rear patio are many special features of the master bedroom

PRICE CODE D

Rear View

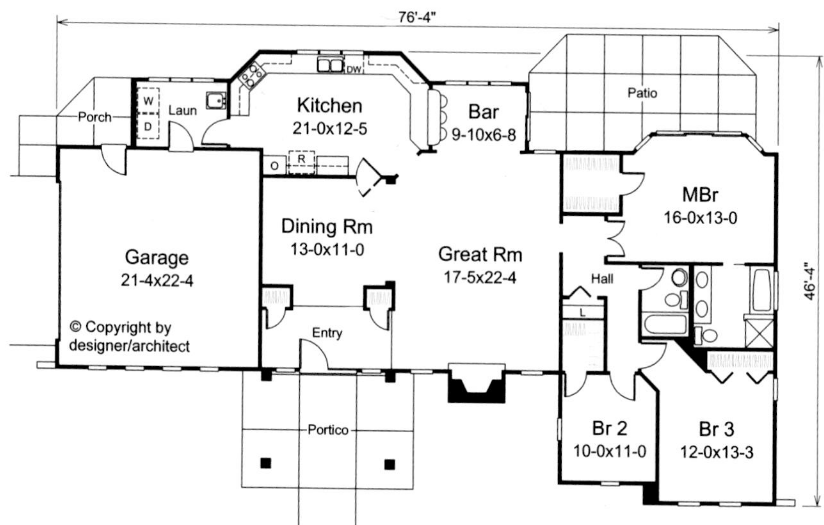
76'-4"
46'-4"
Porch
W
D
Laun
DW
Kitchen
21-0x12-5
Bar
9-10x6-8
Patio
O
R
MBr
16-0x13-0
Dining Rm
13-0x11-0
Garage
21-4x22-4
Great Rm
17-5x22-4
Hall
L
© Copyright by
designer/architect
Entry
Portico
Br 2
10-0x11-0
Br 3
12-0x13-3

To order plans, visit the Menards Building Materials Desk
or visit www.Menards.com.

KINSLEY

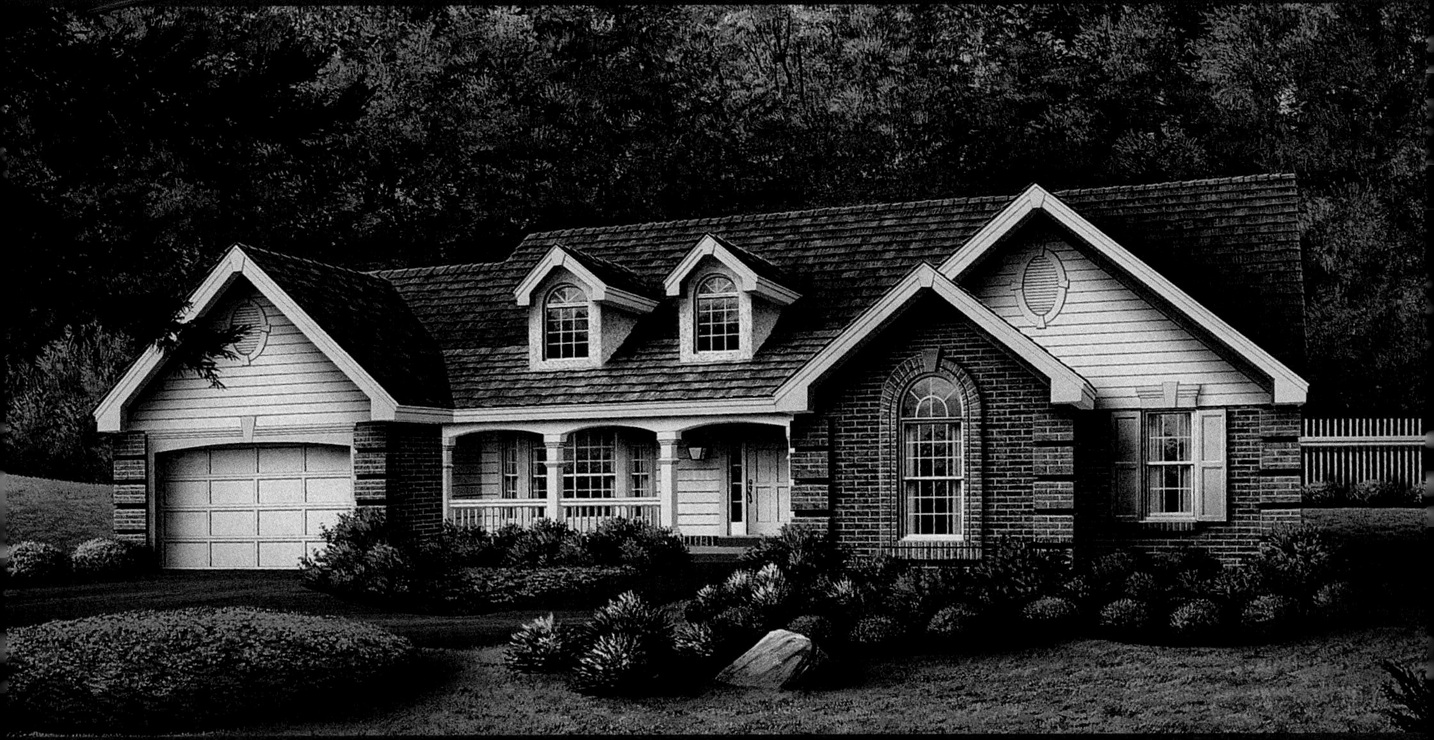

Plan #M06-007D-0049

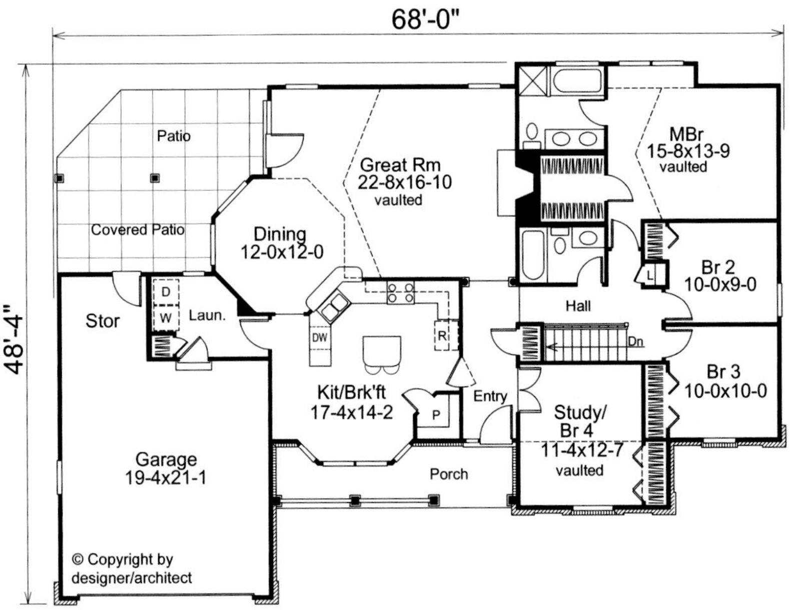

68'-0"
48'-4"
Patio
Covered Patio
Great Rm 22-8x16-10 vaulted
Dining 12-0x12-0
MBr 15-8x13-9 vaulted
Br 2 10-0x9-0
Br 3 10-0x10-0
Hall
Dn
Stor
D
W
Laun.
DW
R
Kit/Brk'ft 17-4x14-2
P
Entry
Study/ Br 4 11-4x12-7 vaulted
Porch
Garage 19-4x21-1

CLASSIC EXTERIOR AND INNOVATIVE INTERIOR

1,791 total square feet of living area

4 bedrooms, 2 baths

2-car garage

Basement foundation, drawings also include crawl space and slab foundations

SPECIAL FEATURES

Vaulted great room and octagon-shaped dining area enjoy a nice view of the patio

The kitchen/breakfast area features a pass-through to the dining area, center island, large walk-in pantry and breakfast area with large bay window

The master bedroom enjoys a vaulted ceiling and a sitting area

2" x 6" exterior walls available, please order plan #M06-007E-0049

PRICE CODE C

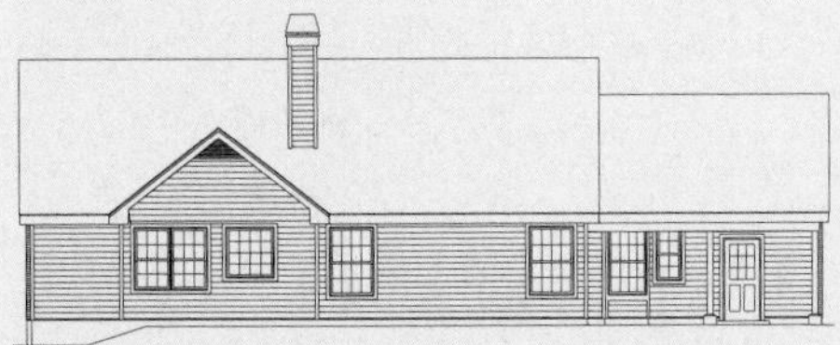

Rear View

PICKFORD PLACE

MENARDS

Plan #M06-077L-0131

FASHIONABLE FAMILY HOME

2,021 total square feet of living area

3 bedrooms, 2 1/2 baths

2-car side entry garage

Basement, slab or crawl space foundation, please specify when ordering

SPECIAL FEATURES

A corner garden tub in the private master bath becomes the ultimate retreat from the stresses of everyday life

A large eating area extends off the kitchen featuring a center island and access to the covered porch with outdoor kitchen

A media/hobby room can be found through double doors in the large great room

The unfinished bonus room has an additional 354 square feet of living area

PRICE CODE E

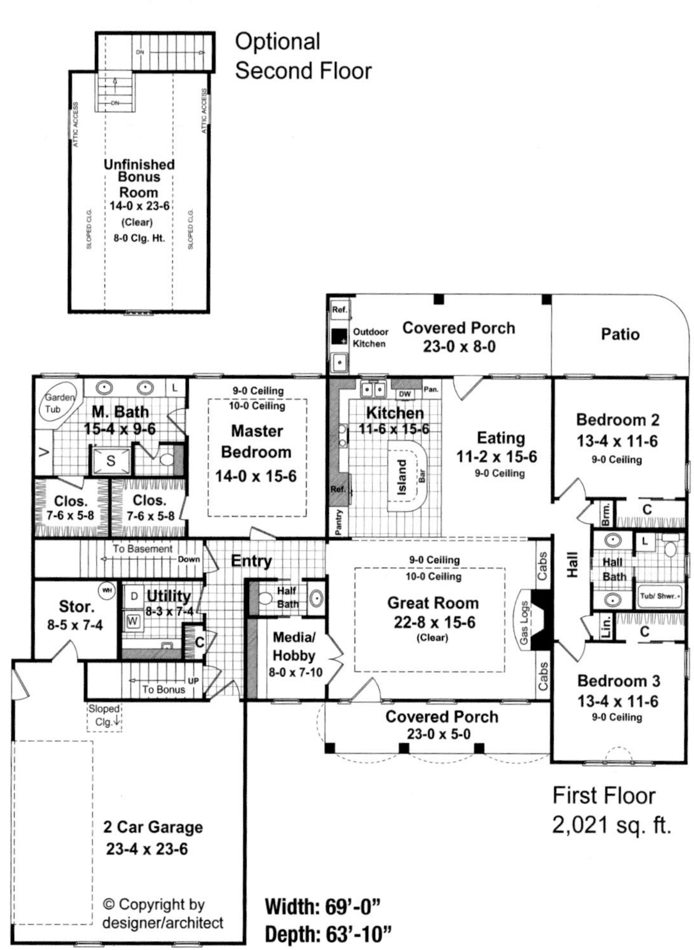

Optional
Second Floor
Unfinished Bonus Room
14-0 x 23-6
(Clear)
8-0 Clg. Ht.
Attic Access
Sloped Clg.
Ref.
Outdoor Kitchen
Covered Porch
23-0 x 8-0
Patio
Garden Tub
M. Bath
15-4 x 9-6
9-0 Ceiling
10-0 Ceiling
Master Bedroom
14-0 x 15-6
Kitchen
11-6 x 15-6
Island
Bar
Pantry
Eating
11-2 x 15-6
9-0 Ceiling
Bedroom 2
13-4 x 11-6
9-0 Ceiling
Clos.
7-6 x 5-8
Clos.
7-6 x 5-8
To Basement
Down
Entry
9-0 Ceiling
10-0 Ceiling
Great Room
22-8 x 15-6
(Clear)
Gas Logs
Cabs
Hall
Hall Bath
Tub/ Shwr.
Stor.
8-5 x 7-4
Utility
8-3 x 7-4
Half Bath
Media/ Hobby
8-0 x 7-10
To Bonus
Sloped Clg.
Covered Porch
23-0 x 5-0
Bedroom 3
13-4 x 11-6
9-0 Ceiling
First Floor
2,021 sq. ft.
2 Car Garage
23-4 x 23-6
© Copyright by designer/architect
Width: 69'-0"
Depth: 63'-10"

To order plans, visit the Menards Building Materials Desk or visit www.Menards.com.

MENARDS

KEMPTON PLACE

Plan #M06-007D-0234

CAR LOVER'S HOME STORES 12 CARS AND RV

2,653 total square feet of living area

3 bedrooms, 2 1/2 baths

12-car garage, 1-RV garage

Walk-out basement foundation

SPECIAL FEATURES

This unique design appears to have only a 3-car garage, but will store and display a collection of 12 mid-size autos plus one small RV in the lower and upper garages accessed from one driveway

The upper garage features a workshop with half bath while the lower garage is open for car maneuvering and placement with light from three 9' glass sliding doors

The mechanical room on the lower level is 151 square feet

PRICE CODE E

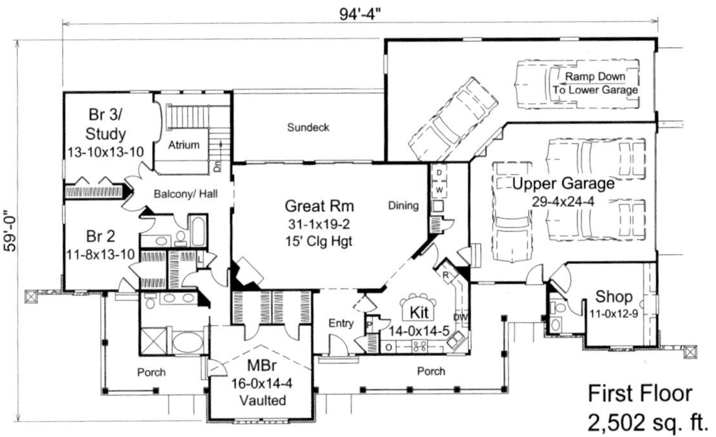

94'-4"
59'-0"
Br 3/
Study
13-10x13-10
Atrium
Dn
Sundeck
Ramp Down
To Lower Garage
Balcony/ Hall
Great Rm
31-1x19-2
15' Clg Hgt
Dining
Upper Garage
29-4x24-4
Br 2
11-8x13-10
Shop
11-0x12-9
Kit
14-0x14-5
Entry
Porch
MBr
16-0x14-4
Vaulted
Porch

First Floor
2,502 sq. ft.

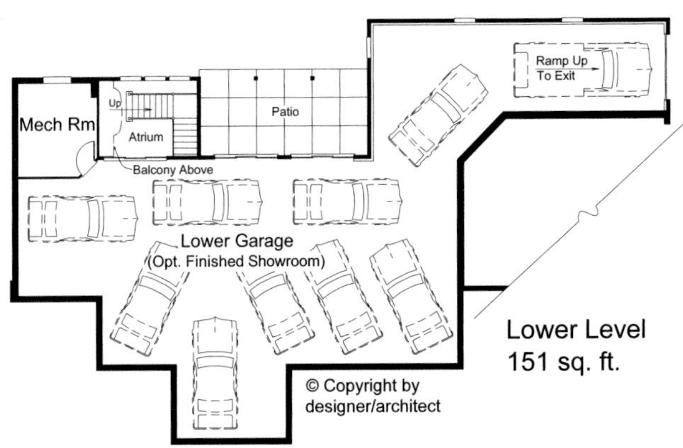

Ramp Up
To Exit
Mech Rm
Up
Atrium
Patio
Balcony Above
Lower Garage
(Opt. Finished Showroom)
© Copyright by
designer/architect

Lower Level
151 sq. ft.

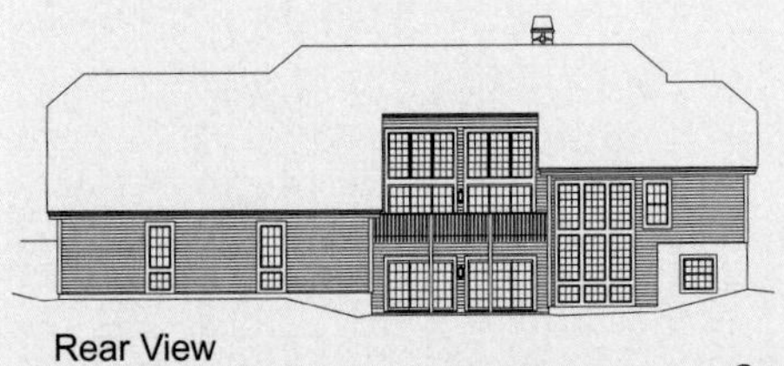

Rear View

To order plans, visit the Menards Building Materials Desk
or visit www.Menards.com.

SAVANNAH

MENARDS

Plan #M06-001D-0080

DOUBLE GABLES FRAME FRONT PORCH

1,832 total square feet of living area

3 bedrooms, 2 baths

2-car detached garage

Crawl space foundation, drawings also include basement and slab foundations

SPECIAL FEATURES

Distinctive master bedroom is enhanced by skylights and a bath with a garden tub, separate shower and a walk-in closet

The U-shaped kitchen features a convenient pantry, laundry area and full view to the breakfast room

The large front porch creates an enjoyable outdoor living

2" x 6" exterior walls available, please order plan #M06-001D-0127

PRICE CODE C

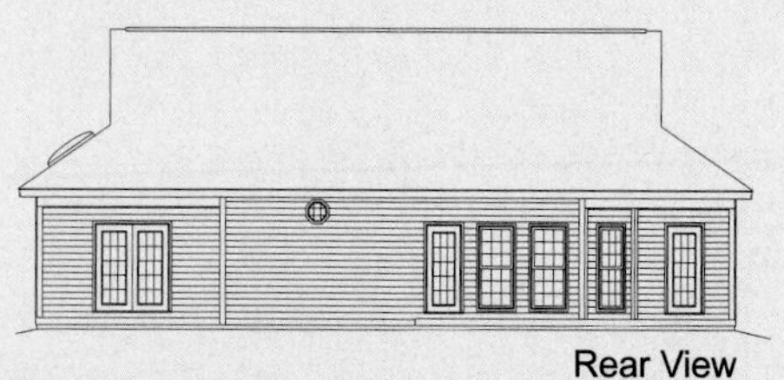

Rear View

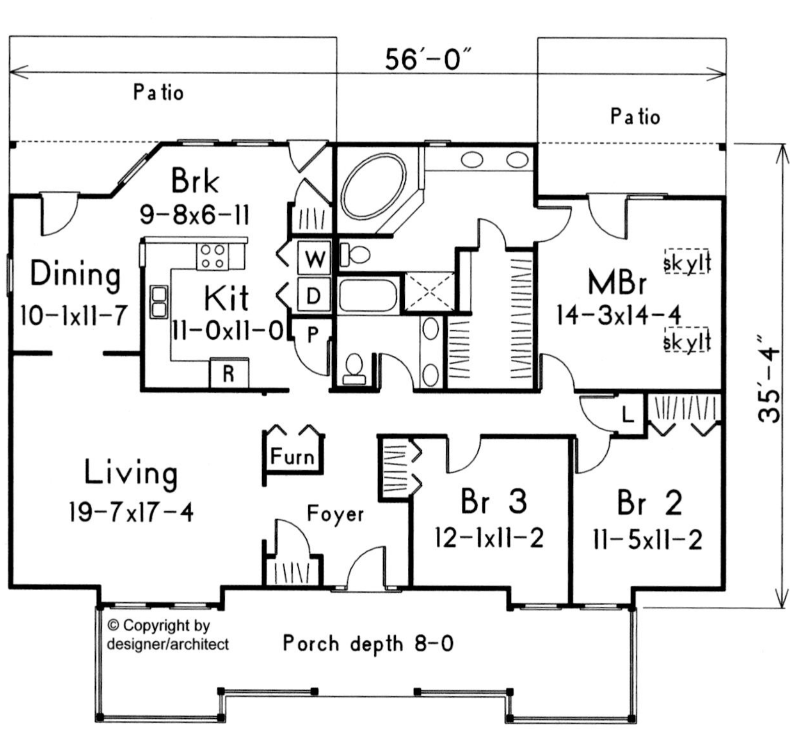
56′-0″
Patio
Patio
Brk
9-8x6-11
Dining
10-1x11-7
Kit
11-0x11-0
W
D
P
R
MBr
14-3x14-4
skylt
skylt
35′-4″
L
Furn
Living
19-7x17-4
Foyer
Br 3
12-1x11-2
Br 2
11-5x11-2
© Copyright by designer/architect
Porch depth 8-0

To order plans, visit the Menards Building Materials Desk or visit www.Menards.com.

MENARDS

FERNLEAF

Plan #M06-055L-0205

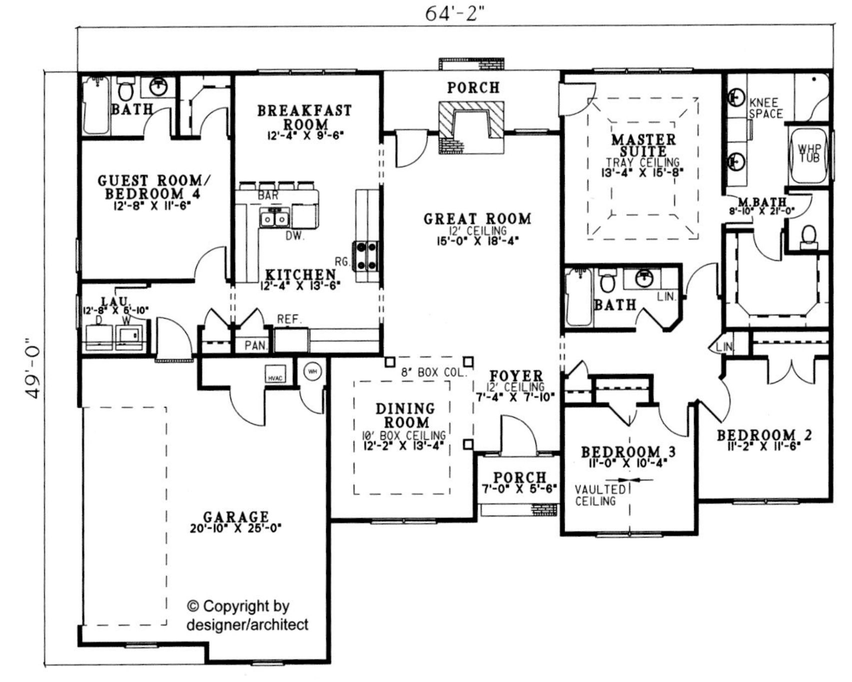

64'-2"
49'-0"
PORCH
BATH
BREAKFAST ROOM
12'-4" X 9'-6"
GUEST ROOM/ BEDROOM 4
12'-8" X 11'-6"
BAR
DW.
RG.
KITCHEN
12'-4" X 13'-6"
GREAT ROOM
12' CEILING
15'-0" X 18'-4"
MASTER SUITE
TRAY CEILING
13'-4" X 15'-8"
KNEE SPACE
WHP TUB
M.BATH
8'-10" X 21'-0"
BATH
LIN.
LIN.
LAU.
12'-8" X 6'-10"
REF.
PAN.
8" BOX COL.
FOYER
12' CEILING
7'-4" X 7'-10"
DINING ROOM
10' BOX CEILING
12'-2" X 13'-4"
PORCH
7'-0" X 5'-6"
BEDROOM 3
11'-0" X 10'-4"
VAULTED CEILING
BEDROOM 2
11'-2" X 11'-6"
GARAGE
20'-10" X 25'-0"
© Copyright by designer/architect

COLUMNS DEFINE DINING ROOM

1,989 total square feet of living area

4 bedrooms, 3 baths

2-car side entry garage

Slab, crawl space, basement or walk-out basement foundation, please specify when ordering

SPECIAL FEATURES

The kitchen includes a counter with seating that opens to the charming breakfast room

The guest bedroom is privately located and includes a bath and walk-in closet

A tray ceiling, deluxe bath and massive walk-in closet enhance the master suite

PRICE CODE D

To order plans, visit the Menards Building Materials Desk or visit www.Menards.com.

EVELYN

MENARDS

Plan #M06-121D-0013

CHARMING HOME WITH ATRIUM

2,100 total square feet of living area

3 bedrooms, 2 baths

2-car garage

Walk-out basement foundation

SPECIAL FEATURES

The spacious great room features a vaulted ceiling, fireplace and staircase to the atrium below

The efficient kitchen has seating for quick and easy meals next to the sunny breakfast area

A bay window, private bath and walk-in closet are some of the amenities of the master bedroom

PRICE CODE B

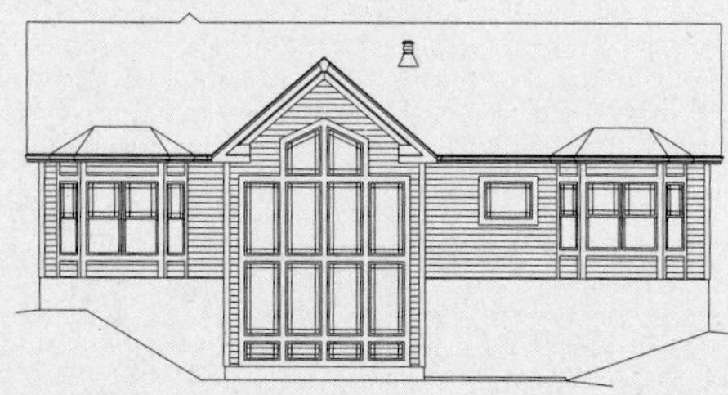

Rear View

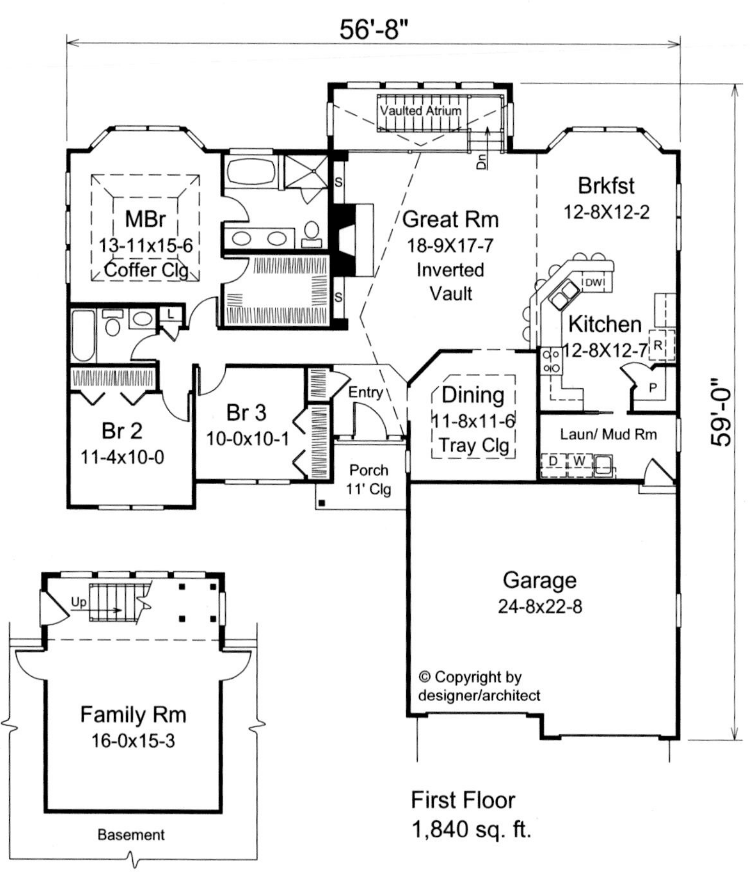
56'-8"
59'-0"
Vaulted Atrium
Dn
MBr
13-11x15-6
Coffer Clg
Great Rm
18-9X17-7
Inverted
Vault
Brkfst
12-8X12-2
DW
Kitchen
12-8X12-7
R
P
Entry
Dining
11-8x11-6
Tray Clg
Laun/ Mud Rm
D
W
Br 2
11-4x10-0
Br 3
10-0x10-1
Porch
11' Clg
Garage
24-8x22-8
© Copyright by
designer/architect
Up
Family Rm
16-0x15-3
Basement
First Floor
1,840 sq. ft.

Lower Level
260 sq. ft.

To order plans, visit the Menards Building Materials Desk or visit www.Menards.com.

MENARDS

SPRING HILL

Plan #M06-068D-0010

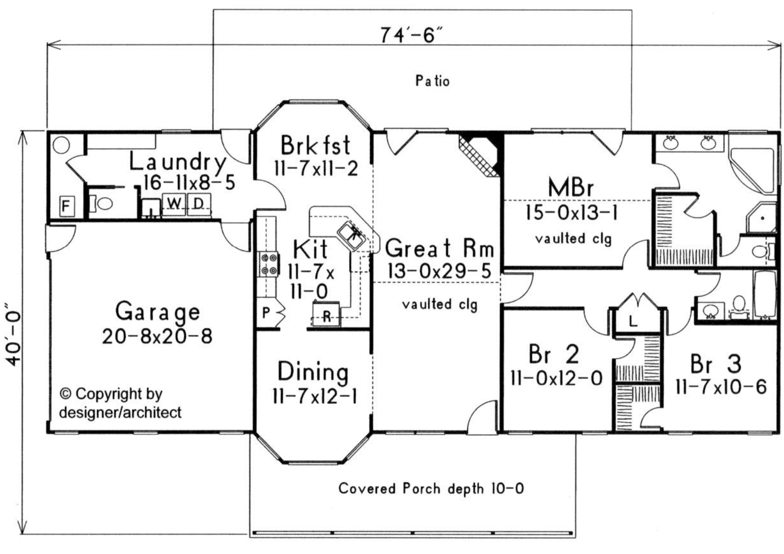

74′-6″
Patio
Laundry
16-11x8-5
F
W D
Brk fst
11-7x11-2
MBr
15-0x13-1
vaulted clg
Kit
11-7x
11-0
P
R
Great Rm
13-0x29-5
vaulted clg
Garage
20-8x20-8
40′-0″
L
Br 2
11-0x12-0
Br 3
11-7x10-6
Dining
11-7x12-1
© Copyright by
designer/architect
Covered Porch depth 10-0

To order plans, visit the Menards Building Materials Desk
or visit www.Menards.com.

BEDROOMS SEPARATE FROM REST OF HOME

1,849 total square feet of living area

3 bedrooms, 2 1/2 baths

2-car side entry garage

Slab foundation, drawings also include crawl space foundation

SPECIAL FEATURES

The enormous laundry room has many extras including a storage area and half bath

The lavish master bath has a corner whirlpool tub, double-bowl vanity, separate shower and walk-in closet

The secondary bedrooms include walk-in closets

The kitchen has a wrap-around eating counter and is positioned between the formal dining area and breakfast room

PRICE CODE C

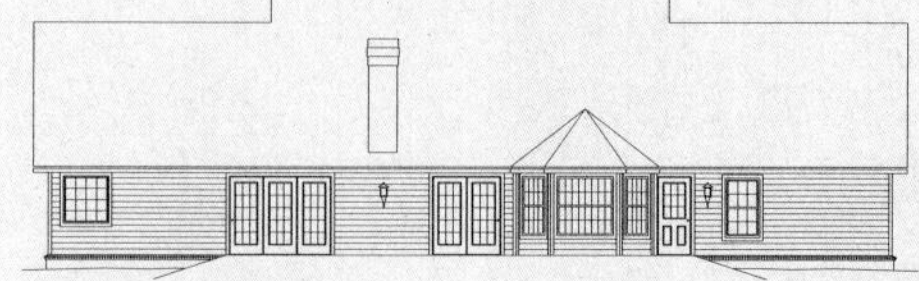

Rear View

MOUNTAINVIEW

MENARDS

Plan #M06-008D-0004

CHARMING COUNTRY FACADE

1,643 total square feet of living area

3 bedrooms, 2 baths

2-car garage

Basement foundation, drawings also include crawl space and slab foundations

SPECIAL FEATURES

An attractive front entry porch gives this ranch a country accent

The spacious family room is the focal point of this design

The kitchen and hobby/laundry room are conveniently located near the gathering areas

The formal living room in the front of the home provides an area for quiet and privacy

The master bedroom has access to a private bath and a generous walk-in closet

PRICE CODE B

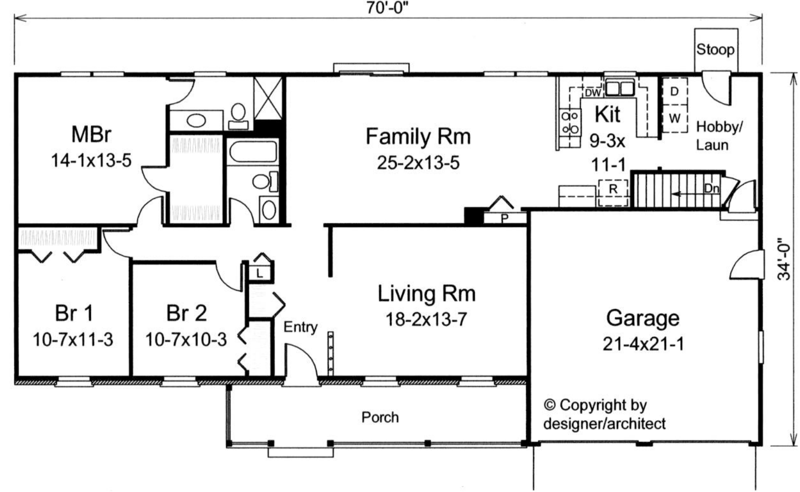
70'-0"
Stoop
DW
Kit
9-3x
11-1
D
W
Hobby/
Laun
MBr
14-1x13-5
Family Rm
25-2x13-5
R
Dn
P
Br 1
10-7x11-3
Br 2
10-7x10-3
L
Entry
Living Rm
18-2x13-7
Garage
21-4x21-1
34'-0"
Porch
© Copyright by
designer/architect

To order plans, visit the Menards Building Materials Desk or visit www.Menards.com.

MENARDS

LAKE ARGYLE

Plan #M06-007D-0214

48'-0"
31'-0"
Deck
Dn
Dining
11-4x14-0
vaulted
Atrium
Dn
Hall
P
Great Room
16-0x16-2
vaulted
MBr
13-5x15-0
vaulted
12'-4" Clg
Kitchen
11-0x11-4
vaulted
R
DW
L
Entry
Porch

First Floor
1,168 sq. ft.

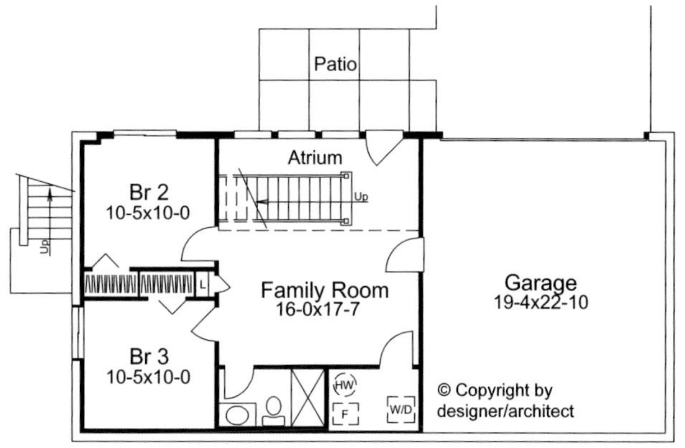
Patio
Atrium
Br 2
10-5x10-0
Up
Up
L
Family Room
16-0x17-7
Garage
19-4x22-10
Br 3
10-5x10-0
HW
F
W/D
© Copyright by
designer/architect

Lower Level
512 sq. ft.

To order plans, visit the Menards Building Materials Desk
or visit www.Menards.com.

TERRIFIC LAKE HOUSE

1,680 total square feet of living area

3 bedrooms, 2 1/2 baths

2-car drive under rear entry garage

Walk-out basement foundation

SPECIAL FEATURES

The vaulted great room, dining and kitchen borrow space and natural light from the atrium to create spacious living

A vaulted ceiling, double entry doors, luxurious bath and large walk-in closet are features of the master bedroom

The lower level consists of a family room/atrium, two secondary bedrooms, a full bath, mechanical closet/laundry and a two-car rear entry garage

PRICE CODE B

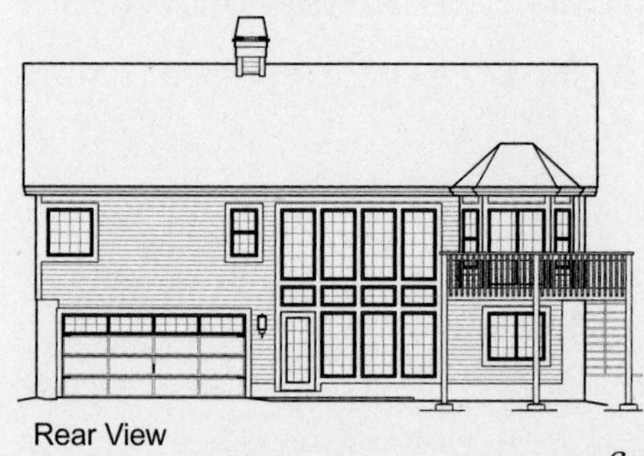

Rear View

LOCKWOOD

MENARDS

Plan #M06-007D-0050

PRESTIGE ABOUNDS IN A CLASSIC RANCH

2,723 total square feet of living area

3 bedrooms, 2 1/2 baths

3-car side entry garage

Basement foundation

SPECIAL FEATURES

A large porch invites you into an elegant foyer that accesses a vaulted study with private hall and coat closet

The great room is second to none, comprised of a fireplace, built-in shelves, a vaulted ceiling and a 1 1/2 story window wall

A spectacular hearth room with vaulted ceiling and masonry fireplace opens to an elaborate kitchen featuring two snack bars, a cooking island and walk-in pantry

PRICE CODE E

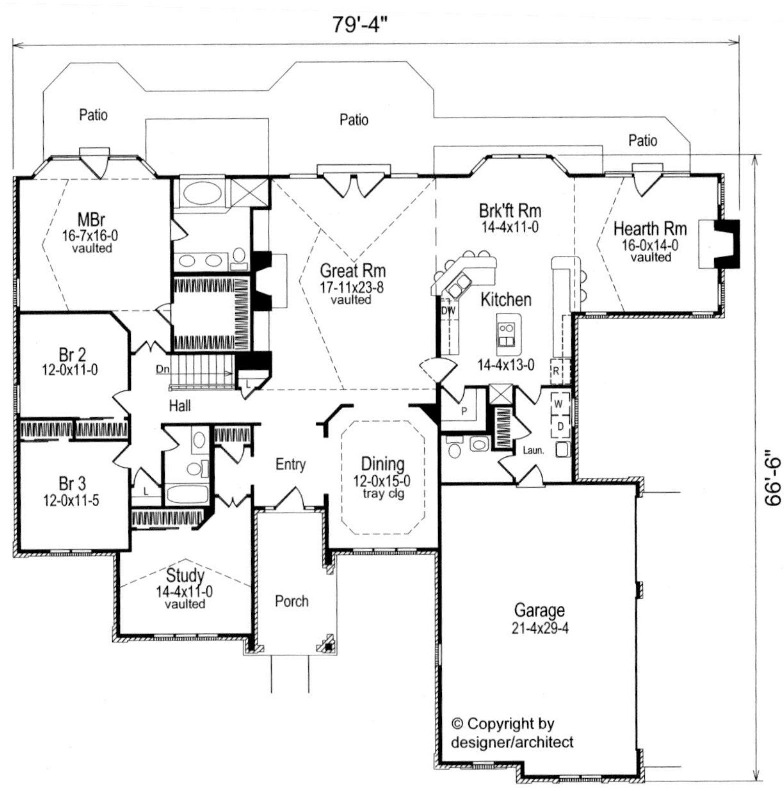
79'-4"
Patio
Patio
Patio
MBr
16-7x16-0
vaulted
Great Rm
17-11x23-8
vaulted
Brk'ft Rm
14-4x11-0
Hearth Rm
16-0x14-0
vaulted
Kitchen
14-4x13-0
DW
Br 2
12-0x11-0
Dn
Hall
Br 3
12-0x11-5
Entry
Dining
12-0x15-0
tray clg
P
R
W
D
Laun.
Study
14-4x11-0
vaulted
Porch
Garage
21-4x29-4
© Copyright by
designer/architect
66'-6"

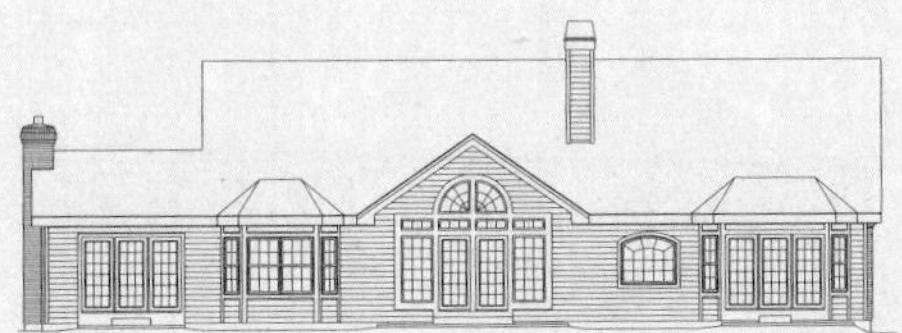

Rear View

To order plans, visit the Menards Building Materials Desk or visit www.Menards.com.

MENARDS

BRISBANE BAY

Plan #M06-055L-0026

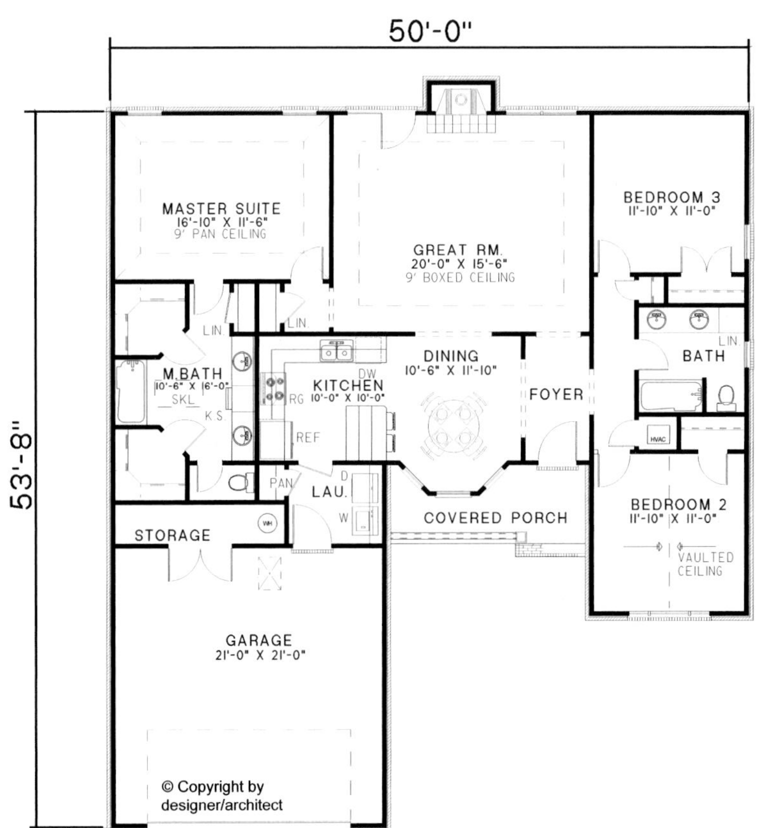

50'-0"
53'-8"
MASTER SUITE
16'-10" X 11'-6"
9' PAN CEILING
GREAT RM.
20'-0" X 15'-6"
9' BOXED CEILING
BEDROOM 3
11'-10" X 11'-0"
LIN
LIN
M.BATH
10'-6" X 16'-0"
SKL
KS
KITCHEN
10'-0" X 10'-0"
RG
DW
REF
DINING
10'-6" X 11'-10"
FOYER
BATH
LIN
HMAC
PAN
LAU.
D
W
WH
COVERED PORCH
BEDROOM 2
11'-10" X 11'-0"
VAULTED
CEILING
STORAGE
GARAGE
21'-0" X 21'-0"
© Copyright by
designer/architect

To order plans, visit the Menards Building Materials Desk or visit www.Menards.com.

BAYED DINING ROOM

1,538 total square feet of living area

3 bedrooms, 2 baths

2-car garage

Slab, walk-out basement, basement, or crawl space foundation, please specify when ordering

SPECIAL FEATURES

Energy efficient home with 2" x 6" exterior walls

Dining and great rooms are highlighted in this design

The master suite has many amenities including double walk-in closets in the private bath

Traditional ranch facade looks great in any neighborhood

PRICE CODE B

BARRON

MENARDS

Plan #M06-077L-0142

MAJESTIC, CENTRAL GREAT ROOM

2,067 total square feet of living area

3 bedrooms, 2 1/2 baths

2-car garage

Slab or crawl space foundation, please specify when ordering

SPECIAL FEATURES

An enormous master bath has separate vanities, a whirlpool tub and a walk-in closet on each end

The flex space would make an excellent formal dining room or home office space

The rear covered porch is a fantastic outdoor retreat and leads onto the open patio

The unfinished bonus room has an additional 379 square feet of living area

PRICE CODE E

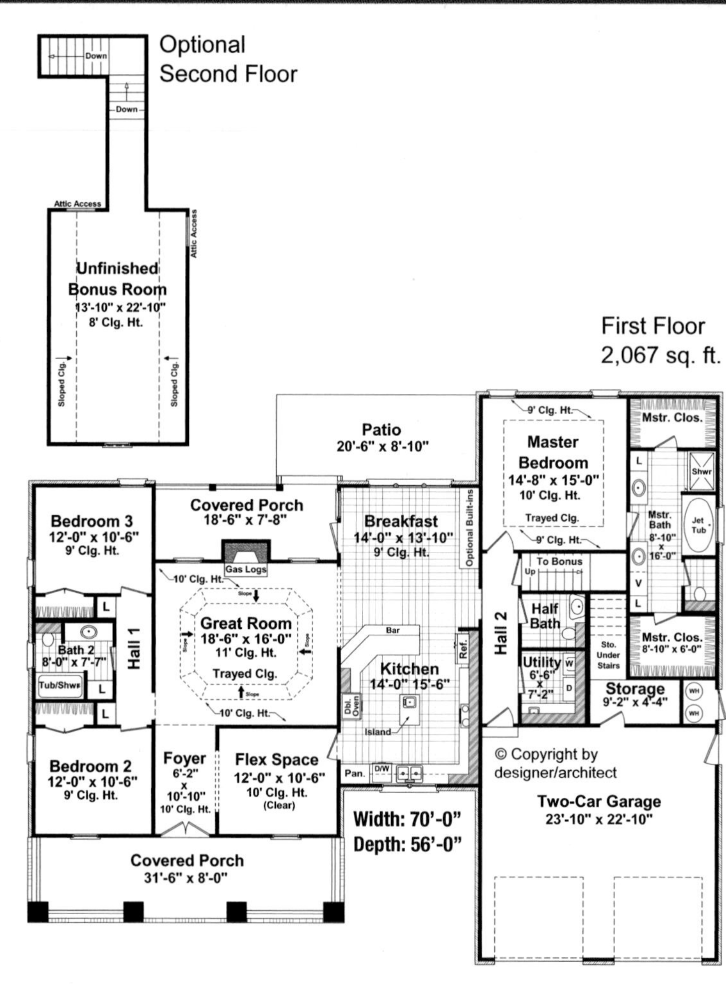

Optional
Second Floor
Down
Attic Access
Unfinished
Bonus Room
13'-10" x 22'-10"
8' Clg. Ht.
Sloped Clg.
First Floor
2,067 sq. ft.
Patio
20'-6" x 8'-10"
Master
Bedroom
14'-8" x 15'-0"
10' Clg. Ht.
Trayed Clg.
9' Clg. Ht.
Mstr. Clos.
Shwr
Mstr.
Bath
8'-10" x 16'-0"
Jet Tub
Bedroom 3
12'-0" x 10'-6"
9' Clg. Ht.
Covered Porch
18'-6" x 7'-8"
Breakfast
14'-0" x 13'-10"
9' Clg. Ht.
Optional Built-ins
Gas Logs
10' Clg. Ht.
Great Room
18'-6" x 16'-0"
11' Clg. Ht.
Trayed Clg.
To Bonus
Up
Half
Bath
Hall 2
Mstr. Clos.
8'-10" x 6'-0"
Bath 2
8'-0" x 7'-7"
Tub/Shwr
Hall 1
Bar
Kitchen
14'-0" x 15'-6"
Dbl. Oven
Island
Ref.
Utility
6'-6" x 7'-2"
Sto. Under Stairs
Storage
9'-2" x 4'-4"
Bedroom 2
12'-0" x 10'-6"
9' Clg. Ht.
Foyer
6'-2" x 10'-10"
10' Clg. Ht.
Flex Space
12'-0" x 10'-6"
10' Clg. Ht.
(Clear)
Pan.
D/W
© Copyright by
designer/architect
Two-Car Garage
23'-10" x 22'-10"
Width: 70'-0"
Depth: 56'-0"
Covered Porch
31'-6" x 8'-0"

To order plans, visit the Menards Building Materials Desk or visit www.Menards.com.

MENARDS

SALINAS

Plan #M06-039L-0026

MULTIPLE WALK-IN CLOSETS

1,542 total square feet of living area

3 bedrooms, 2 baths

2-car garage

Crawl space or slab foundation, please specify when ordering

SPECIAL FEATURES

Varied ceiling heights throughout this home help create a distinctive interior

The master suite encourages privacy and contains a full bath and walk-in closet

The kitchen island incorporates the cooktop creating more counterspace

PRICE CODE C

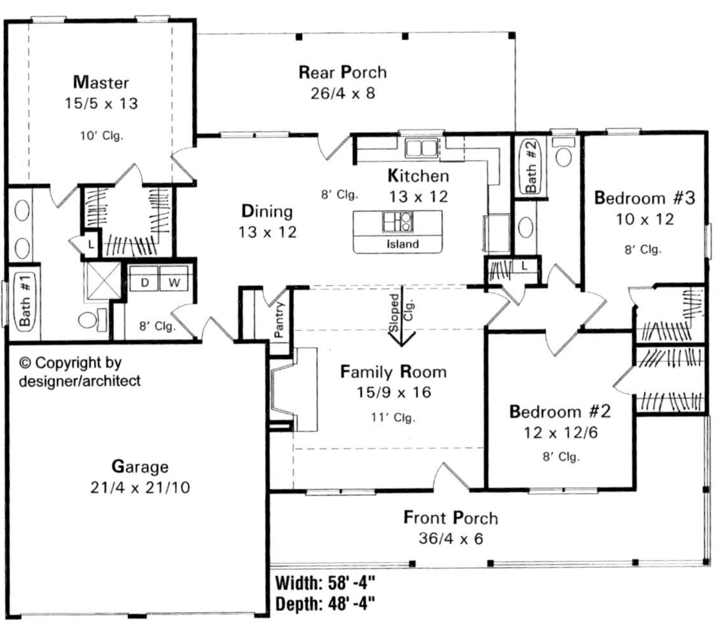

Master
15/5 x 13
10' Clg.
Rear Porch
26/4 x 8
Kitchen
13 x 12
8' Clg.
Island
Dining
13 x 12
Bath #2
Bedroom #3
10 x 12
8' Clg.
L
D
W
Bath #1
8' Clg.
Pantry
Sloped Clg.
L
© Copyright by designer/architect
Family Room
15/9 x 16
11' Clg.
Bedroom #2
12 x 12/6
8' Clg.
Garage
21/4 x 21/10
Front Porch
36/4 x 6
Width: 58' -4"
Depth: 48' -4"

To order plans, visit the Menards Building Materials Desk
or visit www.Menards.com.

WYANDOTTE TRAIL

MENARDS

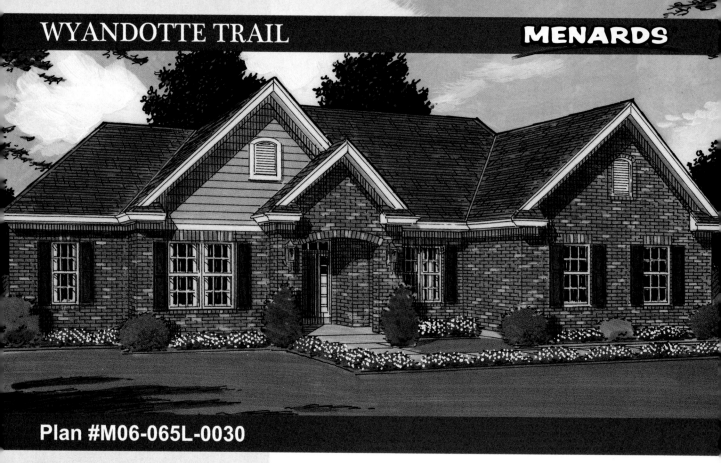

Plan #M06-065L-0030

PERFECT FOR A CASUAL LIFESTYLE

1,860 total square feet of living area

3 bedrooms, 2 baths

2-car side entry garage

Walk-out basement foundation

SPECIAL FEATURES

French doors invite the outdoors in to become part of the great room and breakfast area

The comfortable master bedroom has a deluxe bath, large walk-in closet and a secluded alcove

A convenient snack bar is arranged to offer views to both the breakfast area with angled walls and the great room with fireplace

PRICE CODE C

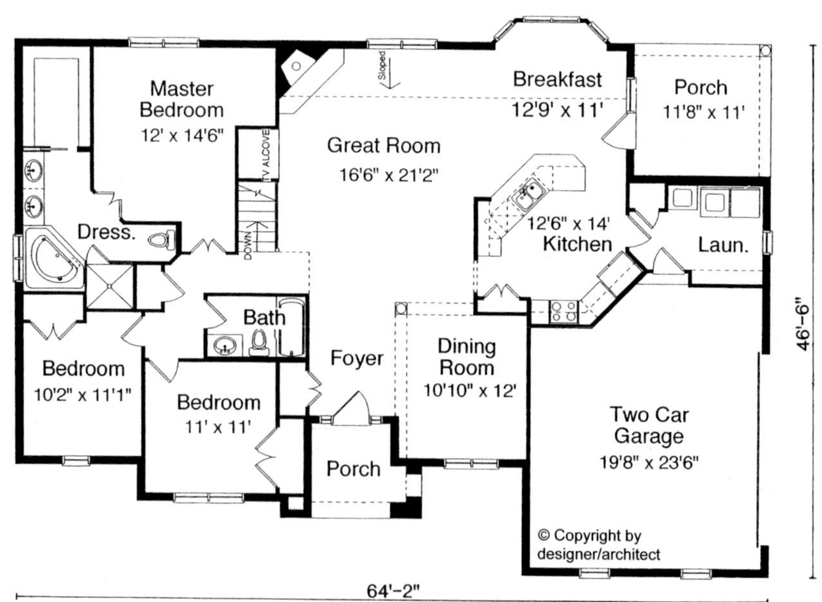

Master Bedroom
12' x 14'6"
Sloped
Breakfast
12'9" x 11'
Porch
11'8" x 11'
TV ALCOVE
Great Room
16'6" x 21'2"
12'6" x 14'
Kitchen
Dress.
DOWN
Laun.
Bath
Bedroom
10'2" x 11'1"
Foyer
Dining Room
10'10" x 12'
Bedroom
11' x 11'
Two Car Garage
19'8" x 23'6"
Porch
46'-6"
© Copyright by designer/architect
64'-2"

To order plans, visit the Menards Building Materials Desk or visit www.Menards.com.

CHESHIRE HILLS

Plan #M06-007D-0207

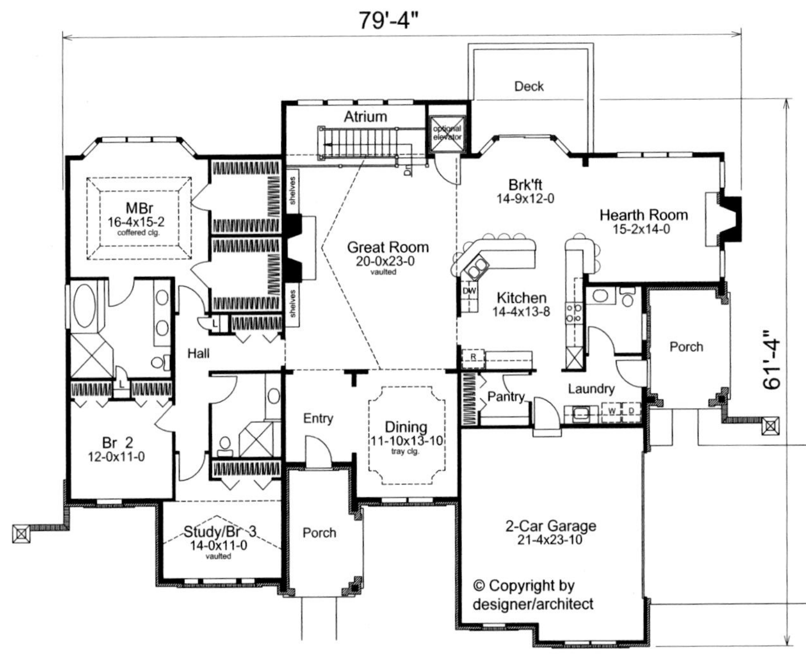
79'-4"
61'-4"
Deck
Atrium
optional elevator
Brk'ft
14-9x12-0
Hearth Room
15-2x14-0
MBr
16-4x15-2
coffered clg.
Great Room
20-0x23-0
vaulted
shelves
Kitchen
14-4x13-8
DW
Porch
Hall
Pantry
Laundry
Entry
Dining
11-10x13-10
tray clg.
Br 2
12-0x11-0
Study/Br 3
14-0x11-0
vaulted
Porch
2-Car Garage
21-4x23-10
© Copyright by
designer/architect

WHEELCHAIR FRIENDLY AND ENERGY EFFICIENT

2,884 total square feet of living area

3 bedrooms, 2 1/2 baths

2-car side entry garage

Walk-out basement foundation

SPECIAL FEATURES

Designed for energy efficiency, this home has R68 ceiling insulation, 2x6 wall construction with R33 insulated vinyl siding, triple-glazed insulated wood windows and doors and a cedar shake roof

All halls, doorways and rooms are designed for wheelchair access

The great room enjoys a fireplace with shelves, space for an optional elevator, and is open to a bright atrium on the lower level with an additional 100 square feet

PRICE CODE D

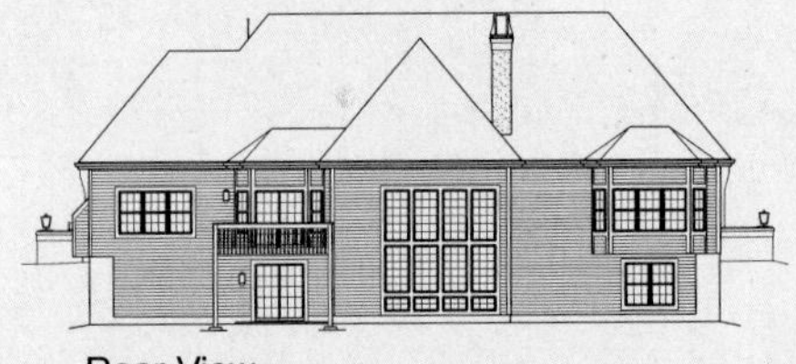

Rear View

To order plans, visit the Menards Building Materials Desk or visit www.Menards.com.

EASTWOOD HILL

MENARDS

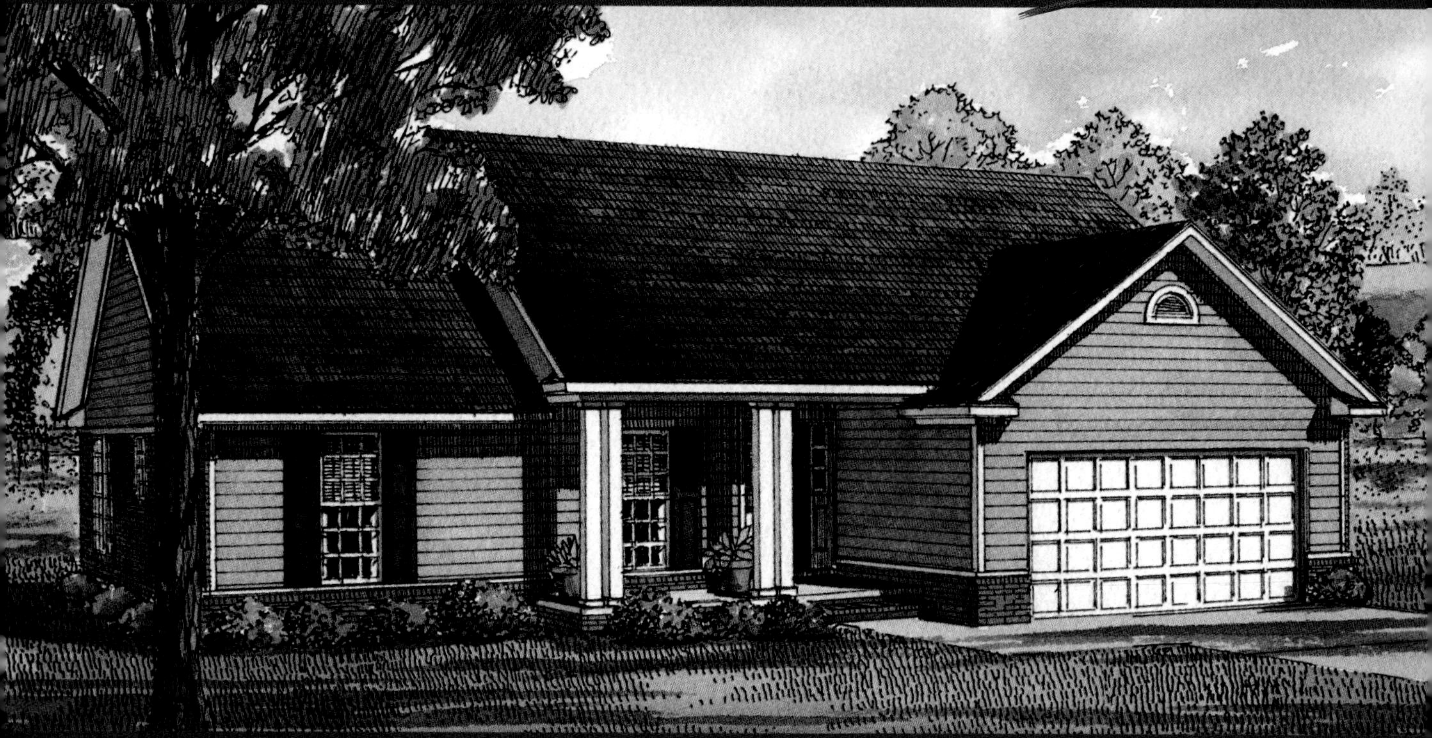

Plan #M06-055L-0017

BUILT-IN COMPUTER DESK

1,525 total square feet of living area

3 bedrooms, 2 baths

2-car garage

Slab, basement, walk-out basement or crawl space foundation, please specify when ordering

SPECIAL FEATURES

A corner fireplace is highlighted in the great room

A unique glass block window over the whirlpool tub in the master bath brightens the interior

An open bar overlooks both the kitchen and great room

The breakfast room leads to an outdoor grilling and covered porch

PRICE CODE D

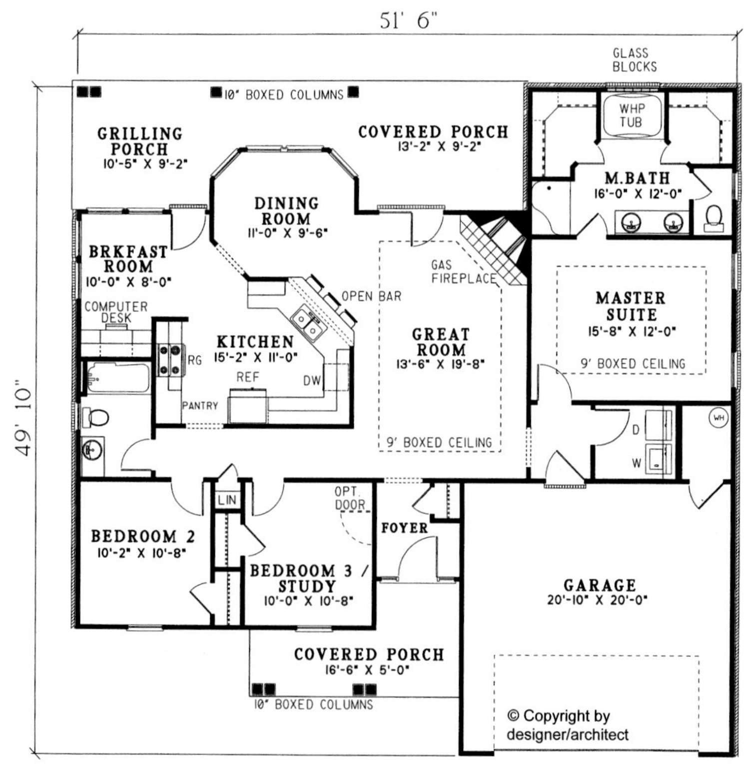

51' 6"
49' 10"
GLASS BLOCKS
10" BOXED COLUMNS
GRILLING PORCH 10'-5" X 9'-2"
COVERED PORCH 13'-2" X 9'-2"
WHP TUB
M.BATH 16'-0" X 12'-0"
DINING ROOM 11'-0" X 9'-6"
BRKFAST ROOM 10'-0" X 8'-0"
GAS FIREPLACE
OPEN BAR
COMPUTER DESK
KITCHEN 15'-2" X 11'-0"
RG
REF
DW
PANTRY
GREAT ROOM 13'-6" X 19'-8"
9' BOXED CEILING
MASTER SUITE 15'-8" X 12'-0"
9' BOXED CEILING
D
W
WH
LIN
OPT. DOOR
FOYER
BEDROOM 2 10'-2" X 10'-8"
BEDROOM 3 / STUDY 10'-0" X 10'-8"
GARAGE 20'-10" X 20'-0"
COVERED PORCH 16'-6" X 5'-0"
10" BOXED COLUMNS

To order plans, visit the Menards Building Materials Desk or visit www.Menards.com.

MENARDS

HAILEY

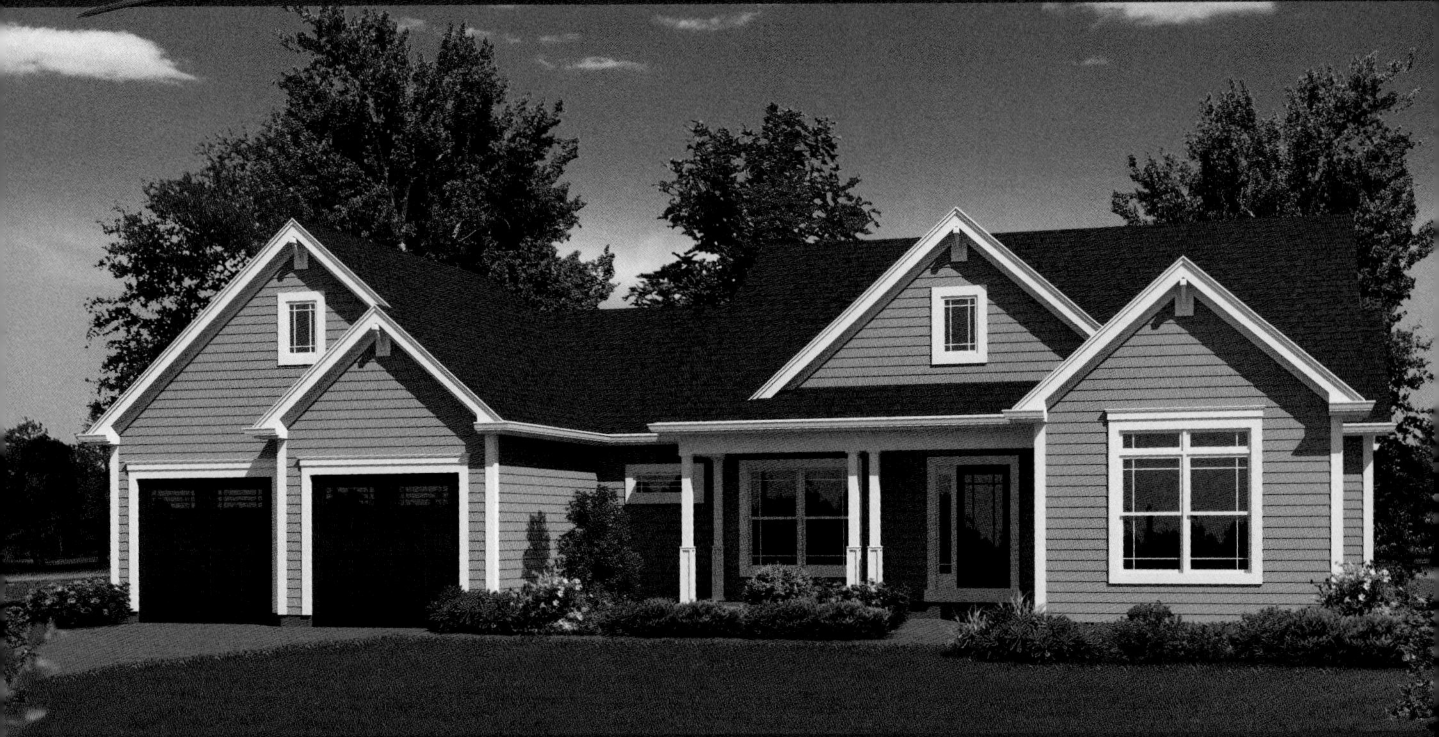

Plan #M06-121D-0020

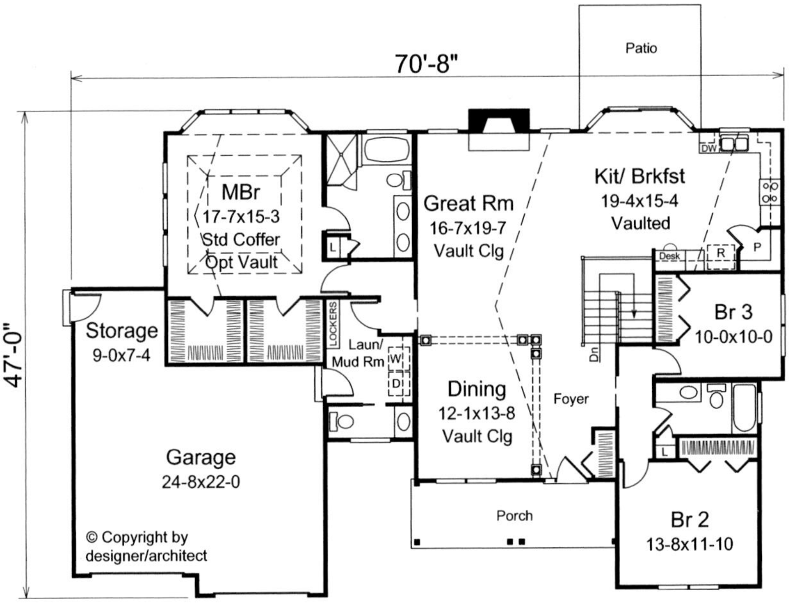

70'-8"
47'-0"
Patio
MBr
17-7x15-3
Std Coffer
Opt Vault
Great Rm
16-7x19-7
Vault Clg
Kit/ Brkfst
19-4x15-4
Vaulted
DW
Desk
R
P
Br 3
10-0x10-0
Storage
9-0x7-4
LOCKERS
Laun/
Mud Rm
W
D
Dn
Dining
12-1x13-8
Vault Clg
Foyer
Garage
24-8x22-0
Porch
Br 2
13-8x11-10

VAULTED CEILINGS ADD CHARISMA

2,037 total square feet of living area

3 bedrooms, 2 1/2 baths

2-car garage

Basement foundation

SPECIAL FEATURES

The vaulted kitchen/breakfast area enjoys a walk-in pantry and a sunny bay window with access to the rear patio

There is extra storage space in the garage that has access to the outdoors

Two spacious walk-in closets and a private bath are some of the amenities of the master bedroom

PRICE CODE B

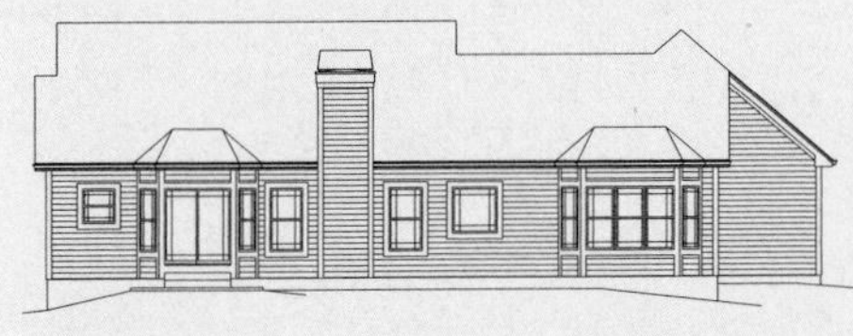

Rear View

To order plans, visit the Menards Building Materials Desk
or visit www.Menards.com.

BOYLAN HEIGHTS

MENARDS

Plan #M06-077L-0181

WELCOMING PORCH

1,919 total square feet of living area

3 bedrooms, 2 1/2 baths

2-car side entry garage

Basement foundation

SPECIAL FEATURES

A raised bar in the kitchen provides excellent serving space

The dining/office is a versatile space that can adapt to your needs

The master bedroom with private bath and walk-in closets is separated from the other bedrooms for privacy

The bonus room above the garage has an additional 338 square feet of living area

PRICE CODE D

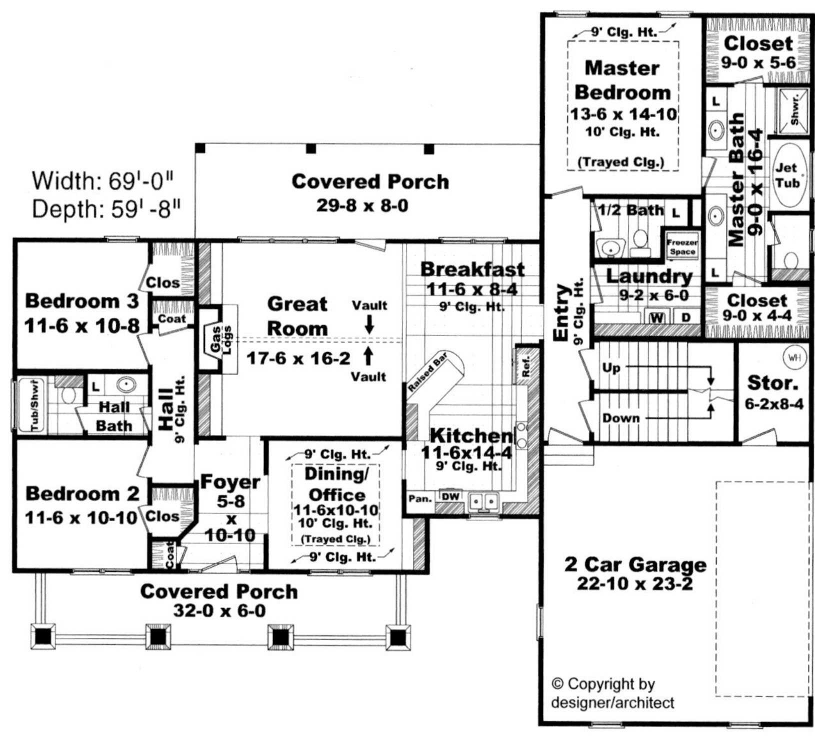

Width: 69'-0"
Depth: 59'-8"
Covered Porch
29-8 x 8-0
Master Bedroom
13-6 x 14-10
10' Clg. Ht.
(Trayed Clg.)
9' Clg. Ht.
Closet
9-0 x 5-6
Master Bath
9-0 x 16-4
Jet Tub
Shwr.
1/2 Bath
Freezer Space
Laundry
9-2 x 6-0
W
D
Closet
9-0 x 4-4
Entry
9' Clg. Ht.
Up
Down
Stor.
6-2x8-4
WH
Bedroom 3
11-6 x 10-8
Clos
Coat
Great Room
17-6 x 16-2
Vault
Vault
Gas Logs
Breakfast
11-6 x 8-4
9' Clg. Ht.
Raised Bar
Ref.
Kitchen
11-6x14-4
9' Clg. Ht.
Pan.
DW
Tub/Shwr
L
Hall Bath
Hall
9' Clg. Ht.
Bedroom 2
11-6 x 10-10
Clos
Coat
Foyer
5-8
x
10-10
Dining/ Office
11-6x10-10
10' Clg. Ht.
(Trayed Clg.)
9' Clg. Ht.
Covered Porch
32-0 x 6-0
2 Car Garage
22-10 x 23-2
© Copyright by designer/architect

To order plans, visit the Menards Building Materials Desk or visit www.Menards.com.

MENARDS

WARREN CLIFF

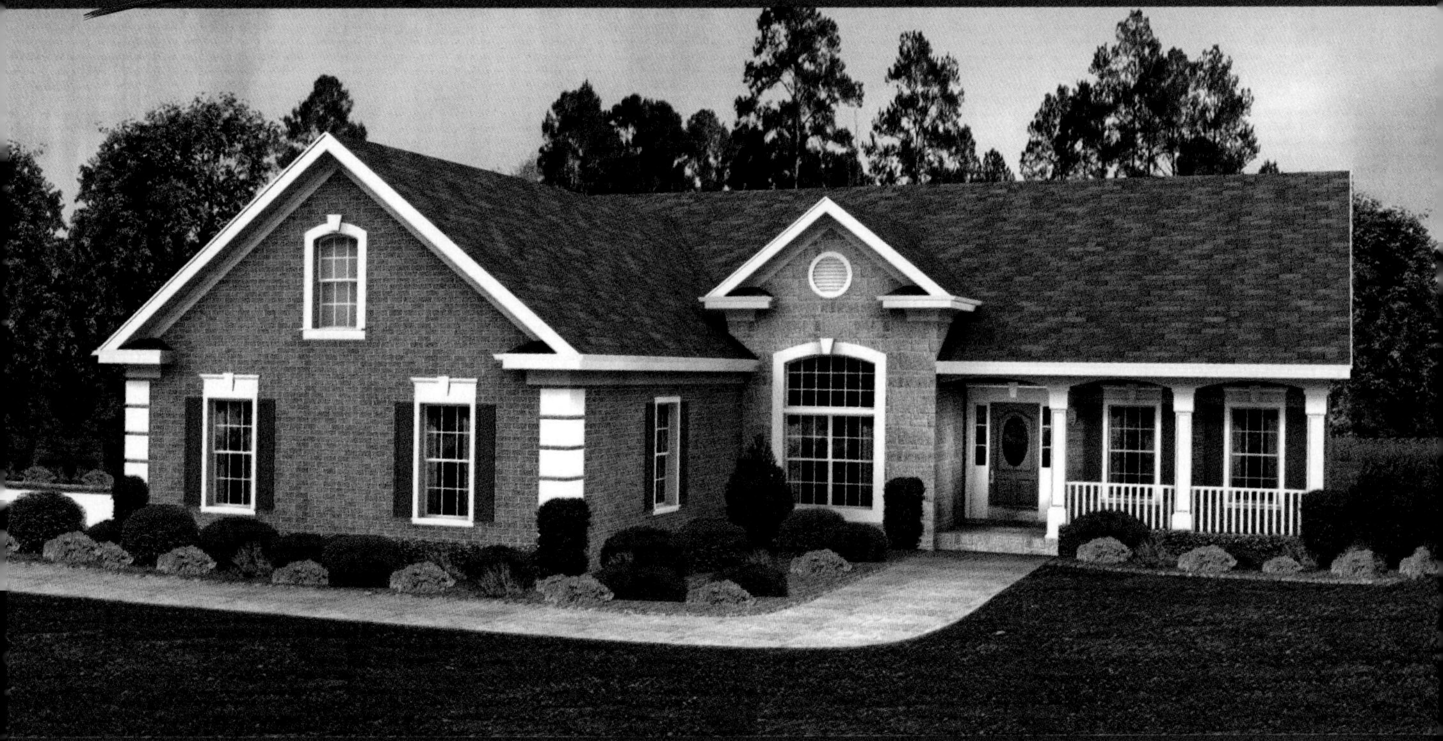

Plan #M06-013L-0046

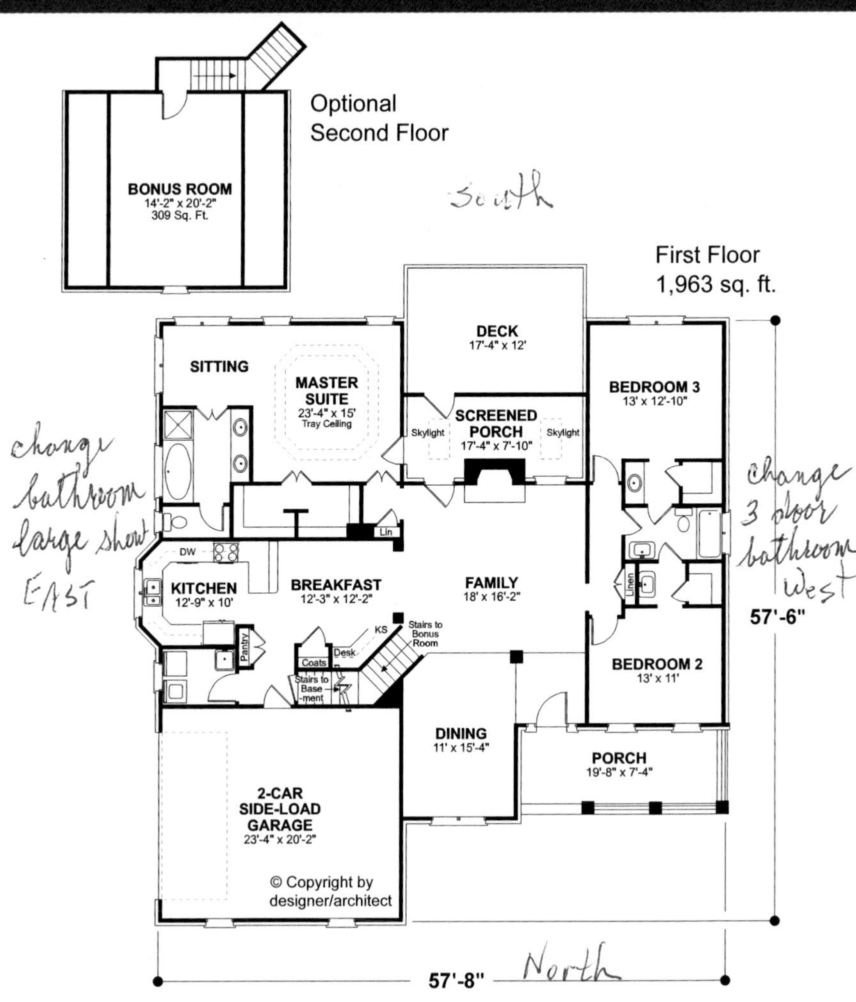

Optional
Second Floor
BONUS ROOM
14'-2" x 20'-2"
309 Sq. Ft.
First Floor
1,963 sq. ft.
SITTING
MASTER SUITE
23'-4" x 15'
Tray Ceiling
DECK
17'-4" x 12'
SCREENED PORCH
17'-4" x 7'-10"
Skylight
Skylight
BEDROOM 3
13' x 12'-10"
DW
Lin
KITCHEN
12'-9" x 10'
BREAKFAST
12'-3" x 12'-2"
FAMILY
18' x 16'-2"
Linen
57'-6"
Pantry
KS
Desk
Coats
Stairs to Bonus Room
Stairs to Base-ment
BEDROOM 2
13' x 11'
DINING
11' x 15'-4"
PORCH
19'-8" x 7'-4"
2-CAR SIDE-LOAD GARAGE
23'-4" x 20'-2"
© Copyright by designer/architect
57'-8"

To order plans, visit the Menards Building Materials Desk or visit www.Menards.com.

FAMILY FRIENDLY HOME

1,963 total square feet of living area

3 bedrooms, 2 baths

2-car side entry garage

Basement foundation

SPECIAL FEATURES

An efficient U-shaped kitchen has counterspace on all sides

The spacious master suite with sunny sitting area makes a quiet retreat

The centrally located family room between all bedroom areas provides a true family gathering area

The screened porch with skylights is well lit, yet sheltered

The second floor bonus room has an additional 309 square feet of living space

PRICE CODE C

COMPTON PLACE

MENARDS

Plan #M06-007D-0213

[illegible] OOM HOME [illegible] ACY ZONES

2,394 total square feet of living area

3 bedrooms, 2 baths

3-car drive under rear entry garage

Walk-out basement foundation

SPECIAL FEATURES

The vaulted living room has a separate entry, arched window and a 14' high see-through fireplace

A large bay window, walk-in pantry and snack bar all help to define the kitchen

Two large bedrooms with walk-in closets share a Jack and Jill bath

The staircase leads to the large laundry room, walk-out basement and three-car garage with shop area

PRICE CODE C

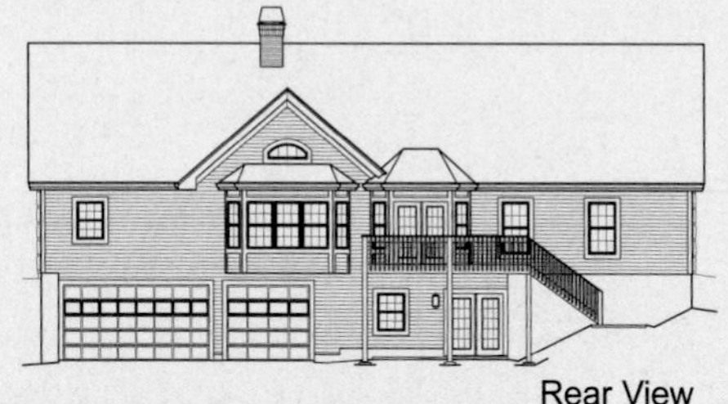

Rear View

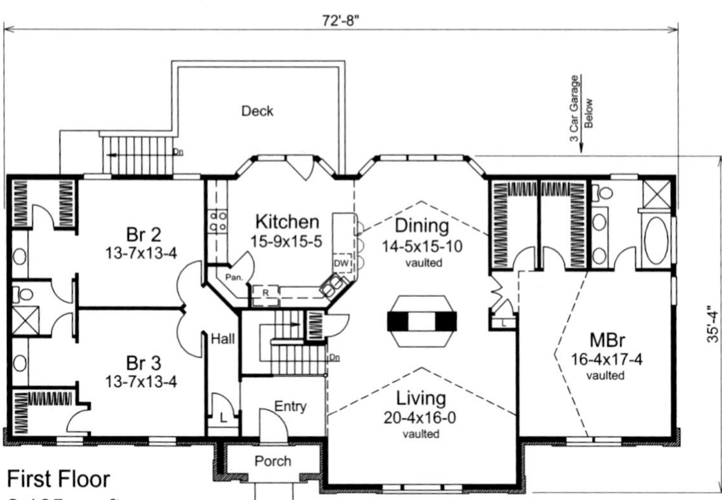
72'-8"
Deck
3 Car Garage Below
Dn
Br 2
13-7x13-4
Kitchen
15-9x15-5
Dining
14-5x15-10
vaulted
Pan.
R
DW
Br 3
13-7x13-4
Hall
Dn
MBr
16-4x17-4
vaulted
35'-4"
L
Entry
Living
20-4x16-0
vaulted
Porch

First Floor
2,165 sq. ft.

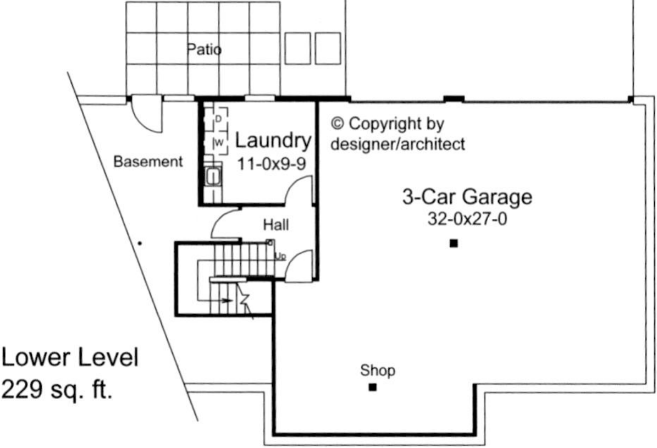
Patio
D
W
Laundry
11-0x9-9
© Copyright by designer/architect
Basement
3-Car Garage
32-0x27-0
Hall
Up
Shop

Lower Level
229 sq. ft.

To order plans, visit the Menards Building Materials Desk or visit www.Menards.com.

SANTA JENITA

Plan #M06-007D-0066

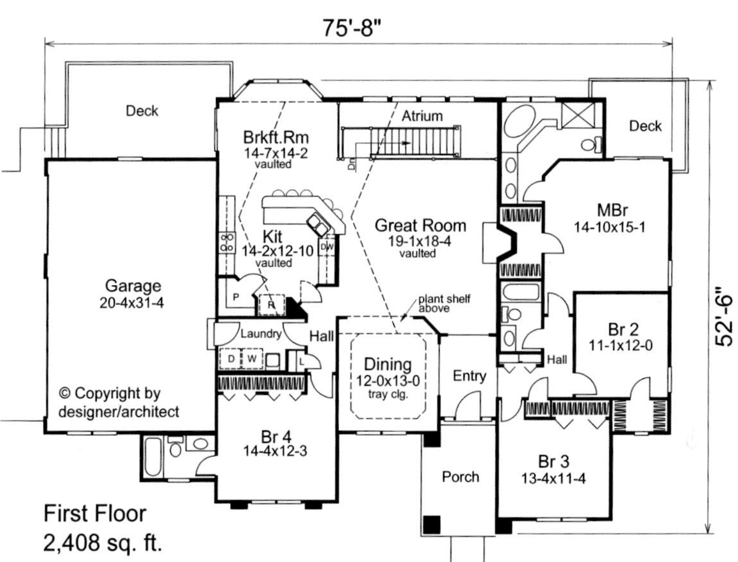
75'-8"
Deck
Brkft.Rm
14-7x14-2
vaulted
Atrium
Dn
Deck
Great Room
19-1x18-4
vaulted
MBr
14-10x15-1
Kit
14-2x12-10
vaulted
DW
Garage
20-4x31-4
P
R
plant shelf above
Laundry
Hall
Dining
12-0x13-0
tray clg.
Entry
Br 2
11-1x12-0
Hall
52'-6"
D
W
L
© Copyright by
designer/architect
Br 4
14-4x12-3
Porch
Br 3
13-4x11-4

First Floor
2,408 sq. ft.

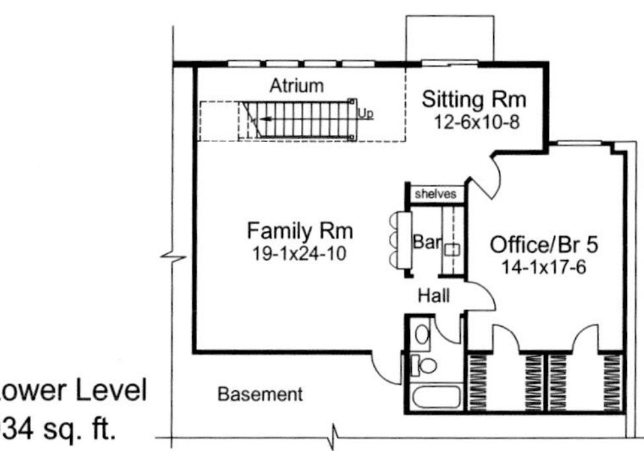
Atrium
Up
Sitting Rm
12-6x10-8
shelves
Family Rm
19-1x24-10
Bar
Office/Br 5
14-1x17-6
Hall
Basement

Lower Level
934 sq. ft.

To order plans, visit the Menards Building Materials Desk
or visit www.Menards.com.

FLORIDIAN ARCHITECTURE WITH MOTHER-IN-LAW SUITE

3,342 total square feet of living area

5 bedrooms, 4 baths

3-car side entry garage

Walk-out basement foundation

SPECIAL FEATURES

Floridian architecture highlights the front facade of this home

Large vaulted great room overlooks an atrium and window wall, adjoins the dining room, spacious breakfast area with bay and pass-through kitchen

Bedroom #4 is perfect for a mother-in-law suite or children home from college, featuring a private bath

PRICE CODE D

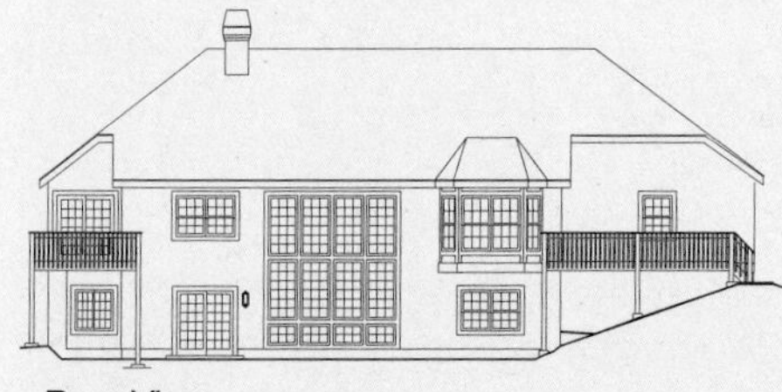

Rear View

STONEHURST

MENARDS

Plan #M06-021D-0006

CHARMING COUNTRY STYLING IN THIS RANCH

1,600 total square feet of living area

3 bedrooms, 2 baths

2-car side entry garage

Slab foundation, drawings also include crawl space and basement foundations

SPECIAL FEATURES

Energy efficient home with 2" x 6" exterior walls

Sunken living room features a massive stone fireplace and 16' vaulted ceiling

The dining room is conveniently located next to the kitchen and divided for privacy

Special amenities include a sewing area, and a large utility area

Sunken master bedroom features a distinctive sitting room

PRICE CODE D

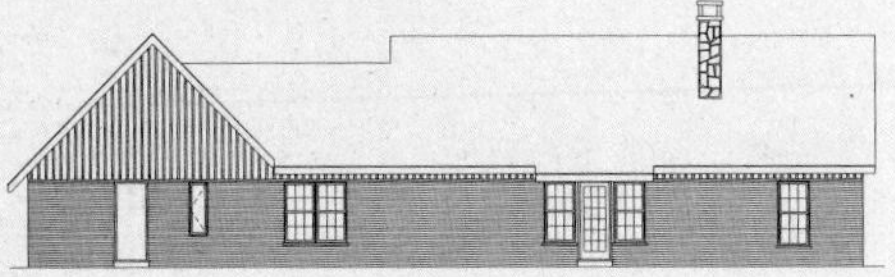

Rear View

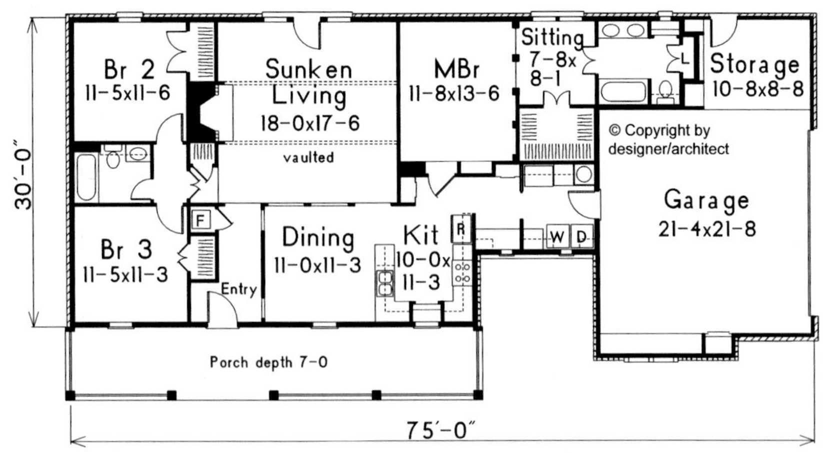

Br 2
11-5x11-6
Sunken
Living
18-0x17-6
vaulted
MBr
11-8x13-6
Sitting
7-8x
8-1
Storage
10-8x8-8
© Copyright by
designer/architect
Garage
21-4x21-8
30'-0"
Br 3
11-5x11-3
F
Entry
Dining
11-0x11-3
Kit
10-0x
11-3
R
W
D
Porch depth 7-0
75'-0"

To order plans, visit the Menards Building Materials Desk or visit www.Menards.com.

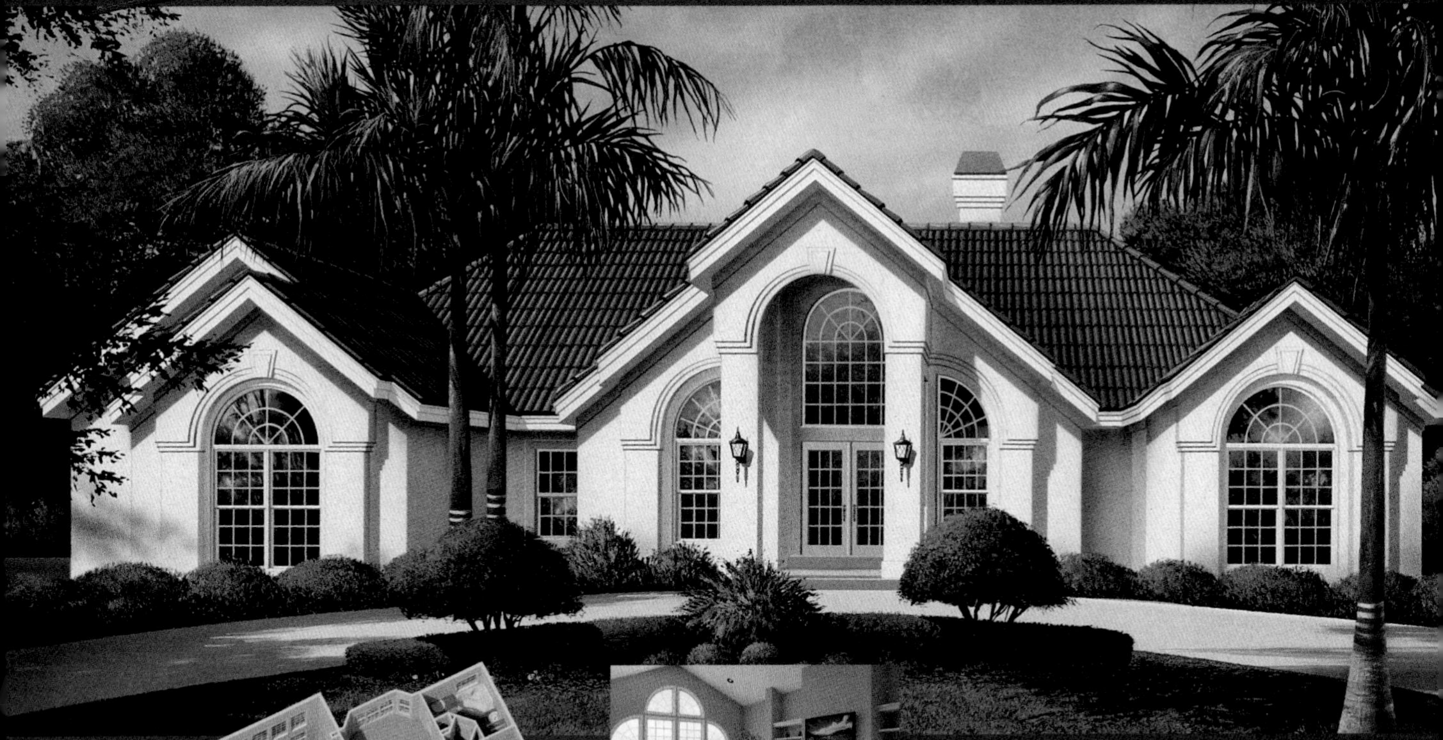

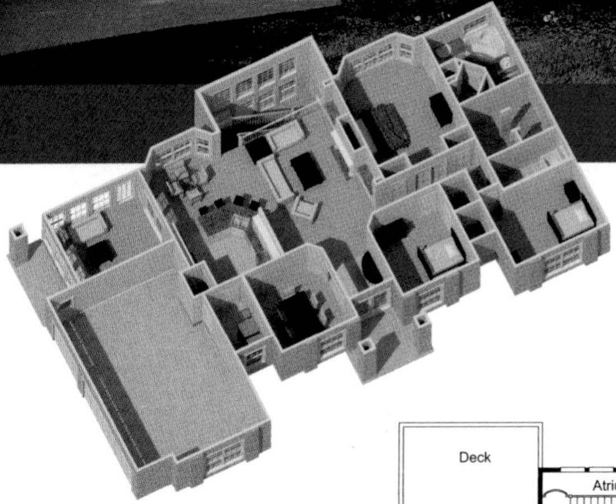

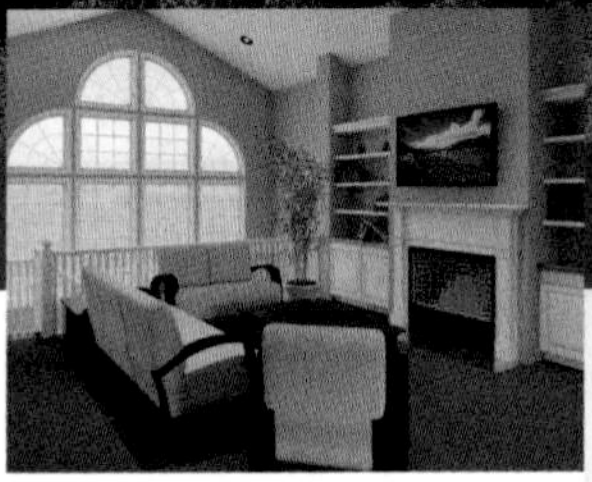

Plan #M06-007D-0098

ATRIUM RANCH WITH TRUE PIZZAZZ

2,398 total square feet of living area

3 bedrooms, 2 baths

3-car side entry garage

Walk-out basement foundation

SPECIAL FEATURES

A grand entry porch leads to a dramatic vaulted entry foyer with a plant shelf

The great room enjoys a 12' vaulted ceiling and atrium featuring 2 1/2 story windows

A conveniently located sunroom and side porch adjoin the breakfast room and garage

763 square feet of optional living area on the lower level

2" x 6" exterior walls available, please order plan #M06-007E-0098

PRICE CODE D

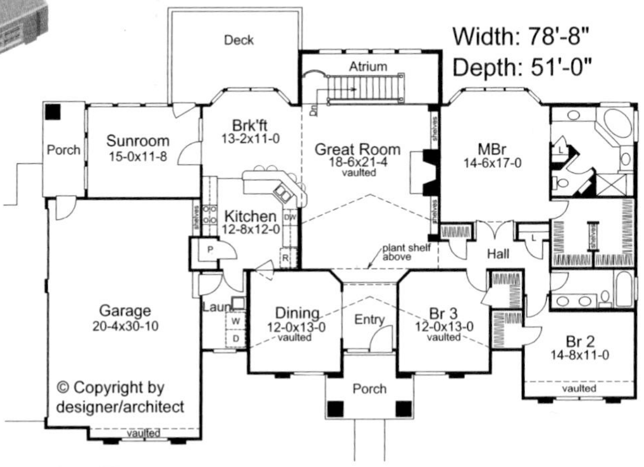

Deck
Atrium
Width: 78'-8"
Depth: 51'-0"
Porch
Sunroom 15-0x11-8
Brk'ft 13-2x11-0
Great Room 18-6x21-4 vaulted
MBr 14-6x17-0
Kitchen 12-8x12-0
plant shelf above
Hall
Garage 20-4x30-10
Laun
Dining 12-0x13-0 vaulted
Entry
Br 3 12-0x13-0 vaulted
Br 2 14-8x11-0
vaulted
Porch

First Floor
2,398 sq. ft.

Atrium
Patio
Opt Family Rm 18-0x21-4
Opt Br 4 14-6x15-7
Hall
Basement

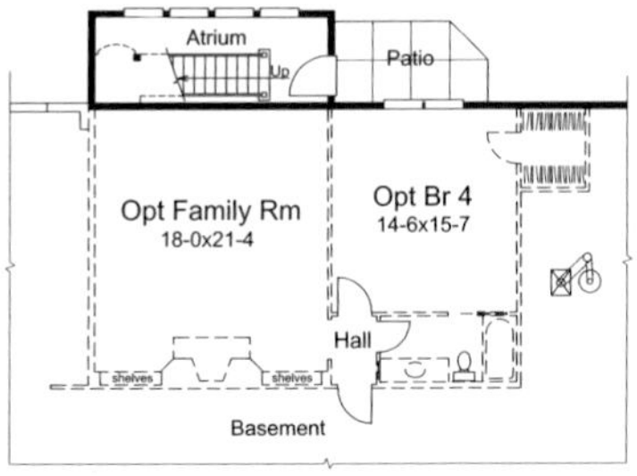

Optional Lower Level

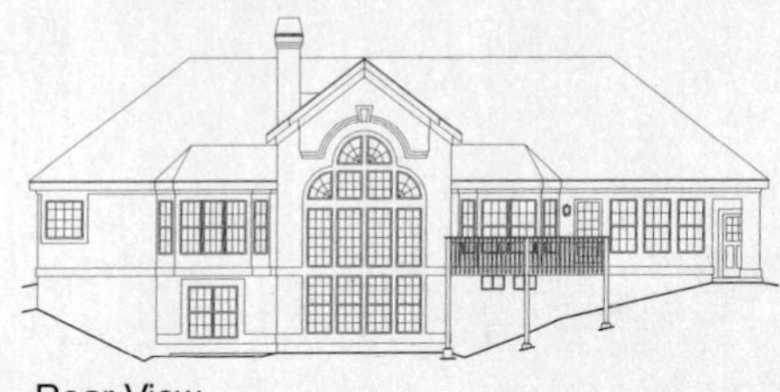

Rear View

To order plans, visit the Menards Building Materials Desk or visit www.Menards.com.

CHERRY SPRING

MENARDS

Plan #M06-055L-0158

OPEN LIVING AREAS

1,636 total square feet of living area

3 bedrooms, 2 baths

2-car garage

Slab or crawl space foundation, please specify when ordering

SPECIAL FEATURES

The grilling porch is large enough for outdoor cooking and entertaining

The bar with seating in the kitchen is great for serving snacks or casual meals

Columns separate the dining room from the rest of the house without enclosing it

PRICE CODE C

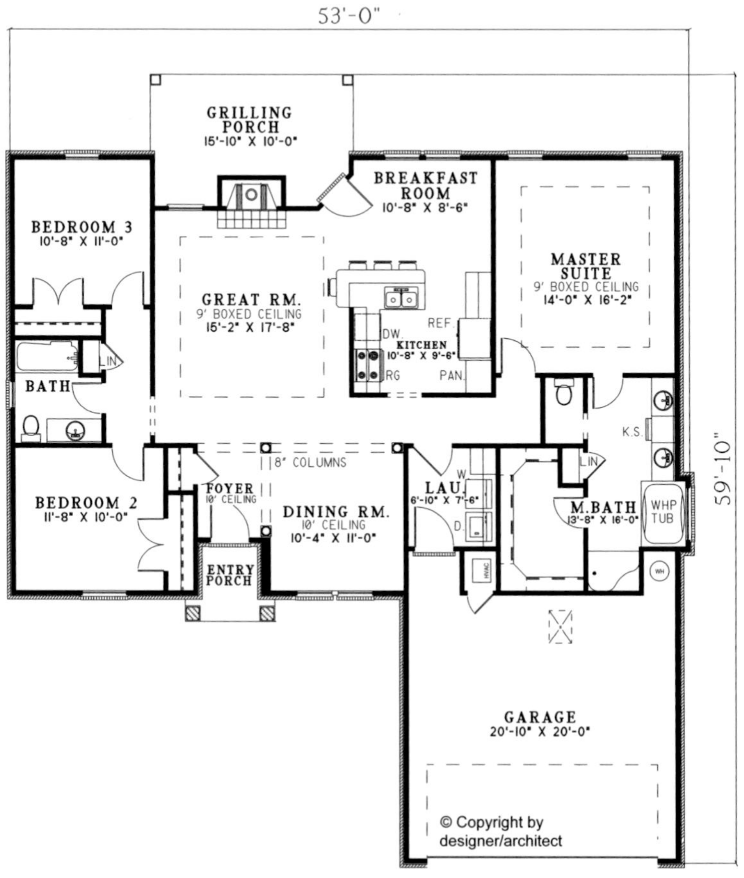

53'-0"
59'-10"
GRILLING PORCH
15'-10" X 10'-0"
BREAKFAST ROOM
10'-8" X 8'-6"
BEDROOM 3
10'-8" X 11'-0"
MASTER SUITE
9' BOXED CEILING
14'-0" X 16'-2"
GREAT RM.
9' BOXED CEILING
15'-2" X 17'-8"
DW
REF
KITCHEN
10'-8" X 9'-6"
RG
PAN.
LIN
BATH
K.S.
8" COLUMNS
LIN
BEDROOM 2
11'-8" X 10'-0"
FOYER
10' CEILING
DINING RM.
10' CEILING
10'-4" X 11'-0"
LAU.
6'-10" X 7'-6"
W
D
M.BATH
13'-8" X 16'-0"
WHP TUB
ENTRY PORCH
GARAGE
20'-10" X 20'-0"
© Copyright by designer/architect

To order plans, visit the Menards Building Materials Desk or visit www.Menards.com.

MENARDS®

SANDRA

Plan #M06-121D-0008

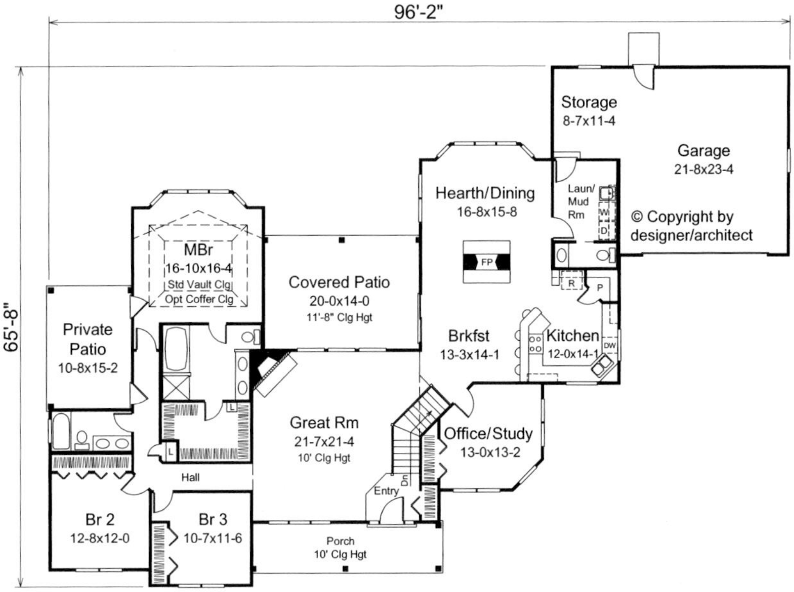

96'-2"
65'-8"
Storage
8-7x11-4
Garage
21-8x23-4
Hearth/Dining
16-8x15-8
Laun/
Mud
Rm
© Copyright by
designer/architect
MBr
16-10x16-4
Std Vault Clg
Opt Coffer Clg
Covered Patio
20-0x14-0
11'-8" Clg Hgt
Private
Patio
10-8x15-2
Brkfst
13-3x14-1
Kitchen
12-0x14-1
Great Rm
21-7x21-4
10' Clg Hgt
Office/Study
13-0x13-2
Hall
Entry
Br 2
12-8x12-0
Br 3
10-7x11-6
Porch
10' Clg Hgt

To order plans, visit the Menards Building Materials Desk or visit www.Menards.com.

GREAT COVERED PATIO FOR OUTDOOR LIVING

2,487 total square feet of living area

3 bedrooms, 2 1/2 baths

2-car garage

Basement foundation

SPECIAL FEATURES

The beautiful vaulted master bedroom features a spacious bath and direct access to a private patio

A see-through fireplace illuminates both the hearth/dining area and the breakfast room while acting as the main focal point in both spaces

A trio of windows, 10' ceiling height and a corner fireplace create a pleasant atmosphere in the great room

PRICE CODE C

Rear View

NATALIE

MENARDS

Plan #M06-121D-0024

CHARMING COUNTRY CRAFTSMAN HOME

1,994 total square feet of living area

3 bedrooms, 2 baths, 2-car garage

Basement foundation

SPECIAL FEATURES

The vaulted entry flows into the spacious great room with corner fireplace and a wall of windows

A large walk-in closet and private bath with double-bowl vanity are some of the amenities of the master bedroom

The kitchen has a walk-in pantry and eating bar that has lovely views of the sunny breakfast area

PRICE CODE B

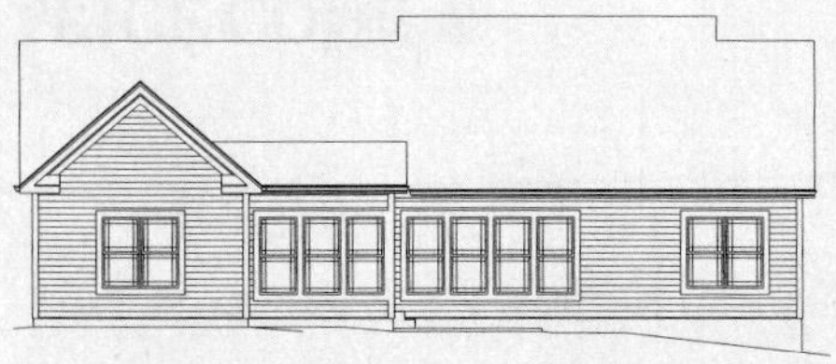

Rear View

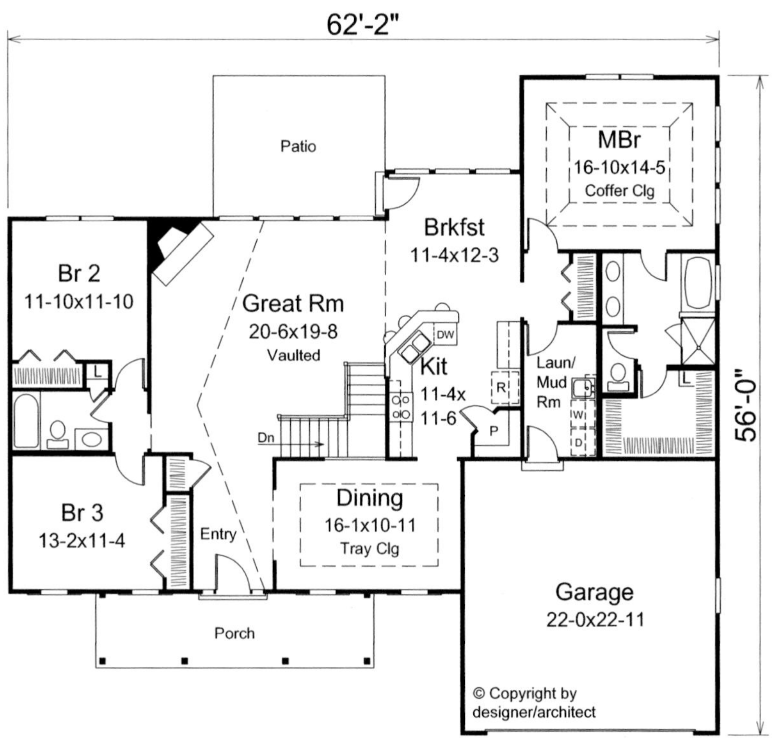
62'-2"
56'-0"
Patio
MBr
16-10x14-5
Coffer Clg
Brkfst
11-4x12-3
Br 2
11-10x11-10
Great Rm
20-6x19-8
Vaulted
DW
Kit
11-4x
11-6
R
P
Laun/
Mud
Rm
W
D
L
Dn
Br 3
13-2x11-4
Entry
Dining
16-1x10-11
Tray Clg
Garage
22-0x22-11
Porch
© Copyright by
designer/architect

To order plans, visit the Menards Building Materials Desk or visit www.Menards.com.

GREENSAVER ATRIUM

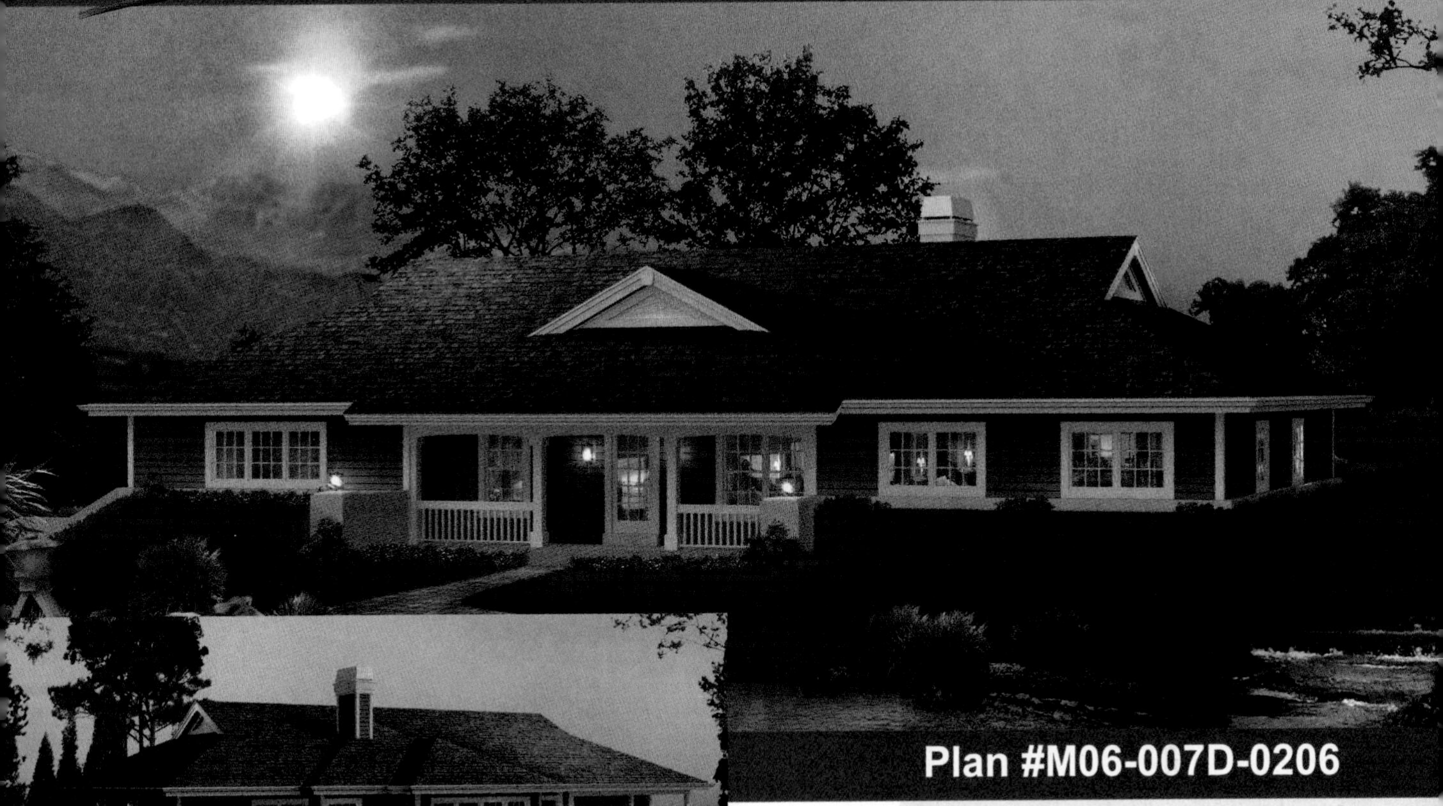

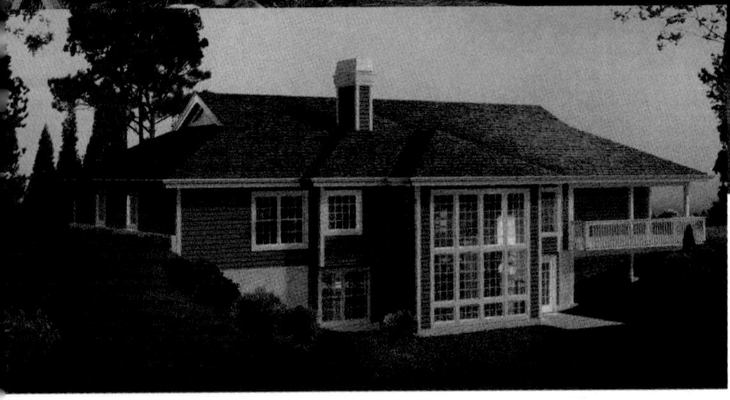

Plan #M06-007D-0206

WHEELCHAIR FRIENDLY & ENERGY EFFICIENT

2,163 total square feet of living area

3 bedrooms, 2 baths

3-car side entry garage

Walk-out basement foundation

SPECIAL FEATURES

Plan includes 2" x 6" and 2" x 8" wall construction and insulated vinyl siding with triple-glazed insulated wood windows and doors

The basement has insulated walls inside and out and a natural cooling system created by a 40' long buried pipe that provides a constant 55-degree earth temperature to help cool the house

The vaulted great room and atrium with two-story window wall provide southern views and warmth from the sun

PRICE CODE C

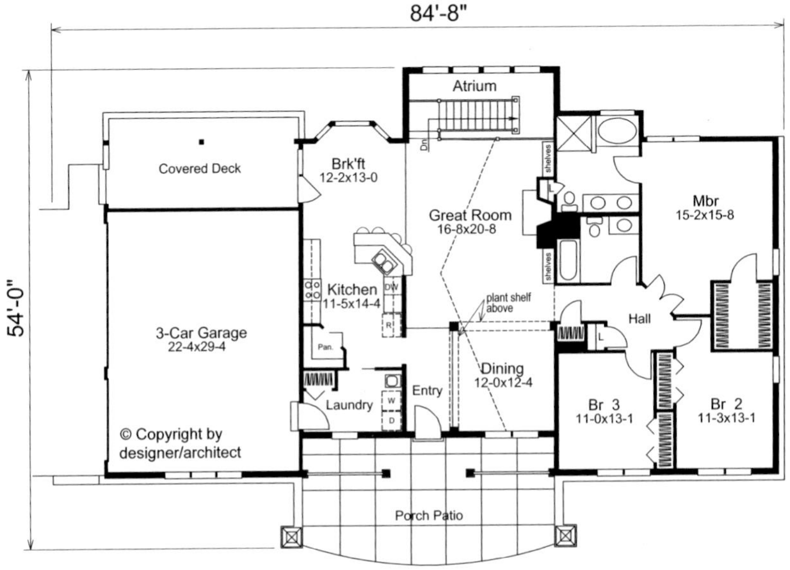

84'-8"

54'-0"

Atrium

Covered Deck

Brk'ft 12-2x13-0

Great Room 16-8x20-8

Mbr 15-2x15-8

Kitchen 11-5x14-4

plant shelf above

Hall

3-Car Garage 22-4x29-4

Dining 12-0x12-4

Entry

Laundry

Br 3 11-0x13-1

Br 2 11-3x13-1

Porch Patio

Rear View

To order plans, visit the Menards Building Materials Desk or visit www.Menards.com.

CARR CREEK

MENARDS

Plan #M06-055L-0203

CENTRALLY LOCATED KITCHEN

2,388 total square feet of living area

4 bedrooms, 2 1/2 baths

2-car side entry garage

Slab or crawl space foundation, please specify when ordering

SPECIAL FEATURES

The foyer opens into the great room that features a gas fireplace, media center and access to the rear porch

Formal dining room, breakfast room with access to the porch and kitchen counter with seating provide plenty of dining space

The master suite enjoys two walk-in closets and a deluxe bath with twin vanities and a whirlpool tub

PRICE CODE D

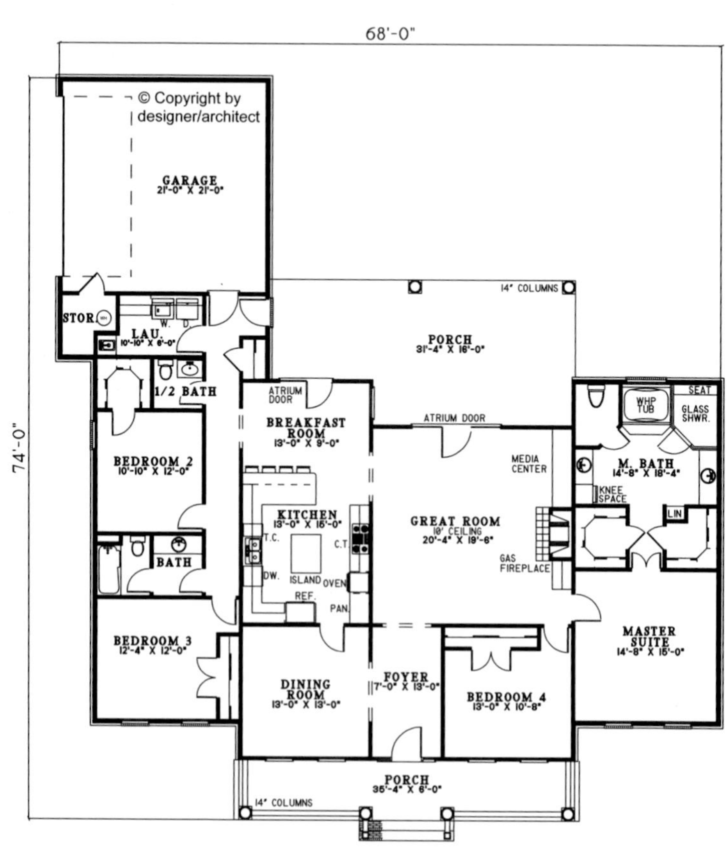

68'-0"
74'-0"
© Copyright by designer/architect
GARAGE 21'-0" X 21'-0"
STOR.
LAU. 10'-10" X 6'-0"
W.
D.
1/2 BATH
14" COLUMNS
PORCH 31'-4" X 16'-0"
ATRIUM DOOR
BREAKFAST ROOM 13'-0" X 9'-0"
ATRIUM DOOR
SEAT
WHP TUB
GLASS SHWR.
BEDROOM 2 10'-10" X 12'-0"
MEDIA CENTER
M. BATH 14'-8" X 18'-4"
KNEE SPACE
LIN
KITCHEN 13'-0" X 16'-0"
T.C.
C.T.
GREAT ROOM 10' CEILING 20'-4" X 19'-6"
BATH
DW.
ISLAND
OVEN
REF.
PAN.
GAS FIREPLACE
BEDROOM 3 12'-4" X 12'-0"
MASTER SUITE 14'-8" X 15'-0"
DINING ROOM 13'-0" X 13'-0"
FOYER 7'-0" X 13'-0"
BEDROOM 4 13'-0" X 10'-8"
PORCH 35'-4" X 6'-0"
14" COLUMNS

To order plans, visit the Menards Building Materials Desk or visit www.Menards.com.

Photo, right - Comfortable and cozy, the family room provides warmth around the fireplace and plenty of places to store family collectibles.

Plan #M06-051L-0246

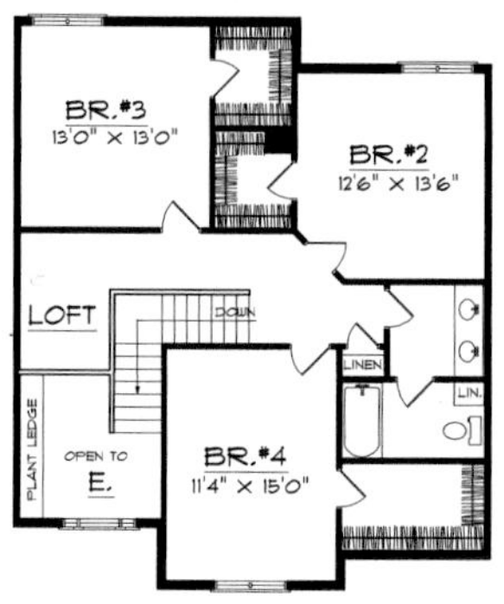

BR.#3
13'0" x 13'0"
BR.#2
12'6" x 13'6"
LOFT
DOWN
LINEN
LIN.
PLANT LEDGE
OPEN TO
E.
BR.#4
11'4" x 15'0"

Second Floor
956 sq. ft.

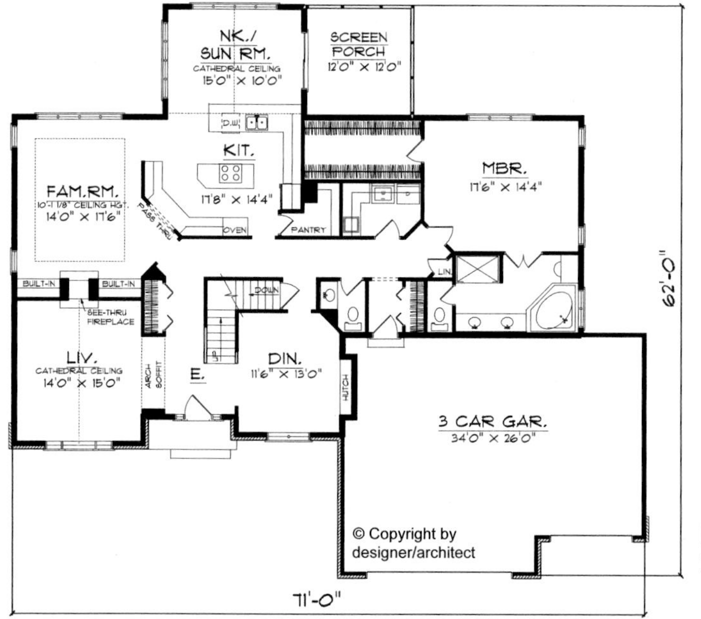

NK./
SUN RM.
CATHEDRAL CEILING
15'0" x 10'0"
SCREEN
PORCH
12'0" x 12'0"
KIT.
17'8" x 14'4"
FAM.RM.
10'-1 1/8" CEILING HGT.
14'0" x 17'6"
PASS THRU
OVEN
PANTRY
MBR.
17'6" x 14'4"
BUILT-IN
BUILT-IN
SEE-THRU
FIREPLACE
LIN
DOWN
LIV.
CATHEDRAL CEILING
14'0" x 15'0"
ARCH. SOFFIT
E.
DIN.
11'6" x 13'0"
HUTCH
3 CAR GAR.
34'0" x 26'0"
62'-0"
71'-0"
© Copyright by
designer/architect

First Floor
2,143 sq. ft.

EVERY BEDROOM HAS A WALK-IN CLOSET

3,099 total square feet of living area

4 bedrooms, 2 1/2 baths

3-car garage

Basement foundation

SPECIAL FEATURES

Energy efficient home with 2" x 6" exterior walls

A see-through fireplace warms both the formal living room and casual family room

The chef of the family will love this gourmet kitchen complete with an abundance of counterspace, a stovetop island and walk-in pantry

The breakfast nook/sun room with access to a screen porch allows the family to enjoy the great outdoors all year long

PRICE CODE F

To order plans, visit the Menards Building Materials Desk
or visit www.Menards.com.

TENNILLE

MENARDS

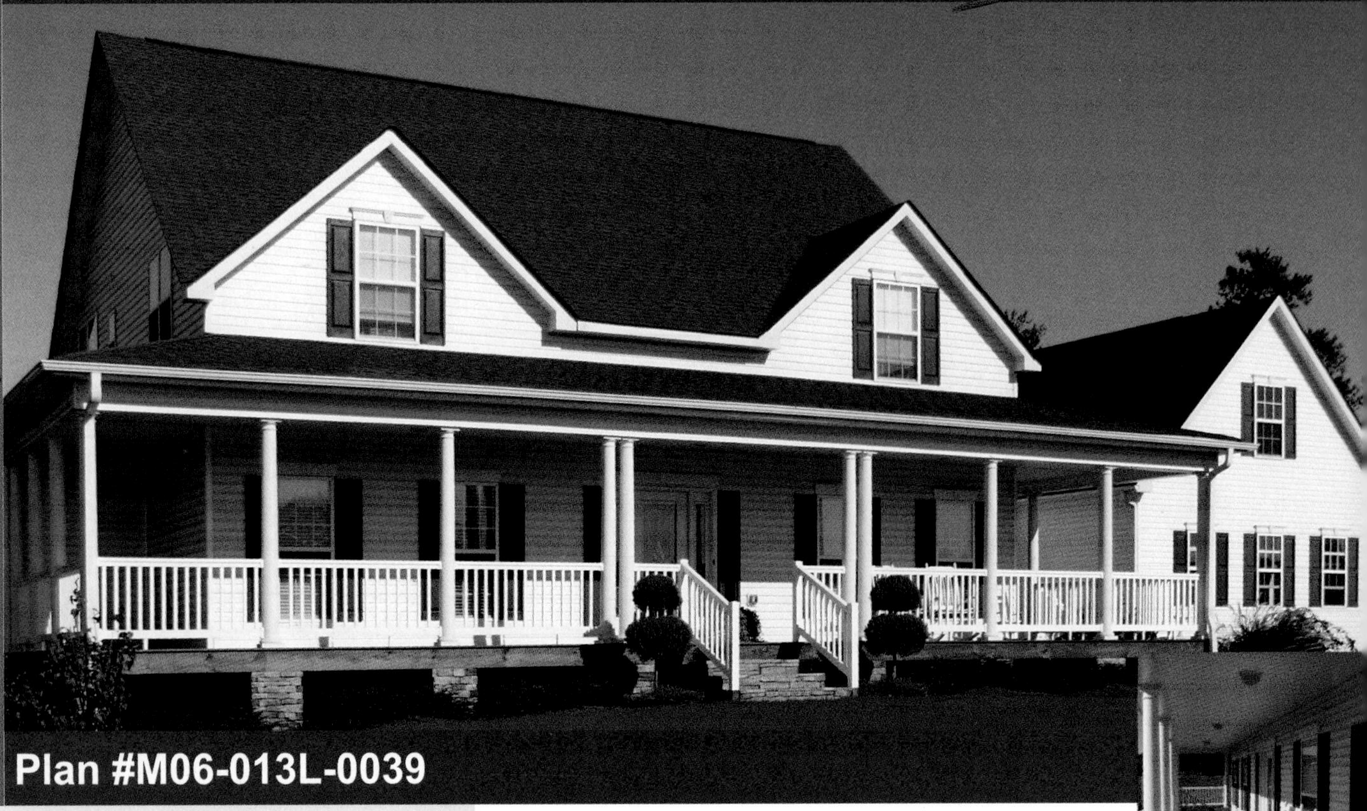

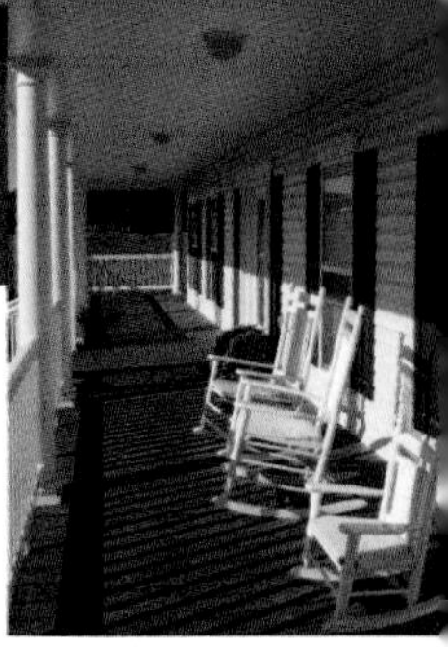

Plan #M06-013L-0039

SPRAWLING FAMILY FARMHOUSE

2,972 total square feet of living area

4 bedrooms, 3 1/2 baths

3-car side entry garage

Walk-out basement, crawl space or slab foundation, please specify when ordering

SPECIAL FEATURES

Extra storage is available beyond bedroom #2 on the second floor

An angled staircase in the entry adds interest

A charming screened porch is accessible from the breakfast area

The bonus room above the garage has an additional 396 square feet of living area

PRICE CODE E

BEDROOM 4
14'9" x 13'0"
OPEN BELOW
BEDROOM 3
14'9" x 13'0"
OPEN BELOW
BEDROOM 2
14'9" x 15'5"

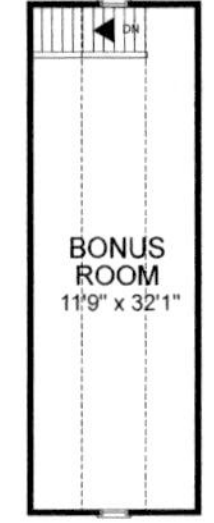
BONUS ROOM
11'9" x 32'1"

Second Floor
986 sq. ft.

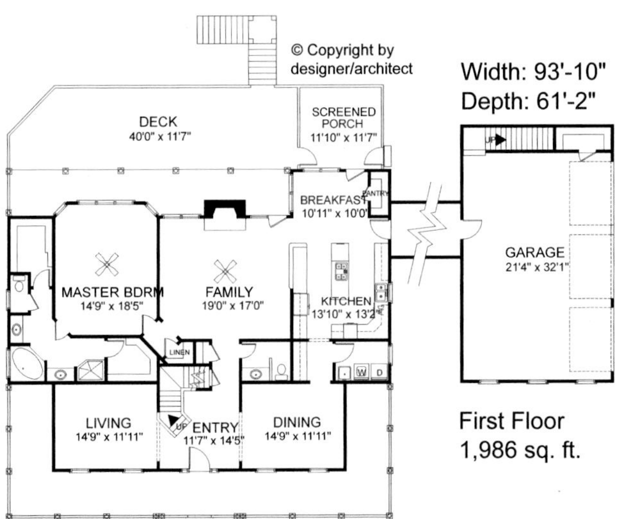
DECK
40'0" x 11'7"
SCREENED PORCH
11'10" x 11'7"
BREAKFAST
10'11" x 10'0"
MASTER BDRM
14'9" x 18'5"
FAMILY
19'0" x 17'0"
KITCHEN
13'10" x 13'2"
GARAGE
21'4" x 32'1"
LINEN
LIVING
14'9" x 11'11"
ENTRY
11'7" x 14'5"
DINING
14'9" x 11'11"

Width: 93'-10"
Depth: 61'-2"

First Floor
1,986 sq. ft.

To order plans, visit the Menards Building Materials Desk or visit www.Menards.com.

BERGAMO MANOR

Plan #M06-055L-0817

EUROPEAN LUXURY

2,889 total square feet of living area

4 bedrooms, 2 1/2 baths

2-car garage

Crawl space or slab foundation, please specify when ordering

SPECIAL FEATURES

Stone, a striking turret and decorative roof lines accent this home and give it a European flair

The luxurious first floor offers a massive great room, plush master suite, quiet office and access to the outdoor living porch furnished with a stone hearth fireplace

The second floor consists of three bedrooms, a shared bath and handy computer center

The second floor bonus room has an additional 378 square feet of living area

PRICE CODE E

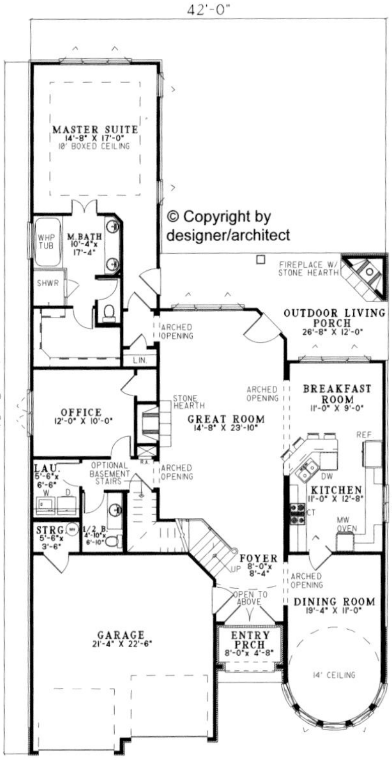

First Floor
1,819 sq. ft.

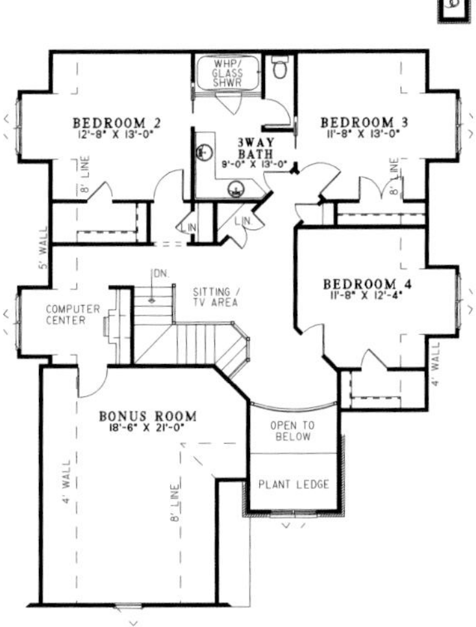

BEDROOM 2
12'-8" X 13'-0"
BEDROOM 3
11'-8" X 13'-0"
3WAY BATH
9'-0" X 13'-0"
BEDROOM 4
11'-8" X 12'-4"
COMPUTER CENTER
SITTING / TV AREA
BONUS ROOM
18'-6" X 21'-0"
OPEN TO BELOW
PLANT LEDGE

Second Floor
1,070 sq. ft.

To order plans, visit the Menards Building Materials Desk or visit www.Menards.com.

OXFORD PARK

MENARDS

Plan #M06-072L-1123

STYLISH CRAFTSMAN SYMMETRY

2,715 total square feet of living area

4 bedrooms, 2 1/2 baths

4-car garage

Walk-out basement or basement foundation, please specify when ordering

SPECIAL FEATURES

Energy efficient home with 2" x 6" exterior walls

The cheerful kitchen has a double-bowl sink in the island, a large corner pantry and opens up to the cheerful dining area

Double doors off the entry hall lead to a sophisticated study with access to the front covered wrap-around porch

The owner's suite has an optional fireplace and offers a generous closet and a private bath with a double-bowl vanity, amazing walk-in shower and a whirlpool tub

PRICE CODE D

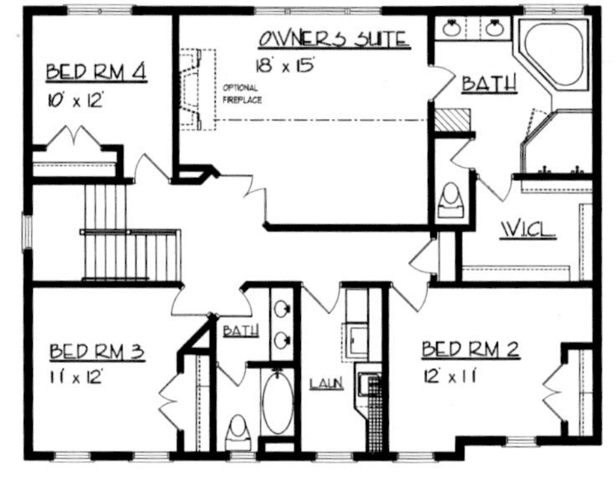
OWNERS SUITE
18' x 15'
BED RM 4
10' x 12'
OPTIONAL FIREPLACE
BATH
W.I.CL.
BATH
BED RM 3
11' x 12'
LAUN
BED RM 2
12' x 11'

Second Floor
1,337 sq. ft.

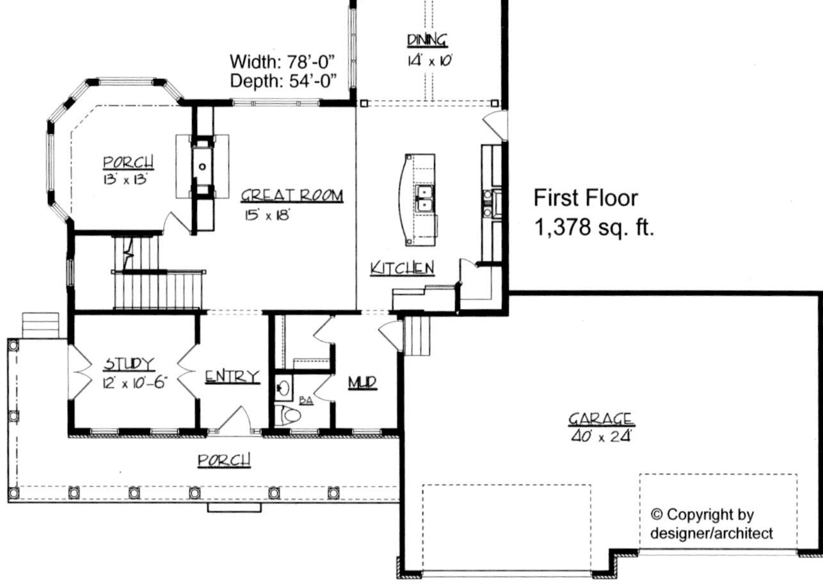
Width: 78'-0"
Depth: 54'-0"
DINING
14' x 10'
PORCH
13' x 13'
GREAT ROOM
15' x 18'
KITCHEN
STUDY
12' x 10'-6"
ENTRY
BA
MUD
GARAGE
40' x 24'
PORCH
© Copyright by designer/architect

First Floor
1,378 sq. ft.

To order plans, visit the Menards Building Materials Desk or visit www.Menards.com.

GUNNISON

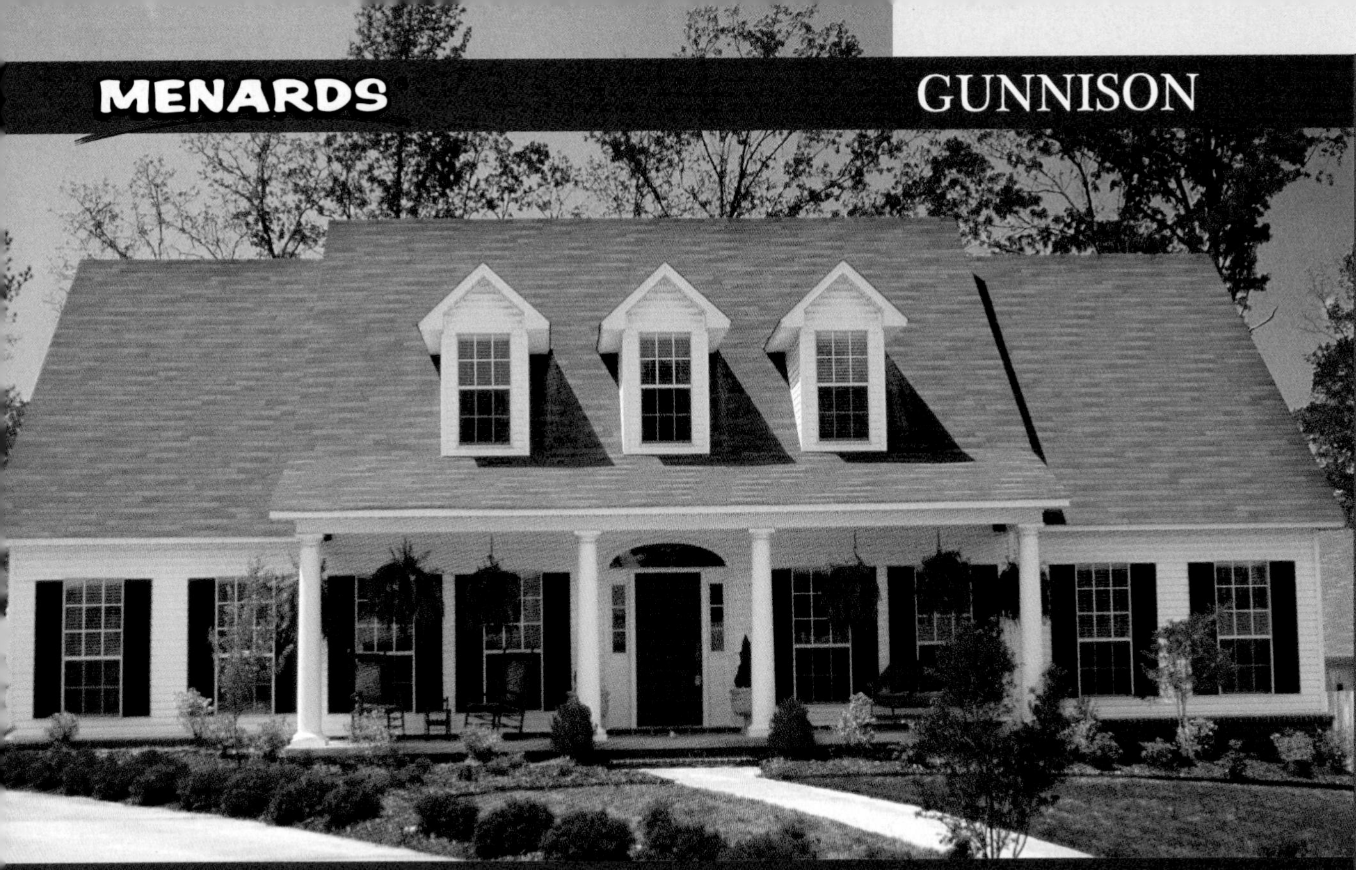

Plan #M06-055L-0212

BONUS ROOM
20'-2" X 19'-4"
GREAT ROOM BELOW
COMPUTER CENTER
BALCONY
BATH
BEDROOM 4
13'-0" X 13'-2"
OPEN TO BELOW
BEDROOM 3
13'-0" X 12'-8"
LINEN
SEAT
SEAT
VAULTED CEILING BELOW

Second Floor
790 sq. ft.

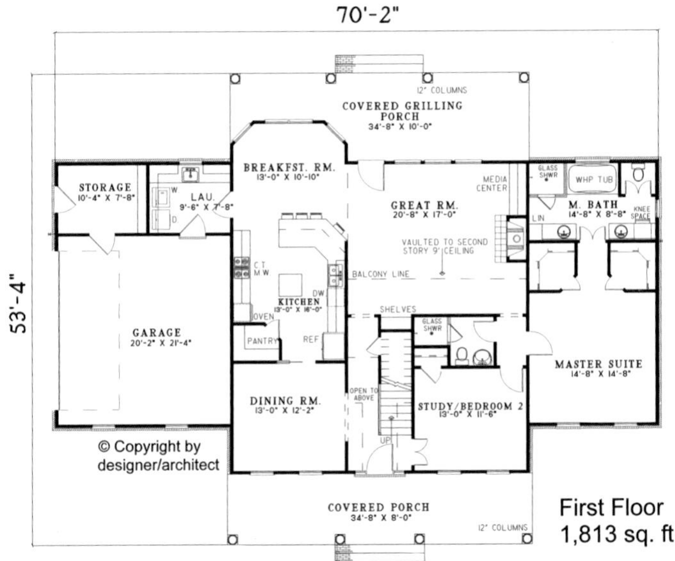
70'-2"
53'-4"
COVERED GRILLING PORCH
34'-8" X 10'-0"
BREAKFST. RM.
13'-0" X 10'-10"
STORAGE
10'-4" X 7'-8"
LAU.
9'-6" X 7'-8"
GREAT RM.
20'-8" X 17'-0"
VAULTED TO SECOND STORY 9' CEILING
MEDIA CENTER
M. BATH
14'-8" X 8'-8"
WHP TUB
KITCHEN
13'-0" X 16'-0"
PANTRY
GARAGE
20'-2" X 21'-4"
MASTER SUITE
14'-8" X 14'-8"
DINING RM.
13'-0" X 12'-2"
STUDY/BEDROOM 2
13'-0" X 11'-6"
COVERED PORCH
34'-8" X 8'-0"
12" COLUMNS

First Floor
1,813 sq. ft.

To order plans, visit the Menards Building Materials Desk
or visit www.Menards.com.

LARGE BAYED BREAKFAST AREA

2,603 total square feet of living area

4 bedrooms, 3 baths

2-car side entry garage

Slab or crawl space foundation, please specify when ordering

SPECIAL FEATURES

The vaulted great room includes a media center, fireplace and access to the covered grilling porch

A convenient storage area is located in the garage

The second floor bedrooms share a unique computer center

The bonus room on the second floor has an additional 410 square feet of living space

PRICE CODE E

GIANCARLO

MENARDS®

Plan #M06-055L-0174

EXCITING GAME ROOM

2,755 total square feet of living area

3 bedrooms, 4 1/2 baths

3-car side entry garage

Slab, crawl space, basement or walk-out basement foundation, please specify when ordering

SPECIAL FEATURES

The breakfast room boasts a two-story vaulted ceiling

Each bedroom has a private bath

The 10' covered porch has plenty of space for eating outdoors or just relaxing

PRICE CODE E

Second Floor
349 sq. ft.

VAULT
OPEN TO BELOW
8' LINE
GAME ROOM
22'-2" X 14'-6"
DN
8' WALL

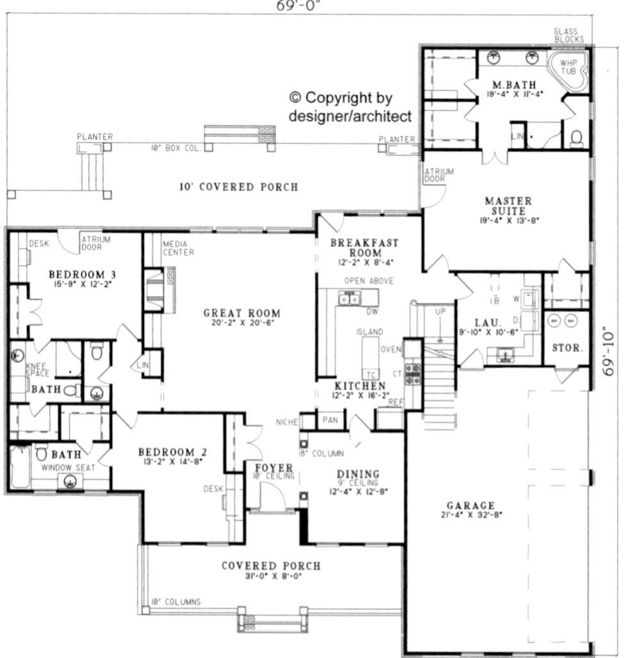
69'-0"
GLASS BLOCKS
WHP TUB
M.BATH
19'-4" X 11'-4"
© Copyright by designer/architect
PLANTER
10" BOX COL.
PLANTER
10' COVERED PORCH
ATRIUM DOOR
MASTER SUITE
19'-4" X 13'-8"
DESK
ATRIUM DOOR
MEDIA CENTER
BREAKFAST ROOM
12'-2" X 8'-4"
BEDROOM 3
15'-9" X 12'-2"
GREAT ROOM
20'-2" X 20'-6"
OPEN ABOVE
DW
ISLAND
OVEN
UP
LAU.
9'-10" X 10'-6"
STOR.
69'-10"
KNEE SPACE
BATH
LIN
KITCHEN
12'-2" X 16'-2"
REF
NICHE
PAN
BATH
WINDOW SEAT
BEDROOM 2
13'-2" X 14'-8"
DESK
FOYER
10' CEILING
10" COLUMN
DINING
9' CEILING
12'-4" X 12'-8"
GARAGE
21'-4" X 32'-8"
COVERED PORCH
31'-0" X 8'-0"
10" COLUMNS

First Floor
2,406 sq. ft.

To order plans, visit the Menards Building Materials Desk or visit www.Menards.com.

KELBY HILL

Plan #M06-065L-0012

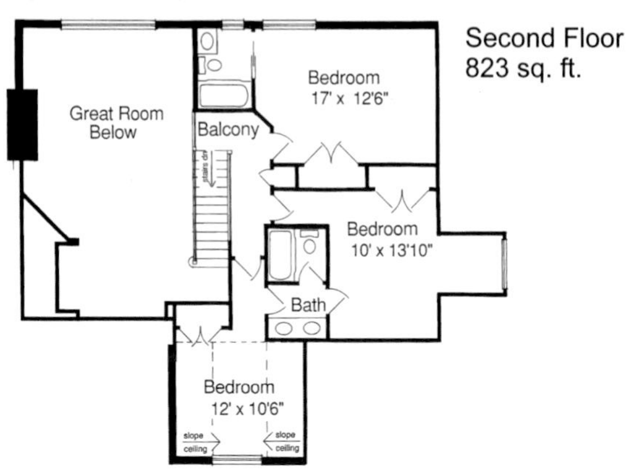
Second Floor
823 sq. ft.
Great Room Below
Balcony
Bedroom
17' x 12'6"
Bedroom
10' x 13'10"
Bath
Bedroom
12' x 10'6"
slope ceiling
slope ceiling

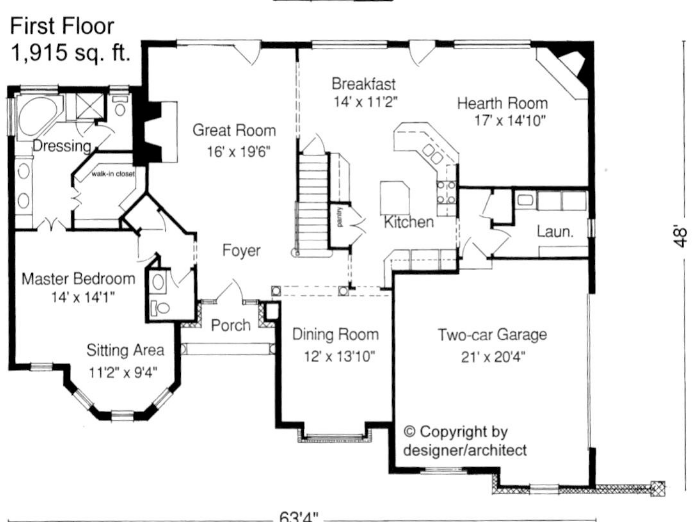
First Floor
1,915 sq. ft.
Dressing
walk-in closet
Great Room
16' x 19'6"
Breakfast
14' x 11'2"
Hearth Room
17' x 14'10"
Kitchen
Laun.
Foyer
Master Bedroom
14' x 14'1"
Porch
Sitting Area
11'2" x 9'4"
Dining Room
12' x 13'10"
Two-car Garage
21' x 20'4"
© Copyright by designer/architect
48'
63'4"

MANY EXCITING FEATURES

2,738 total square feet of living area

4 bedrooms, 3 1/2 baths

2-car side entry garage

Basement foundation

SPECIAL FEATURES

An open entrance offers a spectacular view of the windowed rear wall and fireplace in the great room

The kitchen, breakfast and hearth rooms combine to offer an open and comfortable gathering place

The master bedroom is topped with an 11' ceiling and features a sitting alcove and deluxe bath

PRICE CODE E

To order plans, visit the Menards Building Materials Desk or visit www.Menards.com.

DENBEIGH

MENARDS

Plan #M06-055L-0202

SEE-THROUGH FIREPLACE WARMS LIVING AREAS

3,108 total square feet of living area

3 bedrooms, 2 1/2 baths

3-car side entry garage

Slab or crawl space foundation, please specify when ordering

SPECIAL FEATURES

The two-story great room features French doors to the rear deck

The kitchen and breakfast room combine and include a cooktop island, walk-in pantry and TV cabinet

Second floor bonus rooms provide an additional 485 square feet of living space

PRICE CODE G

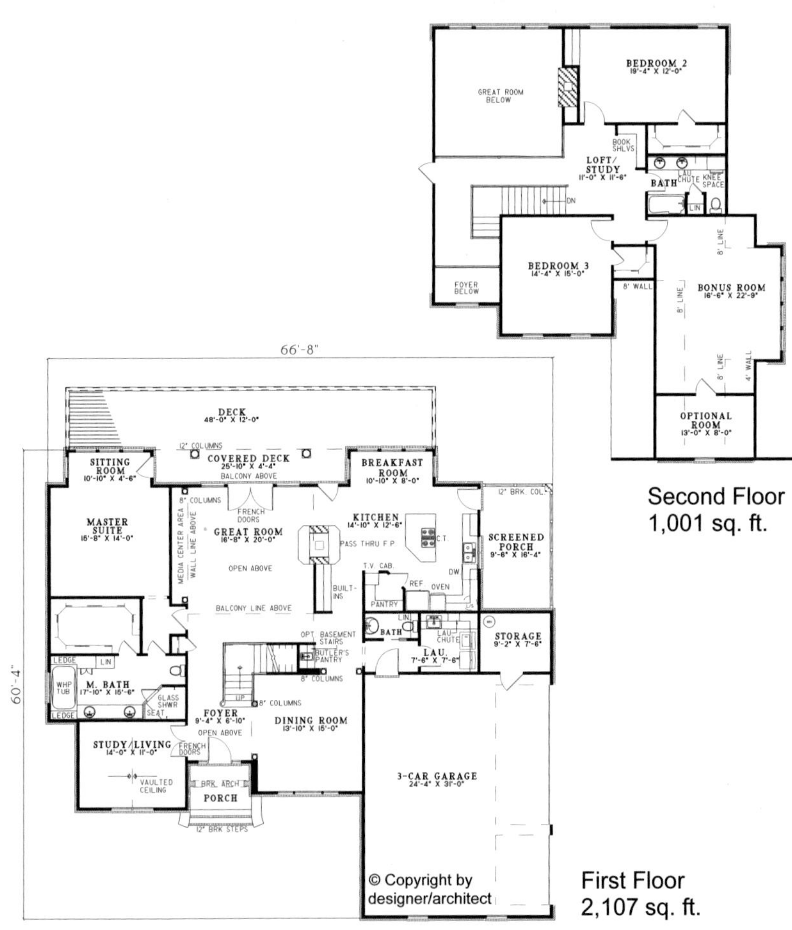

GREAT ROOM BELOW
BEDROOM 2 19'-4" X 12'-0"
LOFT/ STUDY 11'-0" X 11'-6"
BATH
BEDROOM 3 14'-4" X 15'-0"
FOYER BELOW
BONUS ROOM 16'-6" X 22'-9"
OPTIONAL ROOM 13'-0" X 8'-0"
Second Floor
1,001 sq. ft.
66'-8"
60'-4"
DECK 48'-0" X 12'-0"
SITTING ROOM 10'-10" X 4'-6"
COVERED DECK 25'-10" X 4'-4"
BALCONY ABOVE
BREAKFAST ROOM 10'-10" X 8'-0"
MASTER SUITE 16'-8" X 14'-0"
GREAT ROOM 16'-8" X 20'-0"
OPEN ABOVE
KITCHEN 14'-10" X 12'-6"
SCREENED PORCH 9'-6" X 16'-4"
BALCONY LINE ABOVE
PANTRY
BATH
LAU. 7'-6" X 7'-6"
STORAGE 9'-2" X 7'-6"
M. BATH 17'-10" X 15'-6"
FOYER 9'-4" X 6'-10"
DINING ROOM 13'-10" X 15'-0"
STUDY/LIVING 14'-0" X 11'-0"
PORCH
3-CAR GARAGE 24'-4" X 31'-0"
© Copyright by designer/architect
First Floor
2,107 sq. ft.

To order plans, visit the Menards Building Materials Desk or visit www.Menards.com.

BERNICE FARM

Plan #M06-051L-0155

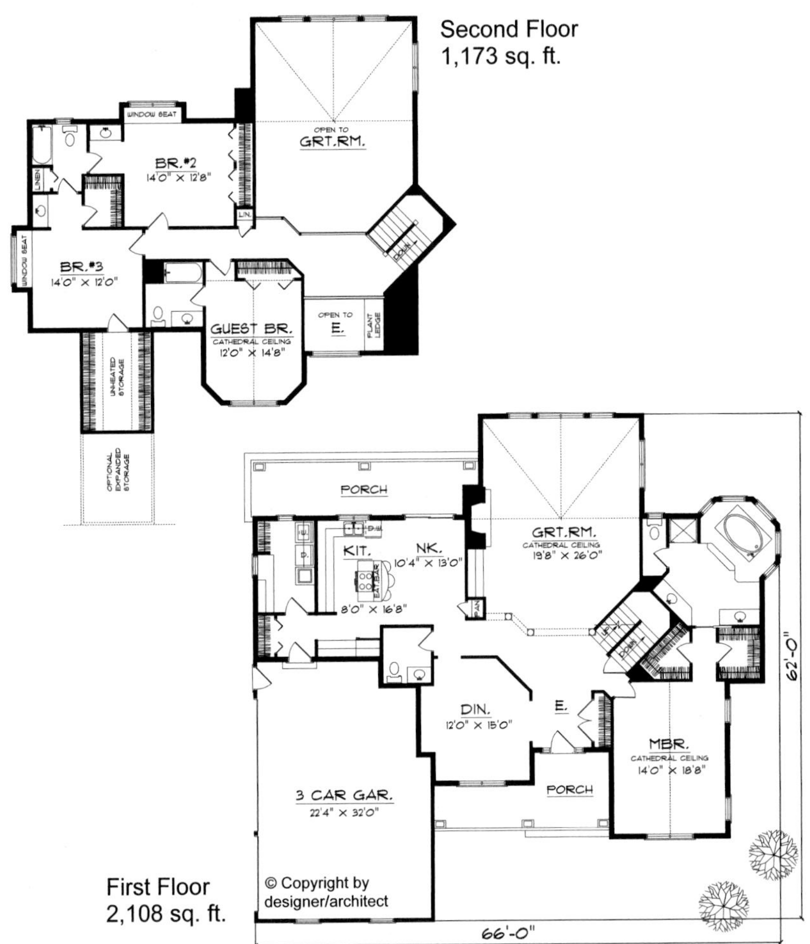
Second Floor
1,173 sq. ft.
WINDOW SEAT
OPEN TO GRT.RM.
BR.#2 14'0" x 12'8"
LINEN
LIN.
WINDOW SEAT
BR.#3 14'0" x 12'0"
GUEST BR. CATHEDRAL CEILING 12'0" x 14'8"
OPEN TO E.
PLANT LEDGE
UNHEATED STORAGE
OPTIONAL EXPANDED STORAGE
PORCH
KIT. 8'0" x 16'8"
NK. 10'4" x 13'0"
GRT.RM. CATHEDRAL CEILING 19'8" x 26'0"
DIN. 12'0" x 15'0"
E.
MBR. CATHEDRAL CEILING 14'0" x 18'8"
PORCH
3 CAR GAR. 22'4" x 32'0"
62'-0"
66'-0"
First Floor
2,108 sq. ft.

To order plans, visit the Menards Building Materials Desk or visit www.Menards.com.

ELEGANT COUNTRY HOME

3,281 total square feet of living area

4 bedrooms, 3 1/2 baths

3-car side entry garage

Basement foundation

SPECIAL FEATURES

Energy efficient home with 2" x 6" exterior walls

The master bedroom is a luxurious retreat with two walk-in closets and a deluxe bath including a whirlpool tub in a bay window

The kitchen features a cooktop island with eating bar and opens to the nook with access onto the rear porch

Bedrooms #2 and #3 each feature a cozy window seat and share a Jack and Jill bath

PRICE CODE F

Rear View

PELHAM PARK

MENARDS®

Luxury Plans

Plan #M06-013L-0031

PEACEFUL SCREENED PORCH FOR RELAXING

2,253 total square feet of living area

4 bedrooms, 3 baths

2-car side entry garage

Walk-out basement, crawl space or slab foundation, please specify when ordering

SPECIAL FEATURES

Two bedrooms on the second floor share a bath

Two walk-in closets, a private bath and a sitting area leading to an outdoor deck are all amenities of the master suite

Bonus room on the second floor has an additional 247 square feet of living area

PRICE CODE D

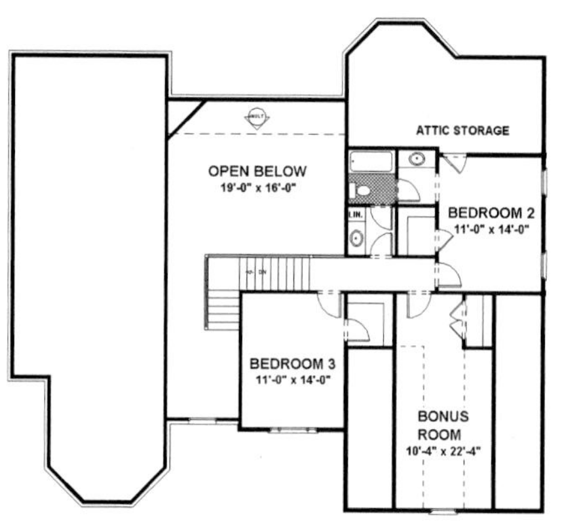
ATTIC STORAGE
OPEN BELOW
19'-0" x 16'-0"
BEDROOM 2
11'-0" x 14'-0"
BEDROOM 3
11'-0" x 14'-0"
BONUS ROOM
10'-4" x 22'-4"

Second Floor
534 sq. ft.

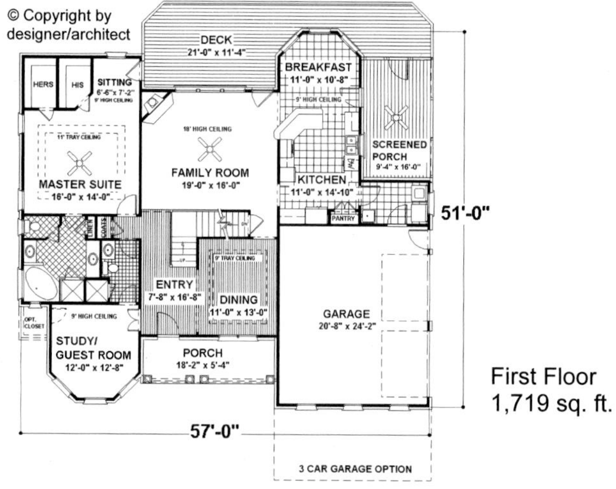
© Copyright by designer/architect
DECK
21'-0" x 11'-4"
BREAKFAST
11'-0" x 10'-8"
HERS
HIS
SITTING
6'-6" x 7'-2"
MASTER SUITE
16'-0" x 14'-0"
FAMILY ROOM
19'-0" x 16'-0"
SCREENED PORCH
9'-4" x 16'-0"
KITCHEN
11'-0" x 14'-10"
PANTRY
51'-0"
ENTRY
7'-8" x 16'-8"
DINING
11'-0" x 13'-0"
GARAGE
20'-8" x 24'-2"
STUDY/ GUEST ROOM
12'-0" x 12'-8"
PORCH
18'-2" x 5'-4"
57'-0"
3 CAR GARAGE OPTION

First Floor
1,719 sq. ft.

To order plans, visit the Menards Building Materials Desk or visit www.Menards.com.

MENARDS

OLIVIA

Luxury Plans

Plan #M06-121D-0001

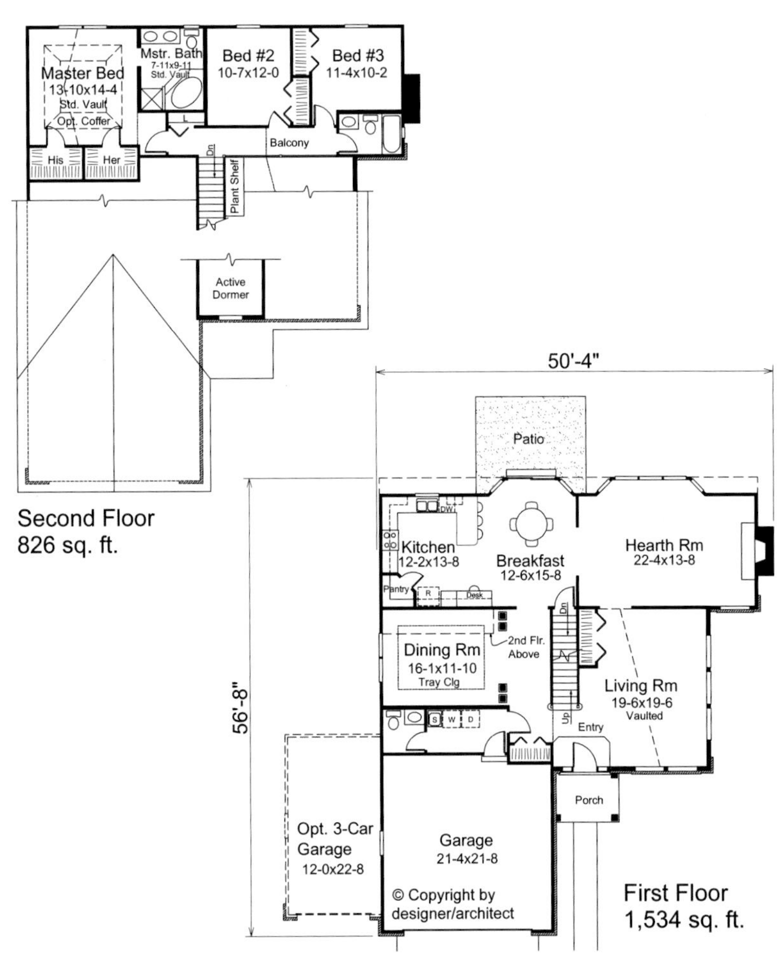
Master Bed
13-10x14-4
Std. Vault
Opt. Coffer
Mstr. Bath
7-11x9-11
Std. Vault
Bed #2
10-7x12-0
Bed #3
11-4x10-2
His
Her
Balcony
Dn
Plant Shelf
Active
Dormer
Second Floor
826 sq. ft.
50'-4"
56'-8"
Patio
Kitchen
12-2x13-8
DW
Pantry
R
Desk
Breakfast
12-6x15-8
Hearth Rm
22-4x13-8
Dn
Dining Rm
16-1x11-10
Tray Clg
2nd Flr.
Above
Living Rm
19-6x19-6
Vaulted
Up
Entry
W
D
Porch
Opt. 3-Car
Garage
12-0x22-8
Garage
21-4x21-8
© Copyright by
designer/architect
First Floor
1,534 sq. ft.

To order plans, visit the Menards Building Materials Desk or visit www.Menards.com.

ARCHED WINDOWS ADDS CURB APPEAL

2,360 total square feet of living area

3 bedrooms, 2 1/2 baths

2-car garage

Basement foundation

SPECIAL FEATURES

The U-shaped kitchen enjoys a large walk-in pantry, desk area and an extended counterspace

The hearth room extends off the bayed breakfast area and features a fireplace

Luxury can be found in the second floor master bedroom including his and her walk-in closets and a private bath

PRICE CODE C

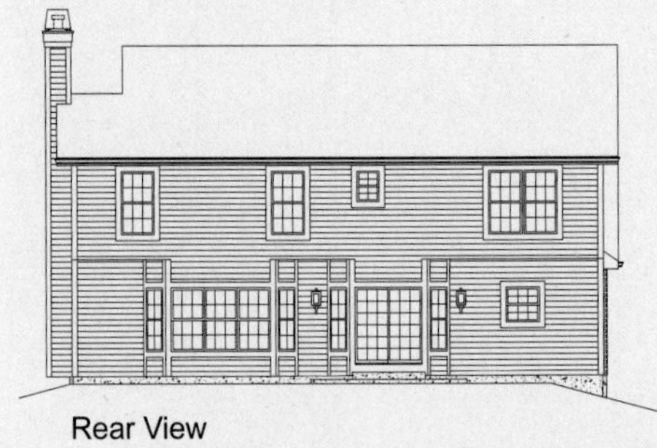

Rear View

FOREST PARK

MENARDS

Luxury Plans

Plan #M06-007D-0209

COVERED PATIO WITH BAR AND SAUNA

2,365 total square feet of living area

4 bedrooms, 3 1/2 baths

2-car garage

Crawl space foundation

SPECIAL FEATURES

The country contemporary exterior packs lots of charm

A winding staircase leading to the second floor's spacious bedrooms is central to this home's carefully designed interior

Both the kitchen and breakfast area view the covered and uncovered rear patios that include skylights, a vaulted ceiling, a walk-in bar and sauna room

The first floor features a private study or guest bedroom with bath and closet

PRICE CODE C

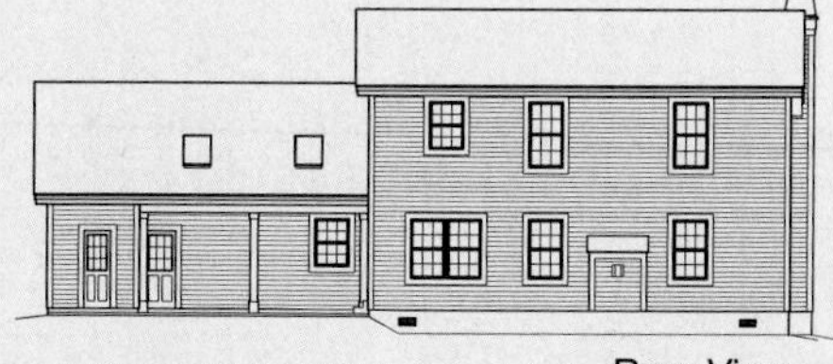

Rear View

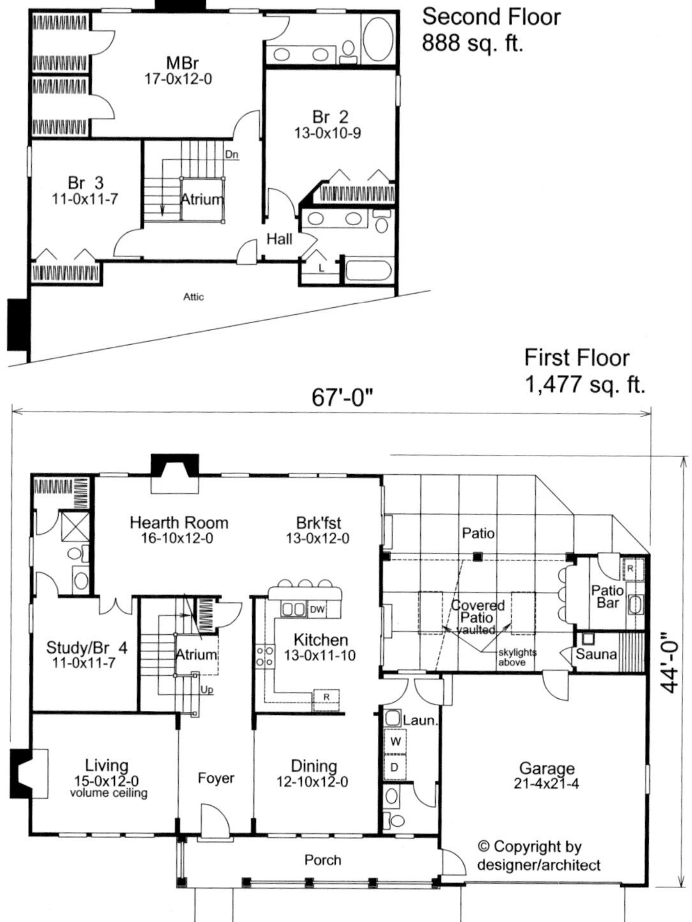
Second Floor
888 sq. ft.
MBr
17-0x12-0
Br 2
13-0x10-9
Br 3
11-0x11-7
Dn
Atrium
Hall
L
Attic
First Floor
1,477 sq. ft.
67'-0"
44'-0"
Hearth Room
16-10x12-0
Brk'fst
13-0x12-0
Patio
DW
Covered
Patio
vaulted
Patio
Bar
R
Kitchen
13-0x11-10
Study/Br 4
11-0x11-7
Atrium
skylights
above
Sauna
Up
R
Laun.
W
D
Living
15-0x12-0
volume ceiling
Foyer
Dining
12-10x12-0
Garage
21-4x21-4
Porch
© Copyright by
designer/architect

To order plans, visit the Menards Building Materials Desk or visit www.Menards.com.

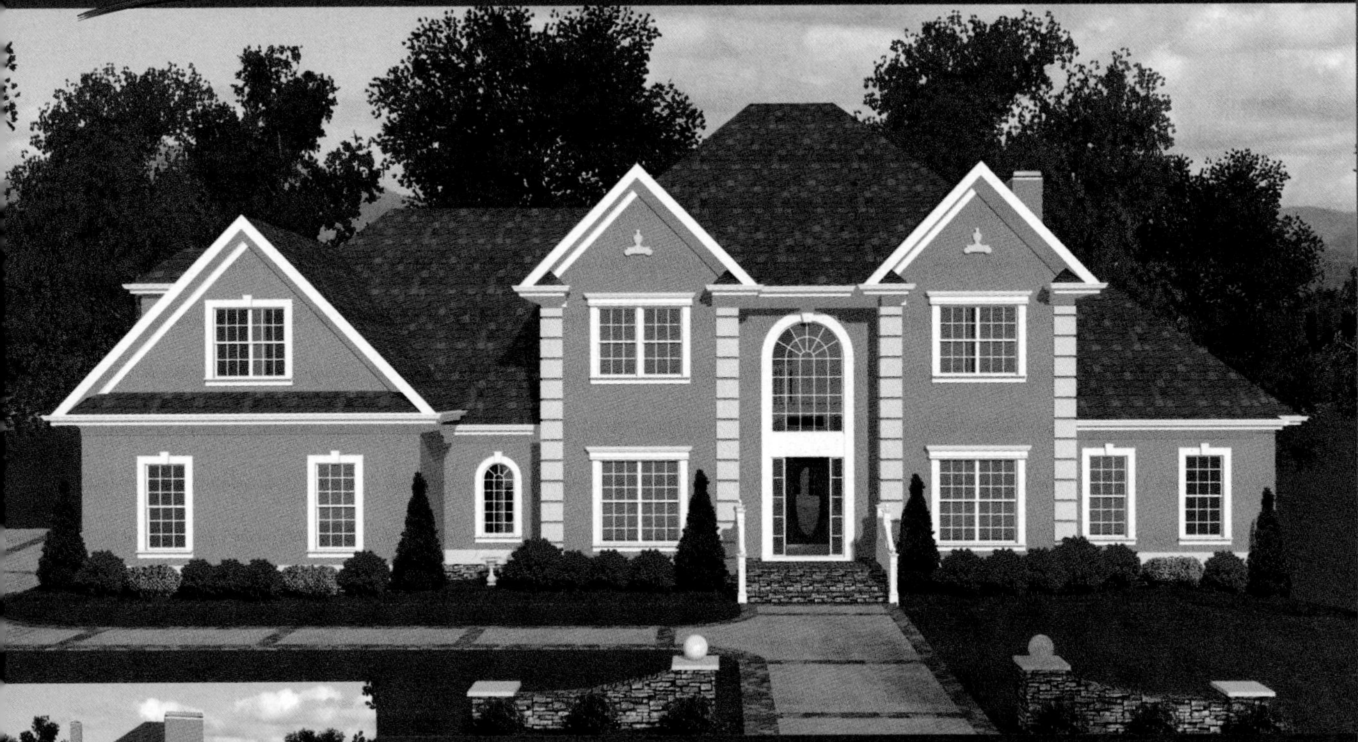

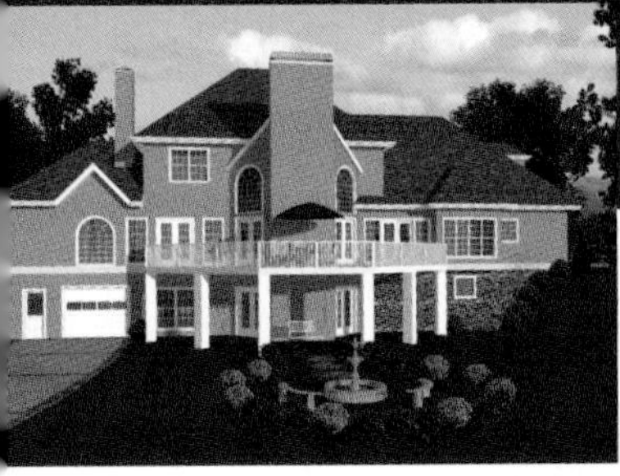

MARIANNA PARK

Plan #M06-013L-0116

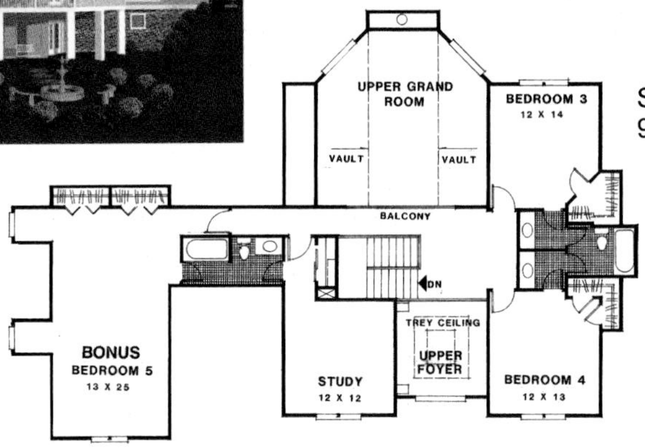

Second Floor
939 sq. ft.

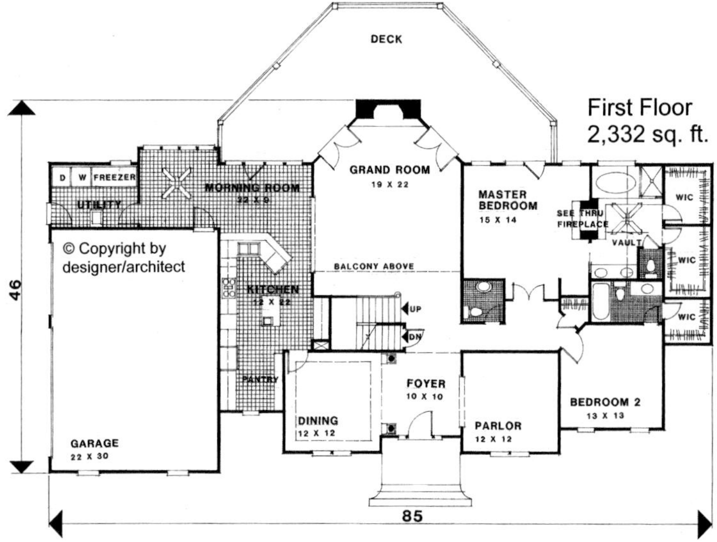
DECK
GRAND ROOM
19 X 22
MASTER BEDROOM
15 X 14
SEE THRU FIREPLACE
VAULT
WIC
WIC
WIC
D
W
FREEZER
UTILITY
MORNING ROOM
© Copyright by designer/architect
KITCHEN
BALCONY ABOVE
UP
DN
PANTRY
FOYER
10 X 10
DINING
12 X 12
PARLOR
12 X 12
BEDROOM 2
13 X 13
GARAGE
22 X 30
46
85

First Floor
2,332 sq. ft.

LARGE OPEN DECK

3,271 total square feet of living area

4 bedrooms, 4 1/2 baths

3-car side entry garage

Walk-out basement foundation

SPECIAL FEATURES

The grand room features a handsome fireplace framed by French doors on both sides leading out to the deck

The see-through fireplace gives the master bedroom a natural focal point

The second floor balcony overlooks the grand room

A bonus room/bedroom #5 above the garage allows for an additional 412 square feet of living area

PRICE CODE E

To order plans, visit the Menards Building Materials Desk or visit www.Menards.com.

DUNGATE

MENARDS®

Plan #M06-013L-0038

IMPRESSIVE BRICK TWO-STORY

2,954 total square feet of living area

4 bedrooms, 3 1/2 baths

2-car side entry garage

Basement or crawl space foundation, please specify when ordering

SPECIAL FEATURES

The master bedroom has a double-door entry into the luxurious bath

A private study has direct access into the master bedroom

The vaulted ceiling and bay window add light and dimension to the breakfast room

PRICE CODE E

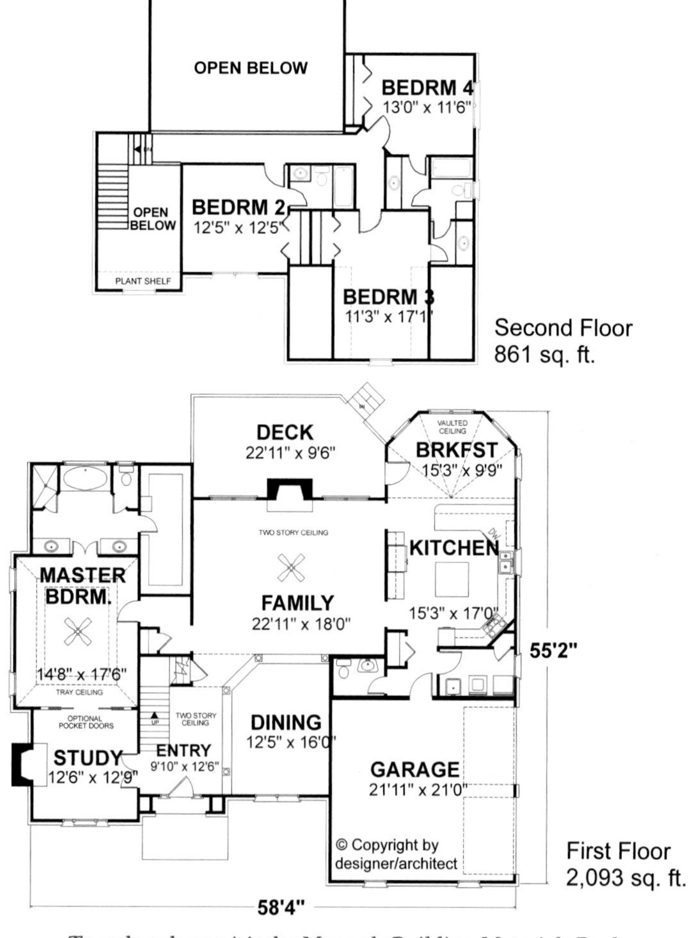
OPEN BELOW
BEDRM 4
13'0" x 11'6"
OPEN BELOW
BEDRM 2
12'5" x 12'5"
PLANT SHELF
BEDRM 3
11'3" x 17'1"
Second Floor
861 sq. ft.
DECK
22'11" x 9'6"
VAULTED CEILING
BRKFST
15'3" x 9'9"
TWO STORY CEILING
KITCHEN
MASTER BDRM.
FAMILY
22'11" x 18'0"
15'3" x 17'0"
55'2"
14'8" x 17'6"
TRAY CEILING
OPTIONAL POCKET DOORS
UP
TWO STORY CEILING
DINING
12'5" x 16'0"
STUDY
12'6" x 12'9"
ENTRY
9'10" x 12'6"
GARAGE
21'11" x 21'0"
© Copyright by designer/architect
First Floor
2,093 sq. ft.
58'4"

To order plans, visit the Menards Building Materials Desk or visit www.Menards.com.

FOREST FALLS

Plan #M06-007D-0211

PRIVATE APARTMENT WITHIN A HOME

3,346 total square feet of living area

5 bedrooms, 4 full baths, 2 half baths

2-car side entry garage

Walk-out basement foundation

SPECIAL FEATURES

The kitchen is open to the informal dining and breakfast areas with views of the rear covered walkway and patio featuring a walk-in bar and sauna room

A covered patio, luxury bath, walk-in closet and bay window are some of the amenities of the first floor master bedroom

In addition to the bedrooms on the second floor, an apartment that has 432 square feet that is included in the total square footage is located to the rear of the home

PRICE CODE E

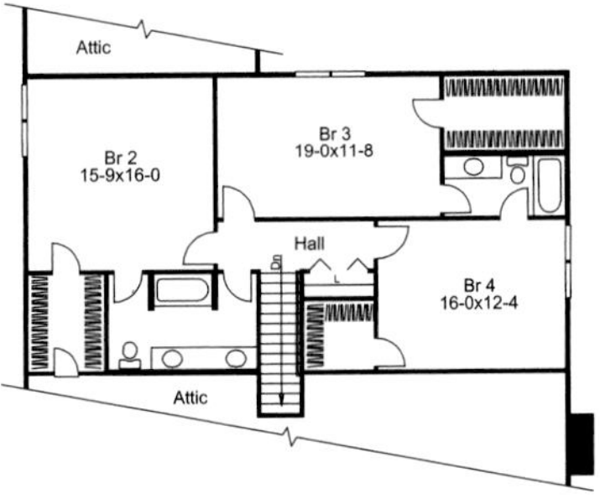

Attic
Br 2
15-9x16-0
Br 3
19-0x11-8
Hall
Br 4
16-0x12-4
Attic

Second Floor
1,170 sq. ft.

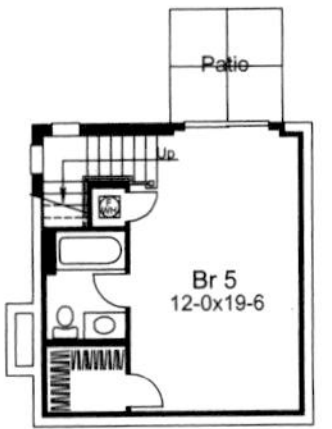

Patio
Br 5
12-0x19-6

Lower Level
380 sq. ft.

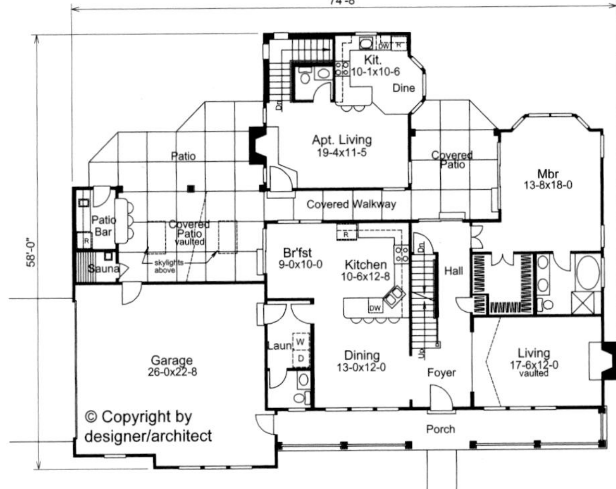

74'-8"
58'-0"
Kit.
10-1x10-6
Dine
Apt. Living
19-4x11-5
Patio
Covered Patio
Mbr
13-8x18-0
Covered Walkway
Patio Bar
Covered Patio vaulted
Sauna
Br'fst
9-0x10-0
Kitchen
10-6x12-8
Hall
Garage
26-0x22-8
Laun
Dining
13-0x12-0
Foyer
Living
17-6x12-0
vaulted
Porch
© Copyright by designer/architect

First Floor
1,796 sq. ft.

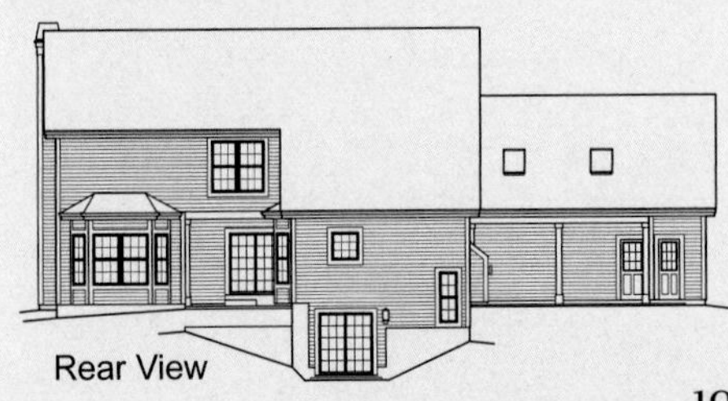

Rear View

To order plans, visit the Menards Building Materials Desk or visit www.Menards.com.

WESTMINSTER HEIGHTS

MENARDS

Plan #M06-007D-0203

TUDOR STYLE HOME

4,409 total square feet of living area

4 bedrooms, 3 1/2 baths

3-car side entry garage

Walk-out basement foundation

SPECIAL FEATURES

A melody of stone, brick, batten shutters and steep roof gables successfully recreate a timeless "Old World" look

A vaulted study, large dining room with tray ceiling and two-story great room with gallery all adjoin a two-story foyer

The kitchen has state-of-the-art features including an island snack bar for six

The master bedroom with coffered ceiling and bayed window has a luxury bath

PRICE CODE F

Rear View

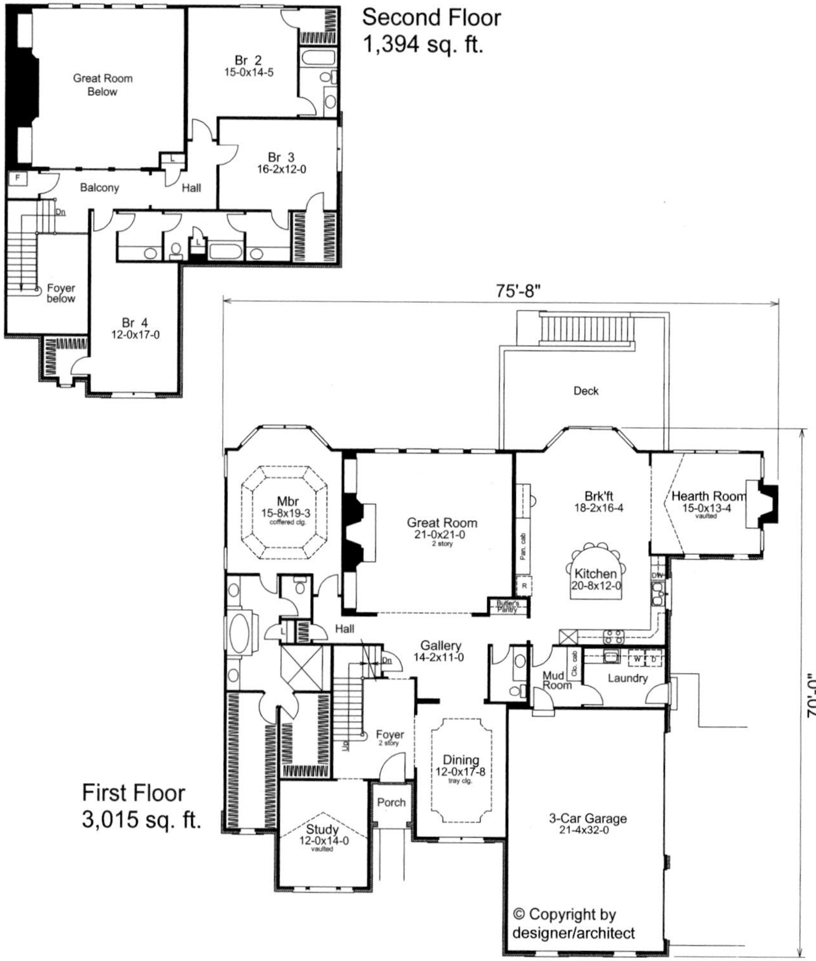
Second Floor
1,394 sq. ft.
Great Room Below
Br 2
15-0x14-5
Br 3
16-2x12-0
Balcony
Hall
Foyer below
Br 4
12-0x17-0
75'-8"
Deck
Mbr
15-8x19-3
Great Room
21-0x21-0
2 story
Brk'ft
18-2x16-4
Hearth Room
15-0x13-4
Kitchen
20-8x12-0
Hall
Gallery
14-2x11-0
Mud Room
Laundry
Foyer
2 story
Dining
12-0x17-8
Porch
Study
12-0x14-0
3-Car Garage
21-4x32-0
70'-0"
First Floor
3,015 sq. ft.
© Copyright by designer/architect

To order plans, visit the Menards Building Materials Desk or visit www.Menards.com.

AUTUMN

Plan #M06-121D-0014

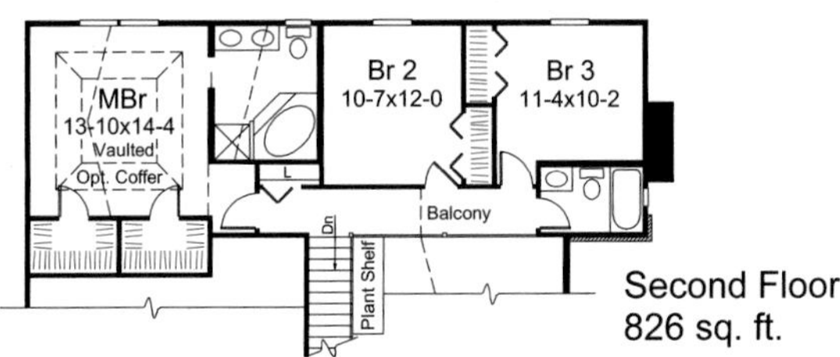

MBr
13-10x14-4
Vaulted
Opt. Coffer
Br 2
10-7x12-0
Br 3
11-4x10-2
Balcony
Dn
Plant Shelf
Second Floor
826 sq. ft.

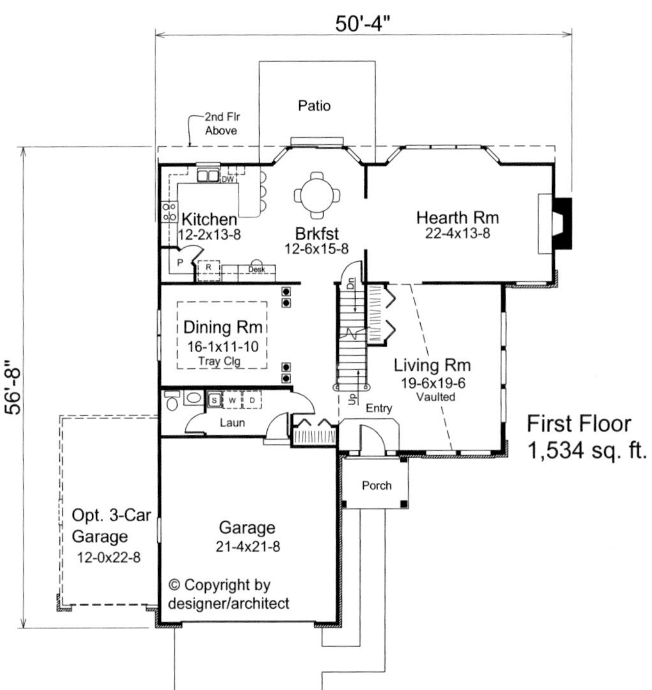

50'-4"
56'-8"
Patio
2nd Flr Above
DW
Kitchen
12-2x13-8
Brkfst
12-6x15-8
Hearth Rm
22-4x13-8
P
R
Desk
Dn
Dining Rm
16-1x11-10
Tray Clg
Living Rm
19-6x19-6
Vaulted
Up
Entry
S
W
D
Laun
Porch
Opt. 3-Car Garage
12-0x22-8
Garage
21-4x21-8
© Copyright by designer/architect
First Floor
1,534 sq. ft.

To order plans, visit the Menards Building Materials Desk or visit www.Menards.com.

ATTRACTIVE STONE EXTERIOR

2,360 total square feet of living area

3 bedrooms, 2 1/2 baths

2-car garage

Basement foundation

SPECIAL FEATURES

A gracious hearth room is brightened by windows and is perfect for relaxing with family next to the cozy fireplace

The kitchen features a walk-in pantry and eating bar for convenience

The vaulted master bedroom has a private bath with whirlpool tub, separate shower and a double-bowl vanity

PRICE CODE C

Rear View

Luxury Plans

SHAMROCK PLACE

MENARDS

Plan #M06-007D-0197

LUXURY LIVING DEFINED

2,764 total square feet of living area

4 bedrooms, 2 1/2 baths
2-car garage

Basement foundation

SPECIAL FEATURES

The exterior has brick, stone, multiple gables, a porch and cedar shake siding

A grand-sized entry accesses a private parlor with double glass doors, dining room with tray ceiling and a powder room

The kitchen enjoys a center island, huge walk-in pantry, built-in double oven and features a 50' vista through the breakfast and family rooms

PRICE CODE E

Rear View

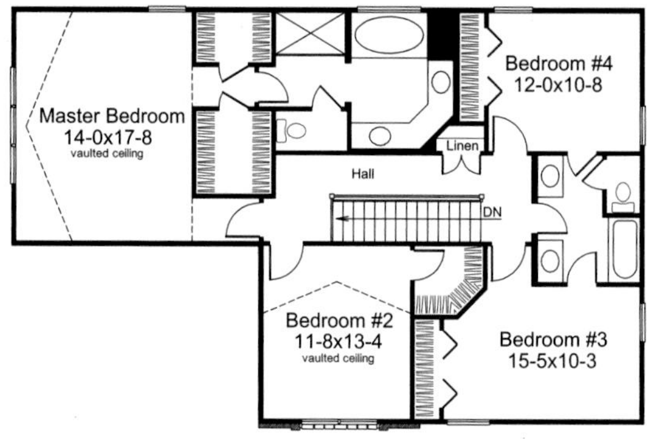
Master Bedroom
14-0x17-8
vaulted ceiling
Bedroom #4
12-0x10-8
Linen
Hall
DN
Bedroom #2
11-8x13-4
vaulted ceiling
Bedroom #3
15-5x10-3

Second Floor
1,332 sq. ft.

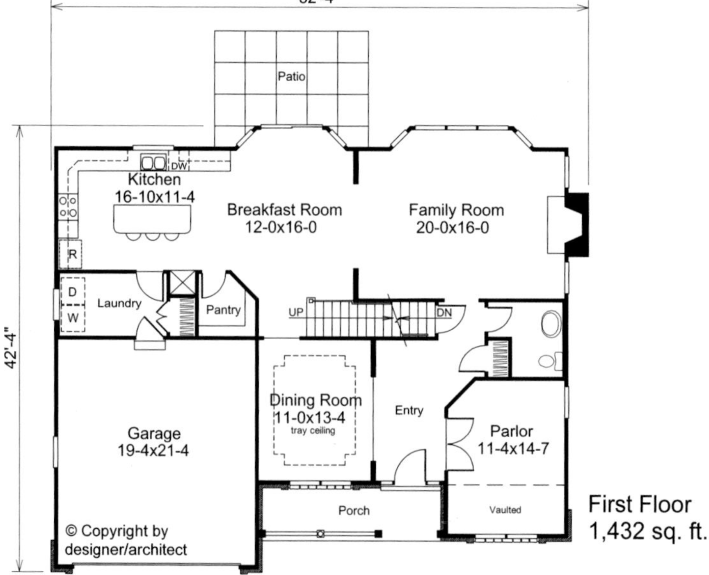
52'-4"
42'-4"
Patio
DW
Kitchen
16-10x11-4
Breakfast Room
12-0x16-0
Family Room
20-0x16-0
R
D
W
Laundry
Pantry
UP
DN
Dining Room
11-0x13-4
tray ceiling
Entry
Parlor
11-4x14-7
Garage
19-4x21-4
Porch
Vaulted
© Copyright by
designer/architect

First Floor
1,432 sq. ft.

To order plans, visit the Menards Building Materials Desk or visit www.Menards.com.

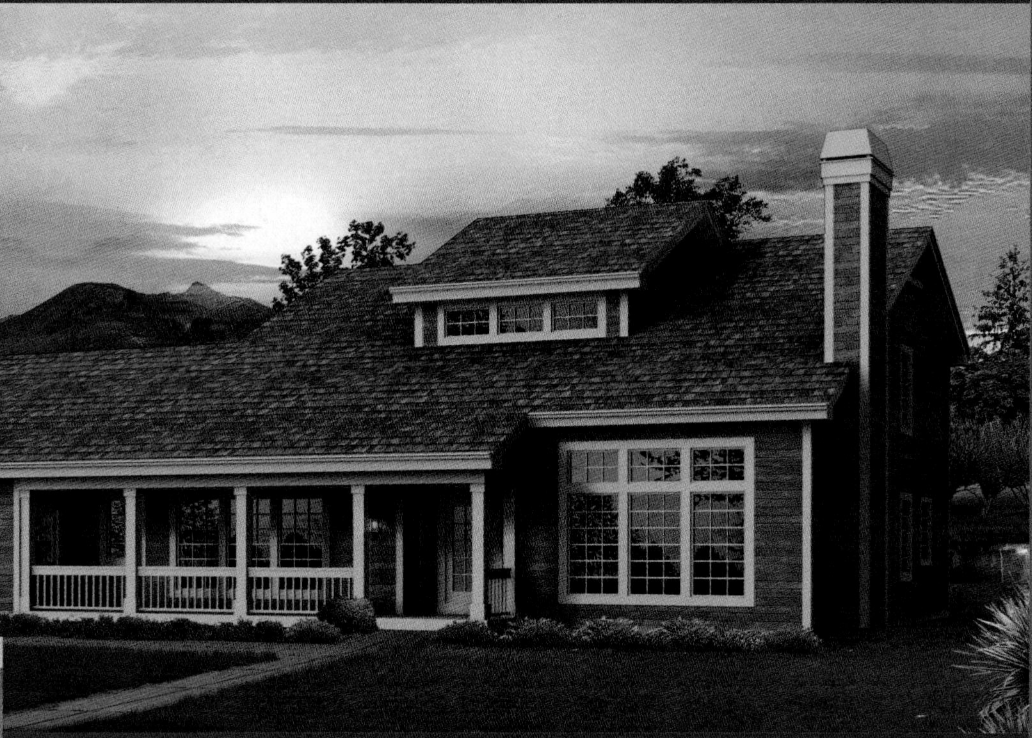

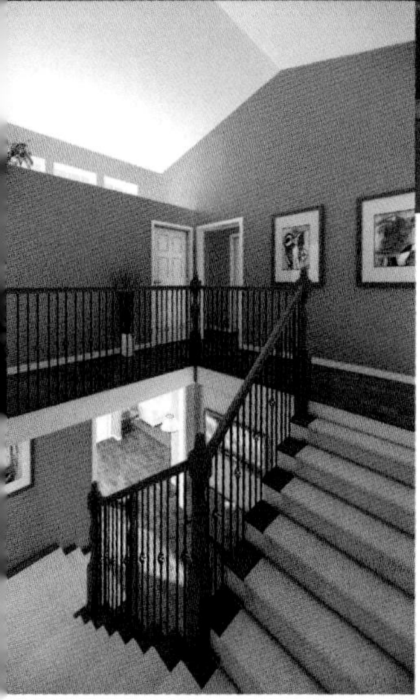

Plan #M06-007D-0208

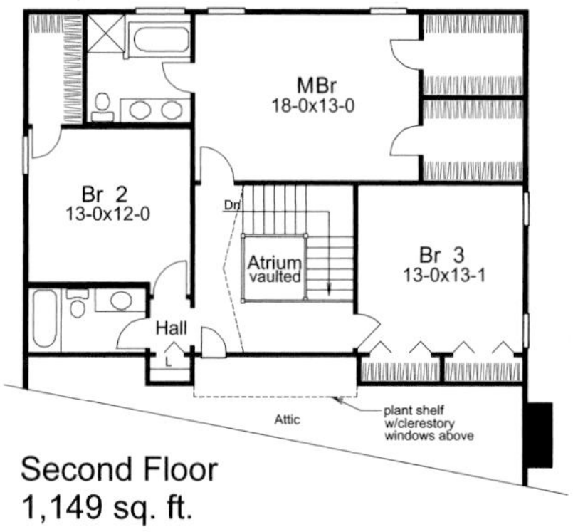

Second Floor
1,149 sq. ft.

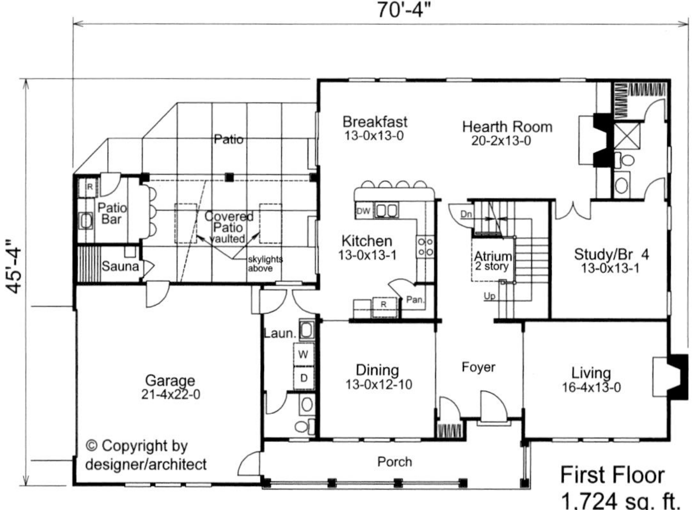
70'-4"
45'-4"
Patio
Breakfast
13-0x13-0
Hearth Room
20-2x13-0
Patio Bar
Covered Patio vaulted
skylights above
Sauna
Kitchen
13-0x13-1
Atrium 2 story
Study/Br 4
13-0x13-1
Pan
Laun.
Garage
21-4x22-0
Dining
13-0x12-10
Foyer
Living
16-4x13-0
© Copyright by designer/architect
Porch

First Floor
1,724 sq. ft.

LOVELY COUNTRY HOME

2,873 total square feet of living area

4 bedrooms, 3 1/2 baths

2-car side entry garage

Basement foundation

SPECIAL FEATURES

A stately foyer leads into a two-story atrium with winding stairs featuring a plant shelf with clerestory windows and vaulted ceiling

The hearth and breakfast rooms offer a 31' vista with adjacent study or private fourth bedroom boasting its own bath and walk-in closet, ideal for guests or live-in mother-in-law

The large covered rear patio area includes a vaulted ceiling with skylights, walk-in wet bar with serving counter and sauna room, perfect for entertaining

PRICE CODE D

Rear View

To order plans, visit the Menards Building Materials Desk or visit www.Menards.com.

ROXBURY

MENARDS

Luxury Plans

Plan #M06-007D-0065

ATRIUM RANCH HOME

3,261 total square feet of living area

6 bedrooms, 3 baths

2-car garage

Walk-out basement foundation

SPECIAL FEATURES

The vaulted great room has an arched colonnade entry, bay windowed atrium with staircase and a fireplace

The vaulted kitchen enjoys bay doors to the deck and a pass-through breakfast bar

The breakfast area offers a bay window and snack bar open to the kitchen with a large laundry room nearby

PRICE CODE D

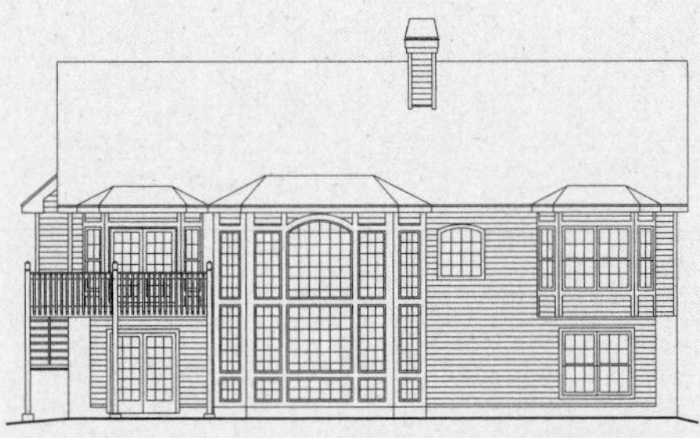

Rear View

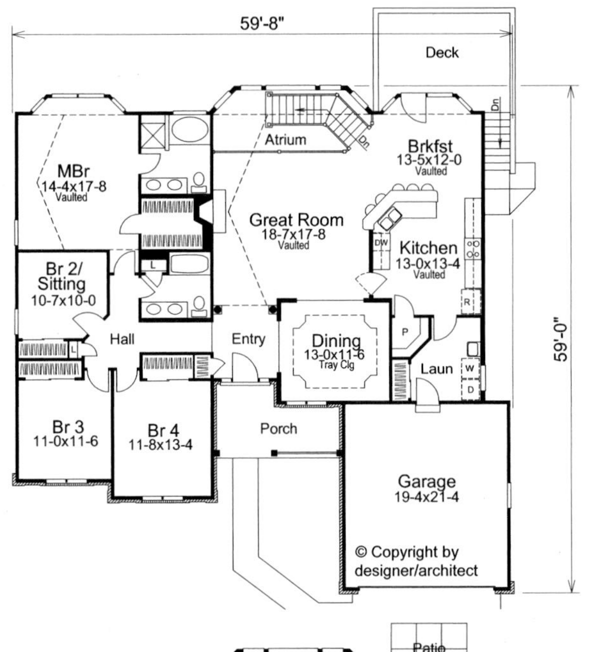

59'-8"
Deck
Atrium
Brkfst
13-5x12-0
Vaulted
MBr
14-4x17-8
Vaulted
Great Room
18-7x17-8
Vaulted
Kitchen
13-0x13-4
Vaulted
Br 2/
Sitting
10-7x10-0
Hall
Entry
Dining
13-0x11-6
Tray Clg
Laun
Br 3
11-0x11-6
Br 4
11-8x13-4
Porch
Garage
19-4x21-4
© Copyright by
designer/architect
59'-0"

First Floor
2,209 sq. ft.

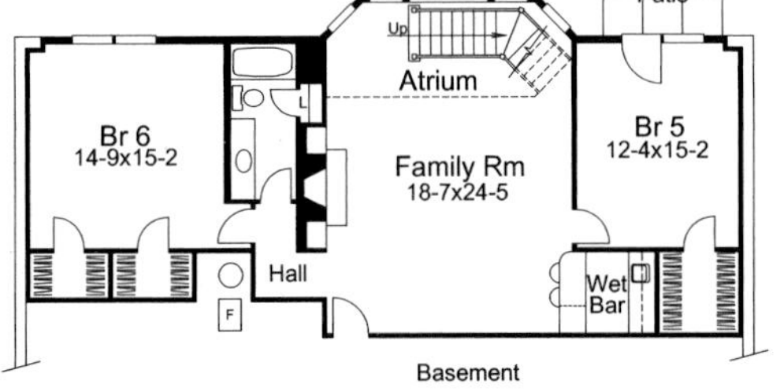

Patio
Up
Atrium
Br 6
14-9x15-2
Family Rm
18-7x24-5
Br 5
12-4x15-2
Hall
Wet
Bar
Basement

Lower Level
1,052 sq. ft.

To order plans, visit the Menards Building Materials Desk
or visit www.Menards.com.

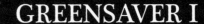

MENARDS

GREENSAVER I

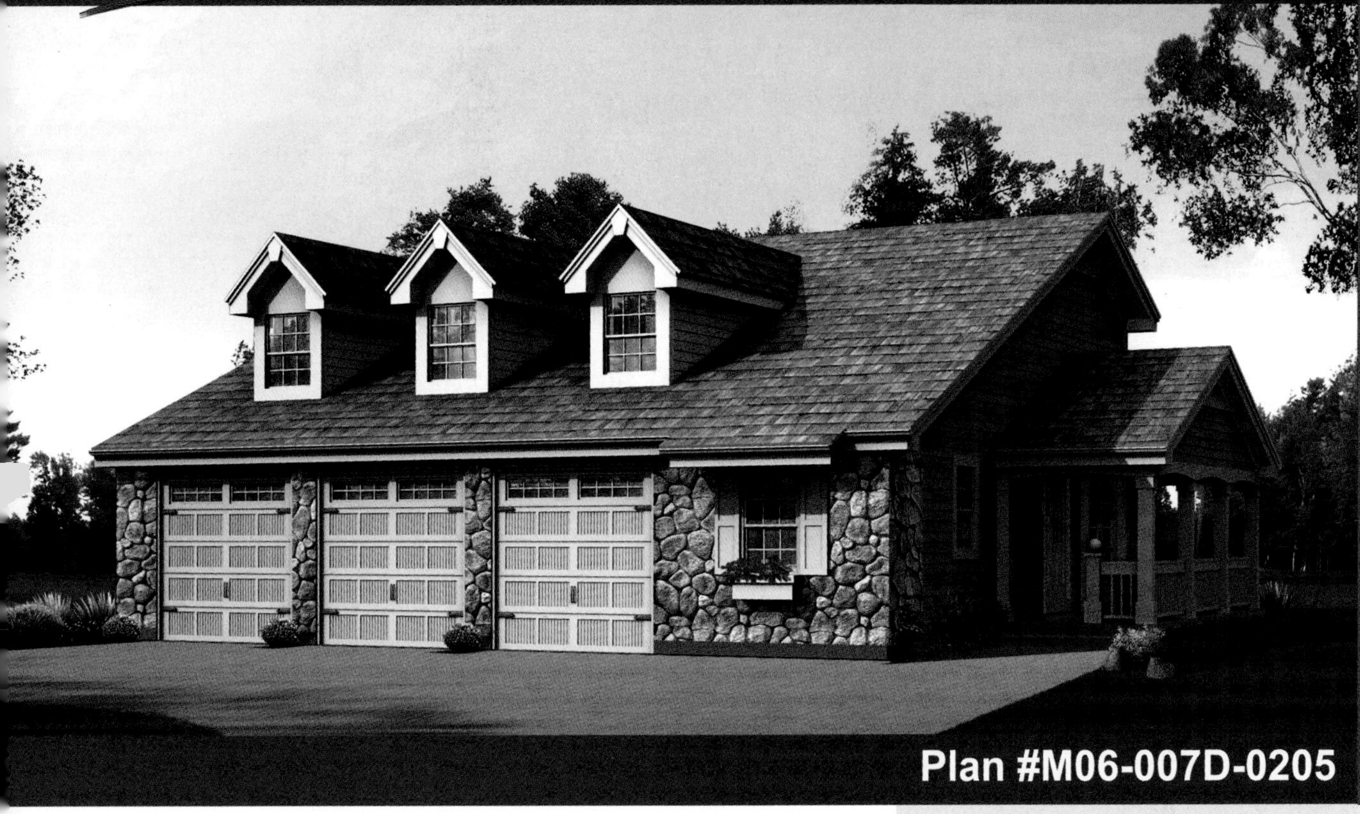

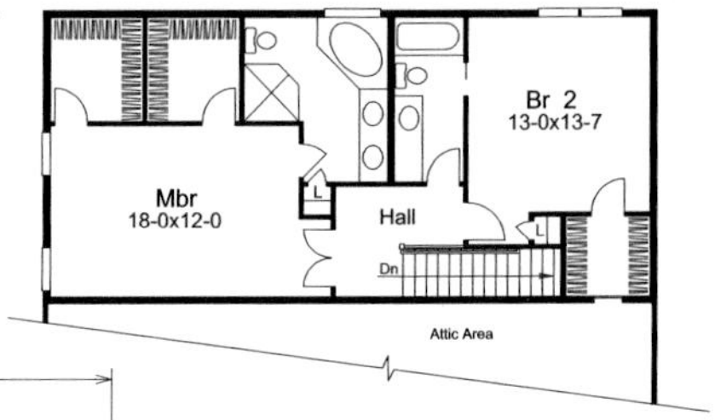

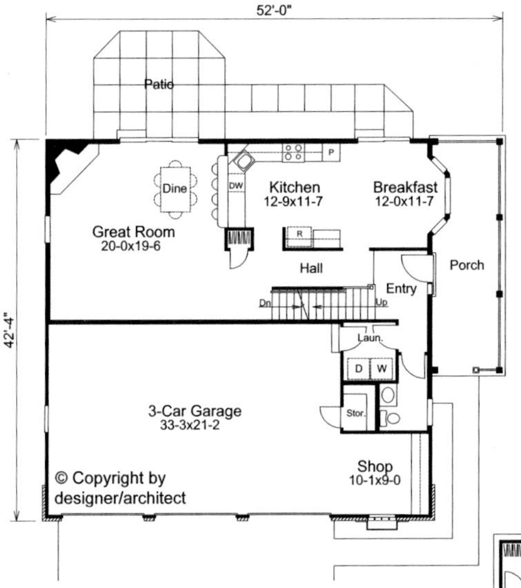

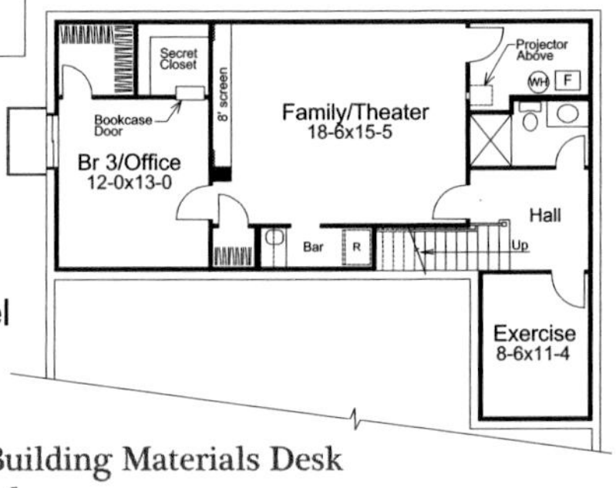

Luxury Plans

Plan #M06-007D-0205

Second Floor
902 sq. ft.

Mbr 18-0x12-0
Br 2 13-0x13-7
Hall
Attic Area

52'-0"
42'-4"

Patio
Dine
Great Room 20-0x19-6
Kitchen 12-9x11-7
Breakfast 12-0x11-7
Hall
Entry
Porch
Laun.
3-Car Garage 33-3x21-2
Stor.
Shop 10-1x9-0

First Floor
1,043 sq. ft.

Secret Closet
Bookcase Door
Br 3/Office 12-0x13-0
Family/Theater 18-6x15-5
Projector Above
Hall
Bar
Exercise 8-6x11-4

Lower Level
937 sq. ft.

To order plans, visit the Menards Building Materials Desk
or visit www.Menards.com.

CAREFULLY DESIGNED FOR EFFICIENCY

2,882 total square feet of living area

3 bedrooms, 3 1/2 baths

3-car garage

Basement foundation

SPECIAL FEATURES

The garage roof deflects winds, the insulated garage acts as a thermal barrier to the home's finished spaces, and triple-glazed insulated wood windows and doors are used in major glass areas

2" x 6" walls with multiple insulating materials create an approximate value of R34 with R70 in the attic

The basement has insulated walls inside and out and a natural cooling system created by a 40' long buried pipe

PRICE CODE D

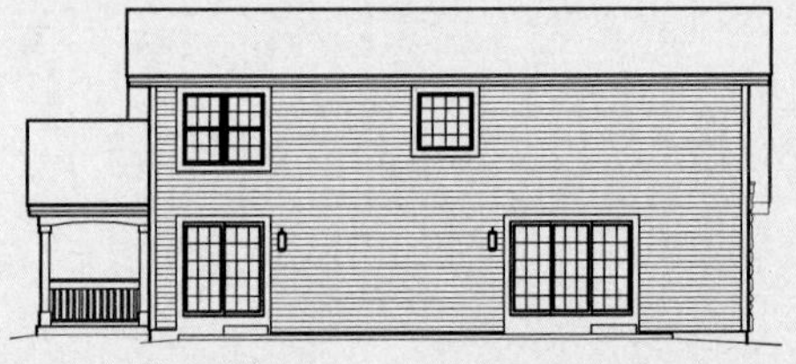

Rear View

LACERNE PLACE

MENARDS

Plan #M06-007D-0250

MASTER BEDROOM IS SECOND TO NONE

4,465 total square feet of living area

4 bedrooms, 3 1/2 baths

3-car side entry garage

Walk-out basement foundation

SPECIAL FEATURES

Arched double-entry 8' doors lead you into a grand foyer with stately staircase

The magnificent kitchen/breakfast room features a large center island, snack bar, menu desk, cabinet pantries, bayed breakfast area and adjacent hearth and dining rooms

The master bedroom has a coffered ceiling, double-entry doors, huge walk-in closets and a lavish bath

PRICE CODE G

Rear View

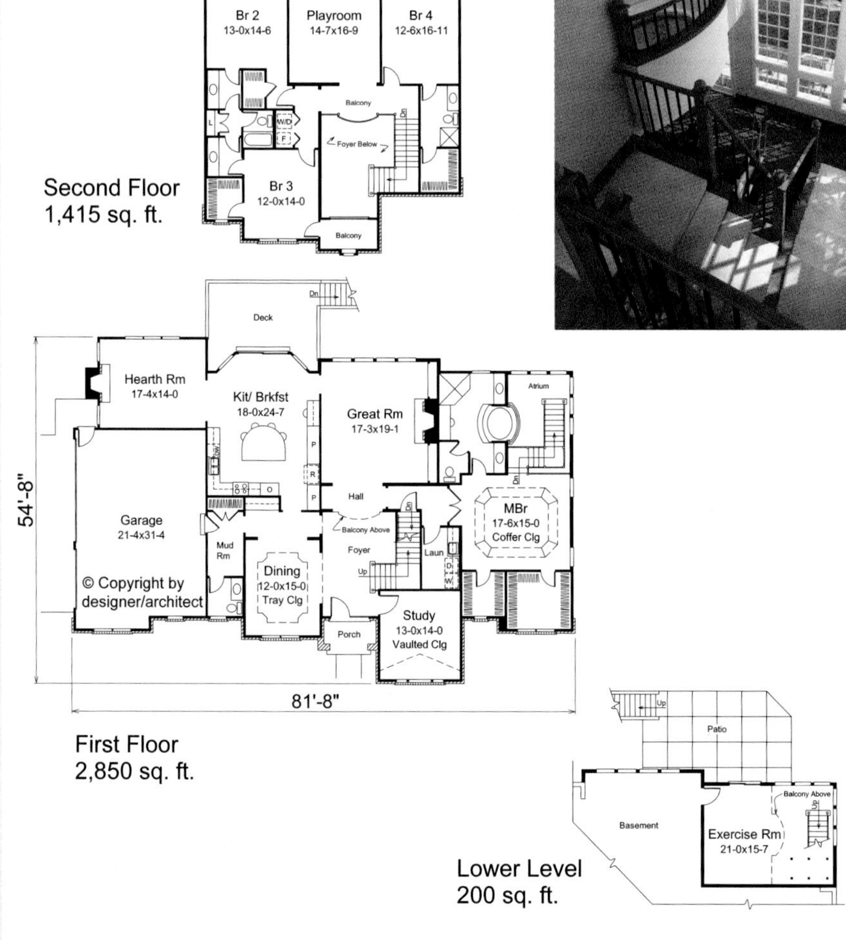

Br 2
13-0x14-6
Playroom
14-7x16-9
Br 4
12-6x16-11
Balcony
Foyer Below
Br 3
12-0x14-0
Balcony
Deck
Hearth Rm
17-4x14-0
Kit/ Brkfst
18-0x24-7
Great Rm
17-3x19-1
Atrium
Garage
21-4x31-4
MBr
17-6x15-0
Coffer Clg
Hall
Balcony Above
Foyer
Mud Rm
Laun
Dining
12-0x15-0
Tray Clg
Study
13-0x14-0
Vaulted Clg
Porch
54'-8"
81'-8"
© Copyright by designer/architect
Patio
Basement
Balcony Above
Exercise Rm
21-0x15-7

Second Floor
1,415 sq. ft.

First Floor
2,850 sq. ft.

Lower Level
200 sq. ft.

To order plans, visit the Menards Building Materials Desk or visit www.Menards.com.

SAMANTHA

Plan #M06-121D-0004

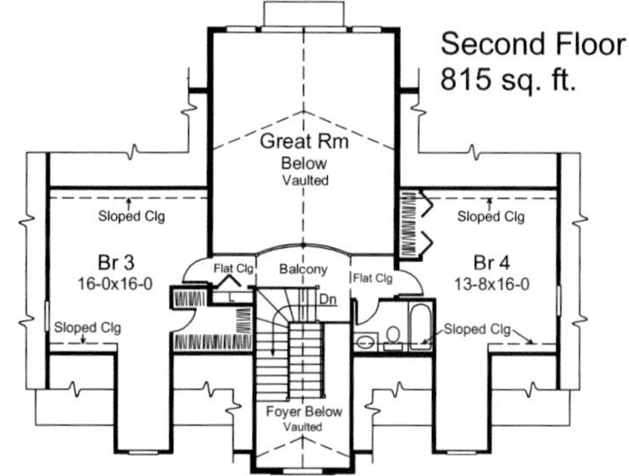
Second Floor
815 sq. ft.
Great Rm
Below
Vaulted
Sloped Clg
Br 3
16-0x16-0
Sloped Clg
Flat Clg
Balcony
Dn
Flat Clg
Sloped Clg
Br 4
13-8x16-0
Sloped Clg
Foyer Below
Vaulted

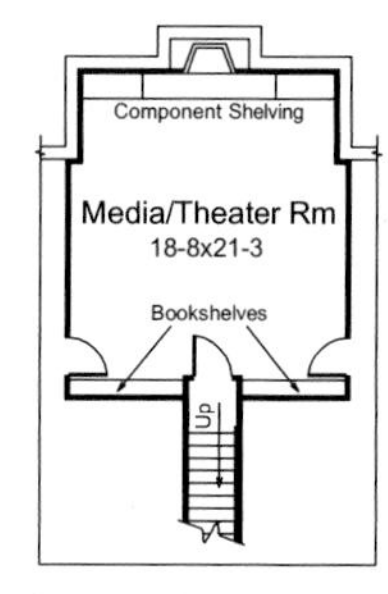
Component Shelving
Media/Theater Rm
18-8x21-3
Bookshelves
Up

Lower Level
396 sq. ft.

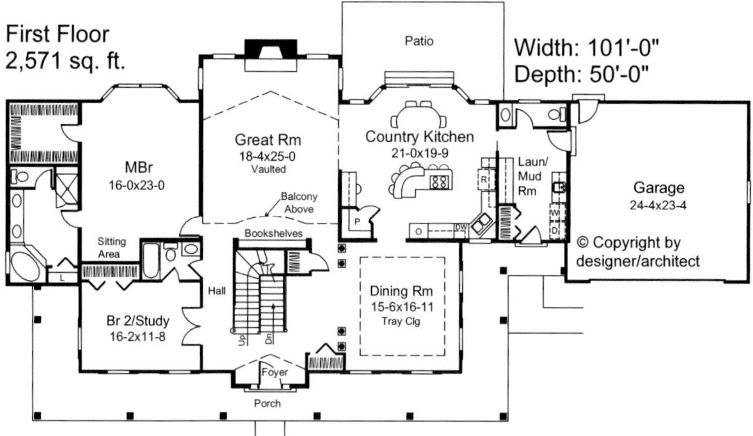
First Floor
2,571 sq. ft.
Patio
Width: 101'-0"
Depth: 50'-0"
MBr
16-0x23-0
Great Rm
18-4x25-0
Vaulted
Balcony
Above
Country Kitchen
21-0x19-9
Laun/
Mud
Rm
Garage
24-4x23-4
© Copyright by
designer/architect
Sitting
Area
Bookshelves
Hall
Dining Rm
15-6x16-11
Tray Clg
Br 2/Study
16-2x11-8
Up
Dn
Foyer
Porch

To order plans, visit the Menards Building Materials Desk
or visit www.Menards.com.

COUNTRY KITCHEN GREAT FOR GATHERING

3,782 total square feet of living area

4 bedrooms, 3 1/2 baths

2-car garage

Basement foundation

SPECIAL FEATURES

A stylish staircase in the foyer ascends to the second floor balcony

The lower level includes a media/theater room with built-in bookshelves

The formal dining room is decorated with an impressive tray ceiling drawing the eye upward

A massive 42" direct vent fireplace and expansive window wall helps bring the outdoors into the vaulted great room

2" x 6" exterior walls available, please order plan #M06-121E-0004

PRICE CODE E

Rear View

WESTERSHIRE PLACE

MENARDS

Plan #M06-007D-0202

OLD ENGLISH LUXURY

6,088 total square feet of living area

4 bedrooms, 4 full baths, 2 half baths

5-car side entry garage

Basement foundation

SPECIAL FEATURES

The two-story foyer invites guests into the grand scale great room

The kitchen includes a 9' island with seating, octagonal breakfast area, vaulted hearth room with fireplace and covered porch

The master bedroom offers a bay window, coffered ceiling and colossal bath with sauna, whirlpool tub and two enormous walk-in closets

A dramatic balcony overlooking the great room and private staircase to the kitchen are some features of the second floor

PRICE CODE H

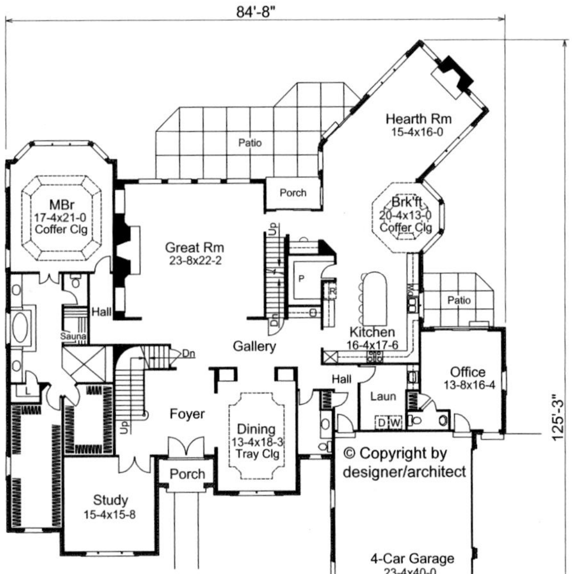

Rear View

84'-8"

125'-3"

Hearth Rm 15-4x16-0

Patio

Porch

MBr 17-4x21-0 Coffer Clg

Great Rm 23-8x22-2

Brk'ft 20-4x13-0 Coffer Clg

Hall

Sauna

Gallery

Kitchen 16-4x17-6

Patio

Office 13-8x16-4

Hall

Laun

Foyer

Dining 13-4x18-3 Tray Clg

Porch

Study 15-4x15-8

First Floor
4,294 sq. ft.

4-Car Garage 23-4x40-0

Storage

1-Car Garage 13-0x23-4

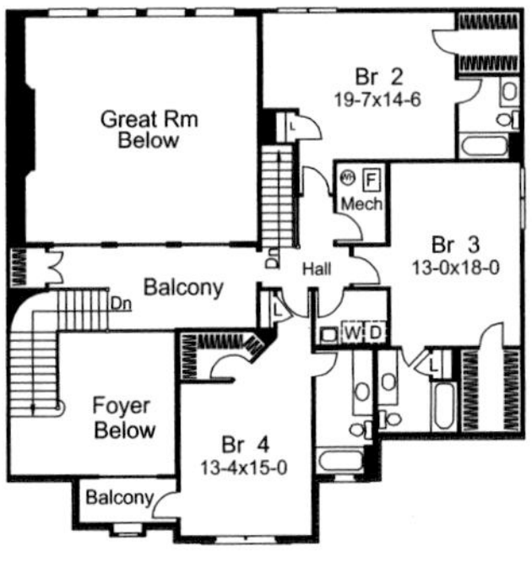

Great Rm Below

Br 2 19-7x14-6

Mech

Br 3 13-0x18-0

Balcony

Hall

Foyer Below

Br 4 13-4x15-0

Balcony

Second Floor
1,794 sq. ft.

To order plans, visit the Menards Building Materials Desk or visit www.Menards.com.

MENARDS KINGSCROSS

Luxury Plans

Plan #M06-055L-0097

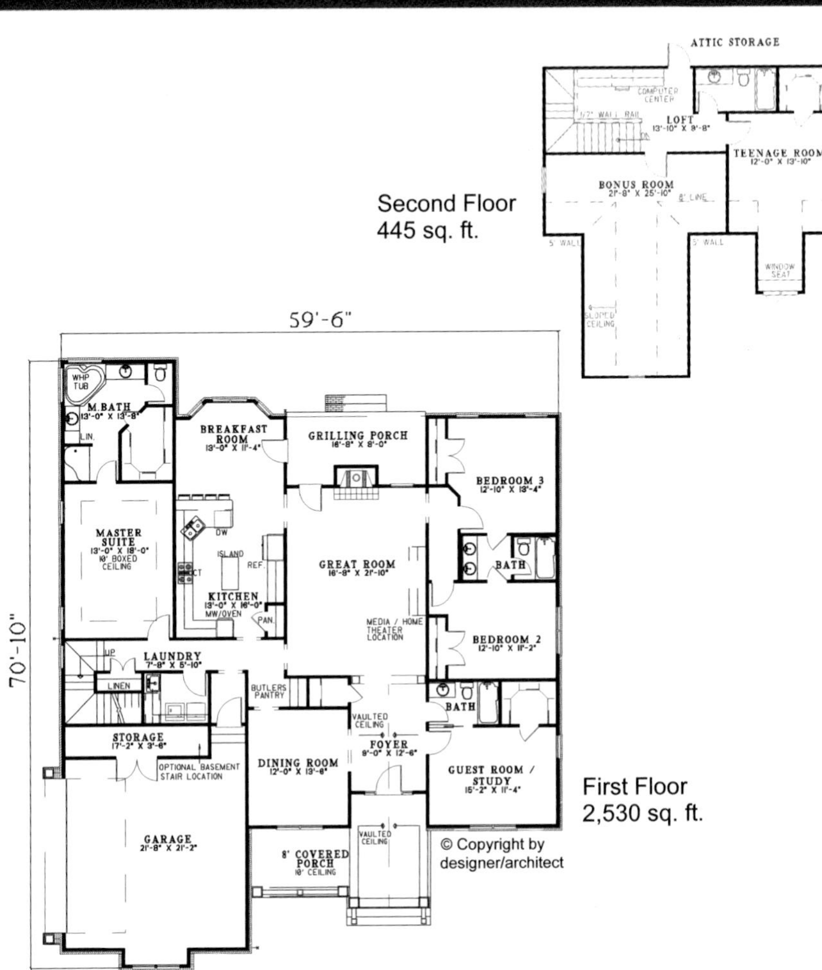

Second Floor
445 sq. ft.
ATTIC STORAGE
COMPUTER CENTER
LOFT
BONUS ROOM
TEENAGE ROOM
WINDOW SEAT
59'-6"
70'-10"
M.BATH
BREAKFAST ROOM
GRILLING PORCH
BEDROOM 3
MASTER SUITE
KITCHEN
GREAT ROOM
BATH
LAUNDRY
BEDROOM 2
STORAGE
BUTLERS PANTRY
BATH
FOYER
DINING ROOM
GUEST ROOM / STUDY
GARAGE
8' COVERED PORCH
First Floor
2,530 sq. ft.

PRIVATE MASTER SUITE

2,975 total square feet of living area

5 bedrooms, 4 baths

2-car side entry garage

Crawl space or slab foundation, please specify when ordering

SPECIAL FEATURES

The dining room has a 12' ceiling and butler's pantry nearby

The second floor bedroom, or "teenage room," has access to a computer center making it an ideal space for a school-aged child or as a home office area

The bonus room has an additional 425 square feet of living area

PRICE CODE E

To order plans, visit the Menards Building Materials Desk or visit www.Menards.com.

ENGLEWOOD

MENARDS®

Plan #M06-013L-0128

CORNER QUOINS ADD ELEGANCE TO EXTERIOR

2,760 total square feet of living area

4 bedrooms, 4 baths

3 1/2-car side entry garage

Basement foundation

SPECIAL FEATURES

Both secondary bedrooms on the second floor have their own full baths and large activity areas

The screened porch off the family room offers a place for outdoor relaxation

A box-bay window adds charm and character to guest bedroom #4

PRICE CODE G

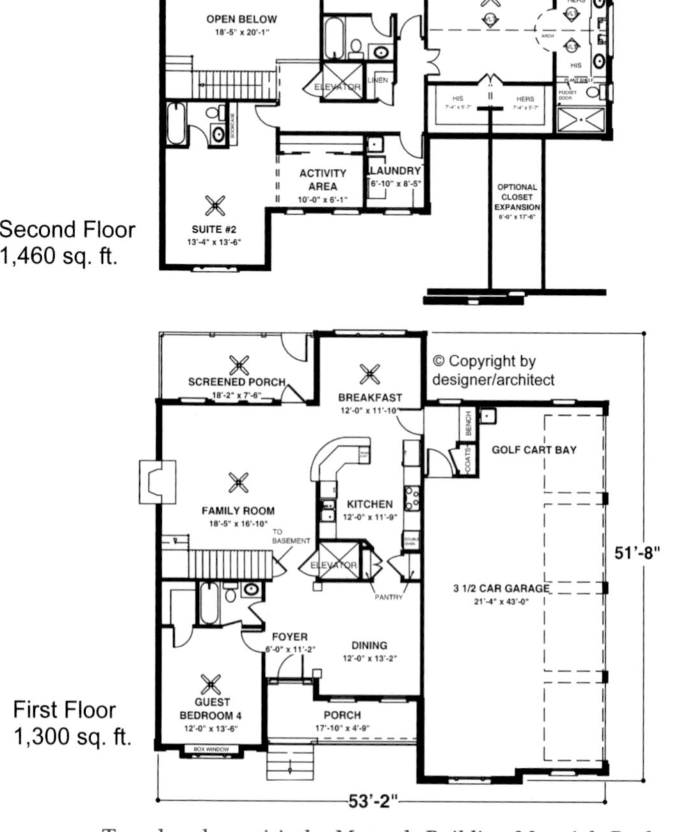
ACTIVITY AREA 9'-0" x 5'-10"
TERRACE
SUITE #3 12'-0" x 12'-0"
MASTER SUITE 15'-0" x 18'-0"
OPEN BELOW 18'-5" x 20'-1"
ELEVATOR
LINEN
HIS
HERS
ACTIVITY AREA 10'-0" x 6'-1"
LAUNDRY 6'-10" x 8'-5"
OPTIONAL CLOSET EXPANSION
SUITE #2 13'-4" x 13'-6"
Second Floor
1,460 sq. ft.
© Copyright by designer/architect
SCREENED PORCH 18'-2" x 7'-6"
BREAKFAST 12'-0" x 11'-10"
GOLF CART BAY
FAMILY ROOM 18'-5" x 16'-10"
KITCHEN 12'-0" x 11'-9"
TO BASEMENT
ELEVATOR
PANTRY
3 1/2 CAR GARAGE 21'-4" x 43'-0"
FOYER 8'-0" x 11'-2"
DINING 12'-0" x 13'-2"
GUEST BEDROOM 4 12'-0" x 13'-6"
PORCH 17'-10" x 4'-9"
BOX WINDOW
51'-8"
53'-2"
First Floor
1,300 sq. ft.

To order plans, visit the Menards Building Materials Desk or visit www.Menards.com.

MENARDS

WELLINGTON MANOR

Plan #M06-055L-0199

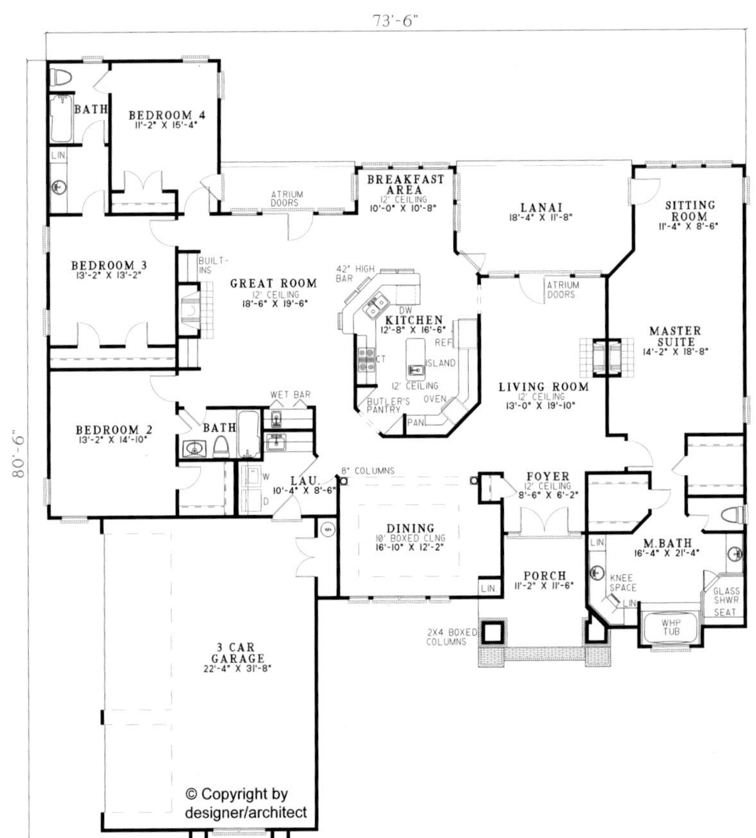

73'-6"
80'-6"
BATH
BEDROOM 4
11'-2" X 15'-4"
LIN
ATRIUM DOORS
BREAKFAST AREA
12' CEILING
10'-0" X 10'-8"
LANAI
18'-4" X 11'-8"
SITTING ROOM
11'-4" X 8'-6"
BEDROOM 3
13'-2" X 13'-2"
BUILT-INS
GREAT ROOM
12' CEILING
18'-6" X 19'-6"
42" HIGH BAR
DW
KITCHEN
12'-8" X 16'-6"
REF
ISLAND
CT
12' CEILING
BUTLER'S PANTRY
OVEN
PAN
ATRIUM DOORS
MASTER SUITE
14'-2" X 18'-8"
LIVING ROOM
12' CEILING
13'-0" X 19'-10"
BEDROOM 2
13'-2" X 14'-10"
WET BAR
BATH
LAU.
10'-4" X 8'-6"
W
D
8" COLUMNS
FOYER
12' CEILING
8'-6" X 6'-2"
DINING
10' BOXED CLNG
16'-10" X 12'-2"
LIN
PORCH
11'-2" X 11'-6"
M.BATH
16'-4" X 21'-4"
LIN
KNEE SPACE
LIN
GLASS SHWR SEAT
WHP TUB
2X4 BOXED COLUMNS
3 CAR GARAGE
22'-4" X 31'-8"
© Copyright by designer/architect

GRAND LIVING AREAS

2,951 total square feet of living area

4 bedrooms, 3 baths

3-car side entry garage

Slab, crawl space, basement or walk-out basement foundation, please specify when ordering

SPECIAL FEATURES

The master suite is luxurious with a see-through fireplace, two walk-in closets, a deluxe bath and a sitting room with access to the lanai

The great room features a 12' ceiling, wet bar, built-in cabinets and a fireplace that also warms the adjoining kitchen and breakfast area

The secondary bedrooms enjoy direct access to the baths

PRICE CODE F

To order plans, visit the Menards Building Materials Desk or visit www.Menards.com.

SHILLINGTON

MENARDS

Plan #M06-065L-0188

CHARMING COUNTRY HOME

1,488 total square feet of living area

3 bedrooms, 2 baths

2-car garage

Basement foundation

SPECIAL FEATURES

An inviting covered porch graces the entry

Vaulted ceilings in the dining and great rooms add spaciousness

The master bedroom enjoys a walk-in closet and luxurious bath with a corner tub

PRICE CODE A

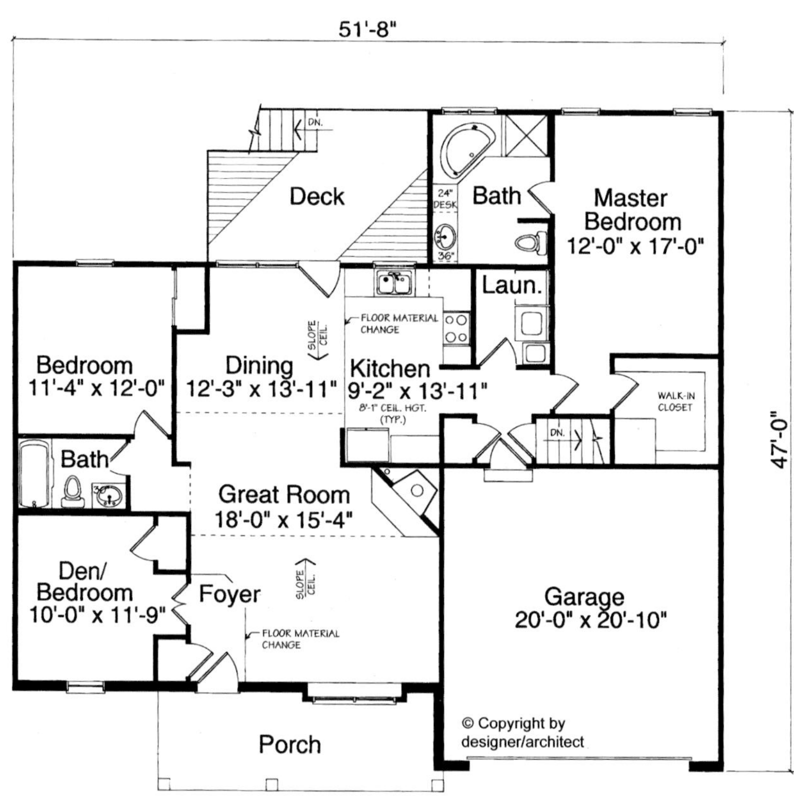

51'-8"
47'-0"
DN.
Deck
24" DESK
36"
Bath
Master Bedroom
12'-0" x 17'-0"
Laun.
FLOOR MATERIAL CHANGE
SLOPE CEIL.
Bedroom
11'-4" x 12'-0"
Dining
12'-3" x 13'-11"
Kitchen
9'-2" x 13'-11"
8'-1" CEIL. HGT. (TYP.)
WALK-IN CLOSET
DN.
Bath
Great Room
18'-0" x 15'-4"
Den/ Bedroom
10'-0" x 11'-9"
Foyer
SLOPE CEIL.
FLOOR MATERIAL CHANGE
Garage
20'-0" x 20'-10"
© Copyright by designer/architect
Porch

To order plans, visit the Menards Building Materials Desk or visit www.Menards.com.

Plan #M06-007D-0232

76'-0"
50'-8"
Br 3 14-4x11-0
Veranda
Garage 24-0x29-4
Dining
Laun
D W
Hall
Great Rm 30-8x17-5
Br 2 10-8x11-0
© Copyright by designer/architect
R
Entry
P
Kit 13-8x15-6
DW
MBr 16-0x13-4 Vaulted
Porch
Porch

COUNTRY HOME WITH CHARM AND GREAT PLANNING

1,915 total square feet of living area

3 bedrooms, 2 1/2 baths

3-car side entry garage

Slab foundation

SPECIAL FEATURES

The great room has a large dining area, corner fireplace and awesome views of the rear veranda

Several corner windows brighten the sink area in the kitchen

The vaulted master bedroom has two walk-in closets, a bath and private porch

The oversized garage has a coat closet, half bath and workbench

PRICE CODE D

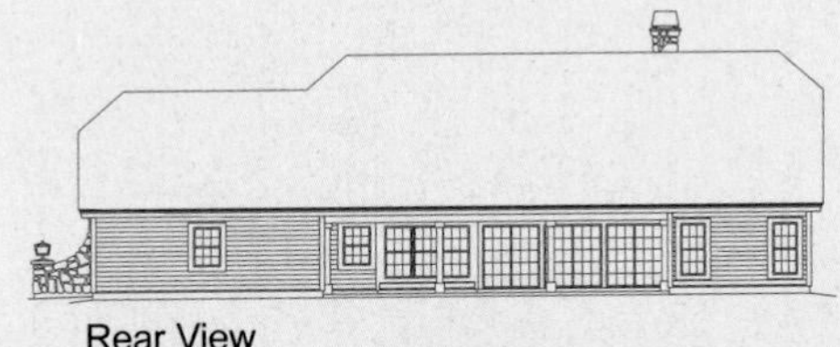

Rear View

To order plans, visit the Menards Building Materials Desk or visit www.Menards.com.

STELLAVILLE

MENARDS®

Plan #M06-013L-0027

SPACIOUS COUNTRY KITCHEN

2,184 total square feet of living area

3 bedrooms, 3 baths

2-car side entry garage

Basement, crawl space or slab foundation, please specify when ordering

SPECIAL FEATURES

The delightful family room has access to the screened porch for enjoyable outdoor living

The secluded master suite is complete with a sitting area and luxurious bath

The formal living room has a double-door entry easily converting it to a study or home office

Two secondary bedrooms have their own baths

Bonus room above garage has an additional 379 square feet of living space

PRICE CODE D

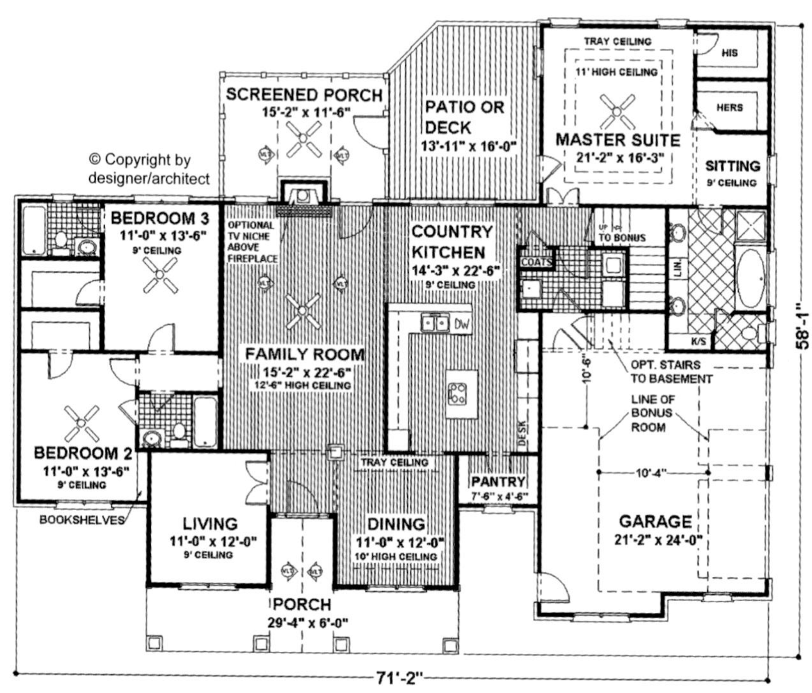

SCREENED PORCH
15'-2" x 11'-6"
PATIO OR DECK
13'-11" x 16'-0"
TRAY CEILING
11' HIGH CEILING
HIS
HERS
MASTER SUITE
21'-2" x 16'-3"
SITTING
9' CEILING
© Copyright by designer/architect
BEDROOM 3
11'-0" x 13'-6"
9' CEILING
OPTIONAL TV NICHE ABOVE FIREPLACE
COUNTRY KITCHEN
14'-3" x 22'-6"
9' CEILING
COATS
UP TO BONUS
LIN.
DW
K/S
FAMILY ROOM
15'-2" x 22'-6"
12'-6" HIGH CEILING
OPT. STAIRS TO BASEMENT
LINE OF BONUS ROOM
10'-6"
DESK
BEDROOM 2
11'-0" x 13'-6"
9' CEILING
TRAY CEILING
PANTRY
7'-6" x 4'-6"
10'-4"
BOOKSHELVES
LIVING
11'-0" x 12'-0"
9' CEILING
DINING
11'-0" x 12'-0"
10' HIGH CEILING
GARAGE
21'-2" x 24'-0"
PORCH
29'-4" x 6'-0"
58'-1"
71'-2"

To order plans, visit the Menards Building Materials Desk or visit www.Menards.com.

MENARDS

GABRIELLA

Plan #M06-121D-0019

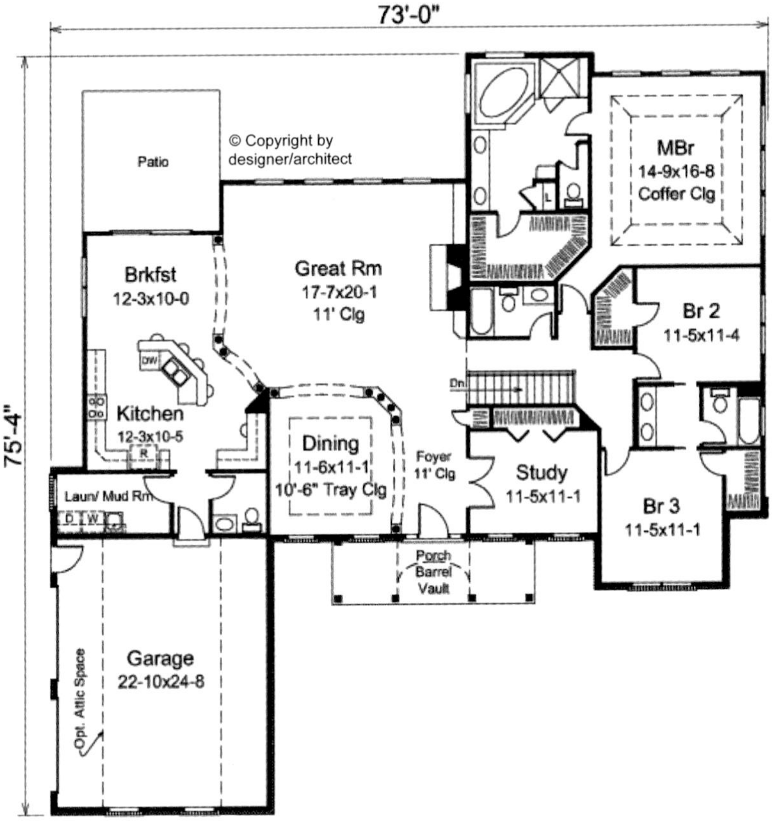

73'-0"

75'-4"

Patio

© Copyright by designer/architect

Brkfst 12-3x10-0

Great Rm 17-7x20-1 11' Clg

MBr 14-9x16-8 Coffer Clg

Br 2 11-5x11-4

Kitchen 12-3x10-5

Dining 11-6x11-1 10'-6" Tray Clg

Foyer 11' Clg

Study 11-5x11-1

Br 3 11-5x11-1

Laun/ Mud Rm

Porch Barrel Vault

Garage 22-10x24-8

Opt. Attic Space

To order plans, visit the Menards Building Materials Desk or visit www.Menards.com.

COLUMNS HIGHLIGHT THE FRONT PORCH

2,814 total square feet of living area

3 bedrooms, 3 1/2 baths

2-car side entry garage

Basement foundation

SPECIAL FEATURES

The spacious great room boasts a warming fireplace and is brightened by multiple windows

The kitchen features a center island with an eating bar for causal meals and a planning center

An amazing private bath with corner whirlpool tub and spacious closet completes the master bedroom

The study could easily be converted to a fourth bedroom

PRICE CODE D

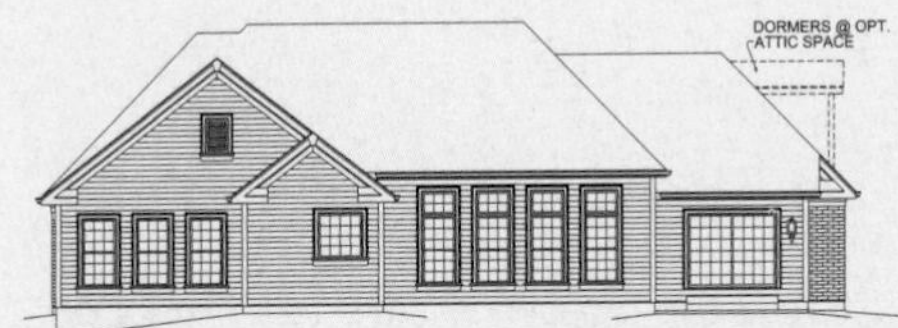
DORMERS @ OPT. ATTIC SPACE

Rear View

STONECROFT

MENARDS

Plan #M06-077L-0053

CLASSIC COUNTRY HOME

1,852 total square feet of living area

3 bedrooms, 2 1/2 baths

2-car garage

Basement, crawl space or slab foundation, please specify when ordering

SPECIAL FEATURES

The stately great room features a vaulted ceiling and a corner gas fireplace

The covered or screened-in porch is a great place to relax and enjoy the outdoors

The future bonus room on the second floor has an additional 370 square feet of living space

PRICE CODE D

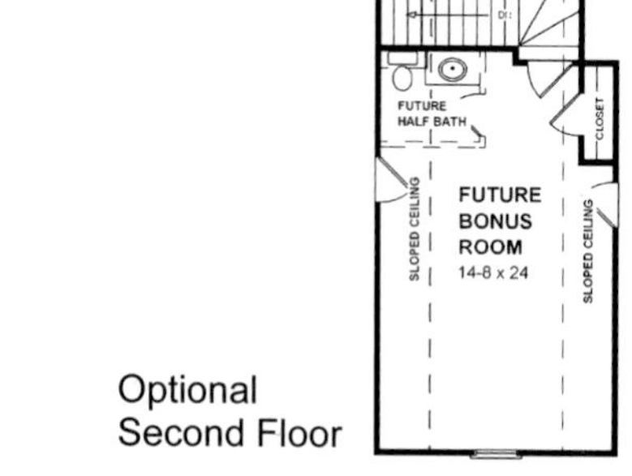
FUTURE HALF BATH
CLOSET
SLOPED CEILING
FUTURE BONUS ROOM
14-8 x 24
SLOPED CEILING

Optional Second Floor

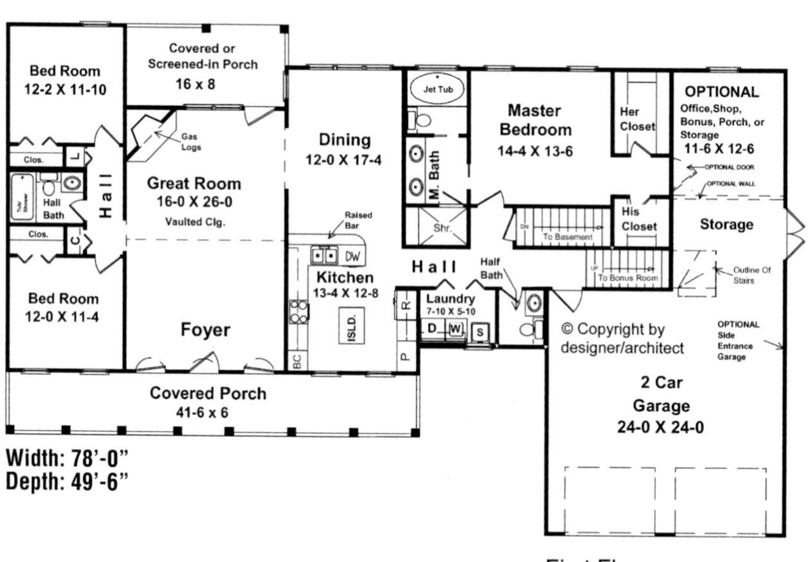
Bed Room
12-2 X 11-10
Covered or Screened-in Porch
16 x 8
Gas Logs
Great Room
16-0 X 26-0
Vaulted Clg.
Clos.
Hall Bath
Hall
Clos.
Bed Room
12-0 X 11-4
Foyer
Dining
12-0 X 17-4
Raised Bar
DW
Kitchen
13-4 X 12-8
ISLD.
BC
Jet Tub
M. Bath
Shr.
Master Bedroom
14-4 X 13-6
Her Closet
His Closet
To Basement
Hall
Half Bath
Laundry
7-10 X 5-10
OPTIONAL
Office,Shop, Bonus, Porch, or Storage
11-6 X 12-6
OPTIONAL DOOR
OPTIONAL WALL
Storage
To Bonus Room
Outline Of Stairs
OPTIONAL Side Entrance Garage
© Copyright by designer/architect
2 Car Garage
24-0 X 24-0
Covered Porch
41-6 x 6
Width: 78'-0"
Depth: 49'-6"

First Floor
1,852 sq. ft.

To order plans, visit the Menards Building Materials Desk or visit www.Menards.com.

MENARDS

WOODFIELD MANOR

Plan #M06-007D-0212

72'-8"
37'-4"
MBr 15-4x12-0
Living 15-8x17-0 vaulted
Brkfst 10-4x11-0
Covered Patio
Kit 10-0 x14-0
Plant shelf above
Hall
Dining 11-2x11-0
Entry
Laun
Garage 19-4x21-4
Br 2 12-4x11-0
Br 3 11-0x11-0
Porch
© Copyright by designer/architect
Stor

COUNTRY RANCH WITH COVERED PATIO

1,568 total square feet of living area

3 bedrooms, 2 baths

2-car garage

Crawl space foundation, drawings also include slab foundation

SPECIAL FEATURES

Classic gables, dormers and decorative circular windows are all combined to create this home's stylish facade

The living room includes a vaulted ceiling with plant shelf and warming fireplace

A walk-in pantry is featured in the well-designed kitchen and is adjacent to a convenient laundry room

The master bedroom with double entry doors is nicely appointed with an over sized bath and large walk-in closet

PRICE CODE A

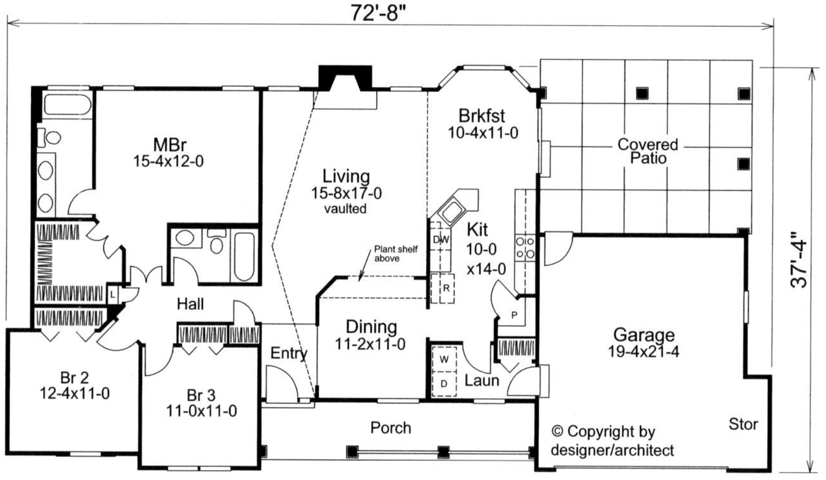

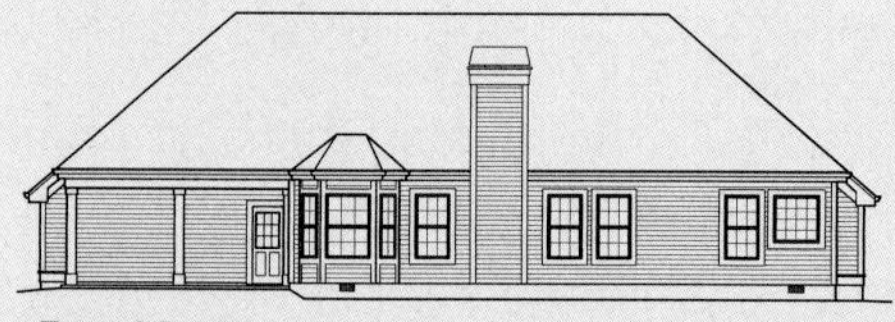
Rear View

To order plans, visit the Menards Building Materials Desk or visit www.Menards.com.

WOOSTOCK

MENARDS

Plan #M06-013L-0155

MAGNIFICENT ONE-LEVEL LIVING

1,800 total square feet of living area

3 bedrooms, 3 baths

3-car side entry garage

Crawl space foundation

SPECIAL FEATURES

The wonderful family room boasts a 10' ceiling and opens nicely to the eating area and cozy kitchen

The chef of the family is sure to love this cheerful kitchen equipped with a uniquely-shaped island, plenty of counterspace and a functional pass-thru to the formal dining room

Luxurious master suite includes two closets, a separate shower, a double-bowl vanity and access to the screen porch

The optional bonus room above the garage has an additional 503 square feet of living area

PRICE CODE B

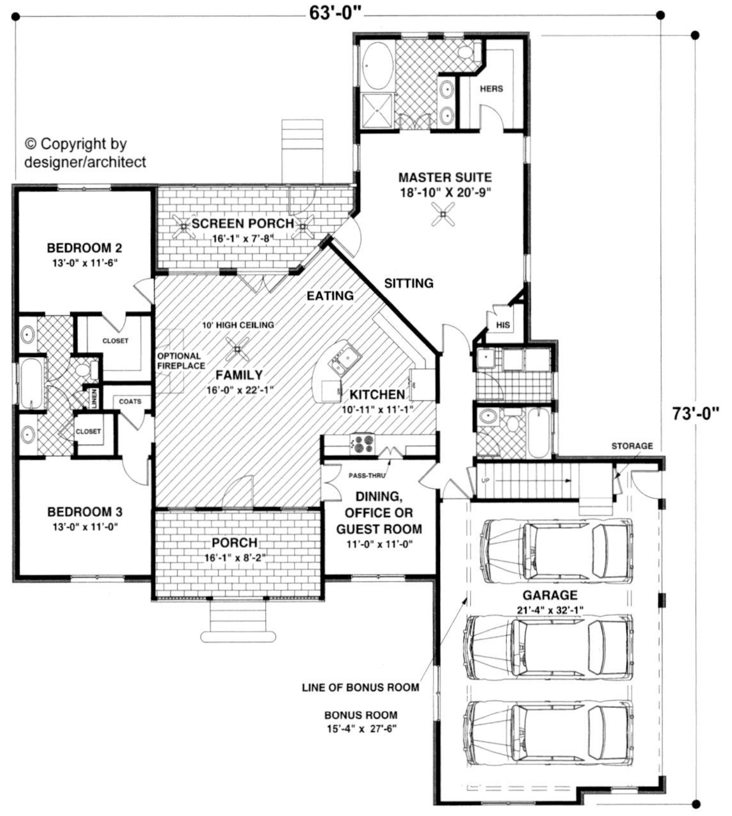

63'-0"
73'-0"
© Copyright by designer/architect
HERS
MASTER SUITE 18'-10" X 20'-9"
SCREEN PORCH 16'-1" x 7'-8"
BEDROOM 2 13'-0" x 11'-6"
SITTING
EATING
10' HIGH CEILING
CLOSET
OPTIONAL FIREPLACE
FAMILY 16'-0" x 22'-1"
KITCHEN 10'-11" x 11'-1"
HIS
LINEN
COATS
CLOSET
PASS-THRU
STORAGE
UP
DINING, OFFICE OR GUEST ROOM 11'-0" x 11'-0"
BEDROOM 3 13'-0" x 11'-0"
PORCH 16'-1" x 8'-2"
GARAGE 21'-4" x 32'-1"
LINE OF BONUS ROOM
BONUS ROOM 15'-4" x 27'-6"

To order plans, visit the Menards Building Materials Desk or visit www.Menards.com.

MENARDS®

ABIGAIL

Plan #M06-121D-0011

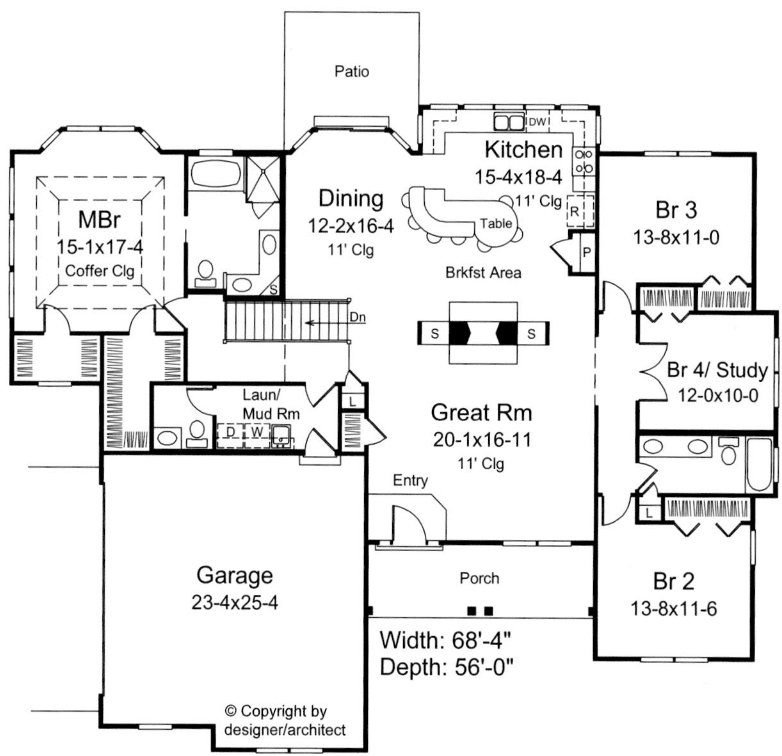

Patio
Kitchen
15-4x18-4
11' Clg
DW
R
P
Dining
12-2x16-4
11' Clg
Table
Brkfst Area
MBr
15-1x17-4
Coffer Clg
S
Dn
Br 3
13-8x11-0
Br 4/ Study
12-0x10-0
Laun/
Mud Rm
D
W
L
Great Rm
20-1x16-11
11' Clg
Entry
Garage
23-4x25-4
Porch
Br 2
13-8x11-6
Width: 68'-4"
Depth: 56'-0"
© Copyright by
designer/architect

To order plans, visit the Menards Building Materials Desk or visit www.Menards.com.

LOVELY SEE-THROUGH FIREPLACE

2,241 total square feet of living area

4 bedrooms, 2 1/2 baths

2-car side entry garage

Basement foundation

SPECIAL FEATURES

11' ceilings can be found in the entry, great room, kitchen and dining area

The large kitchen island with breakfast bar also includes a table extension providing enough dining space for up to seven people

The elegant master bedroom is topped with a coffered ceiling and enjoys amenities such as two walk-in closets and a private bath

PRICE CODE C

Rear View

FLORENCE

MENARDS

Plan #M06-017D-0005

COMFORTABLE ONE-STORY COUNTRY HOME

1,367 total square feet of living area

3 bedrooms, 2 baths

2-car garage

Basement foundation, drawings also include slab foundation

SPECIAL FEATURES

Energy efficient home with 2" x 6" exterior walls

Neat front porch shelters the entrance

The dining room has a full wall of windows and convenient storage area

The breakfast area leads to the rear terrace through sliding doors

The large living room features a high ceiling, skylight and fireplace

PRICE CODE B

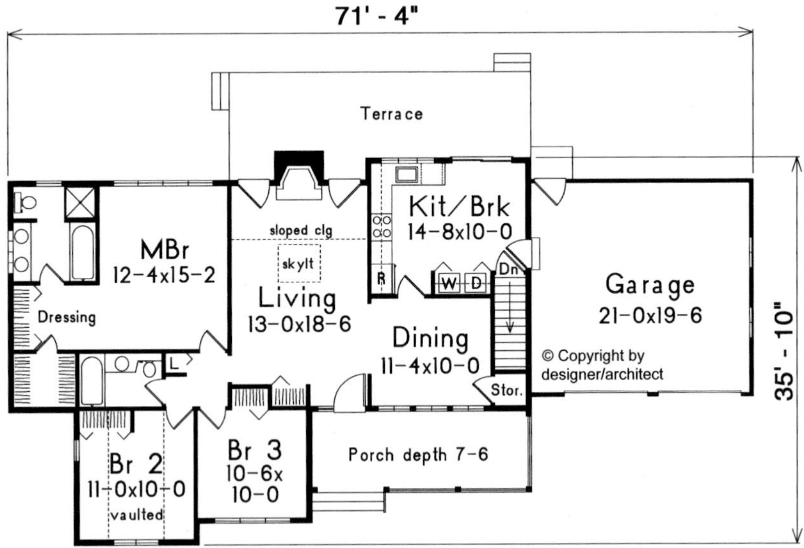

71' - 4"
Terrace
MBr
12-4x15-2
sloped clg
skylt
Living
13-0x18-6
Kit/Brk
14-8x10-0
R
W
D
Dn
Dressing
L
Dining
11-4x10-0
Stor.
Garage
21-0x19-6
© Copyright by designer/architect
35' - 10"
Br 2
11-0x10-0
vaulted
Br 3
10-6x
10-0
Porch depth 7-6

Rear View

To order plans, visit the Menards Building Materials Desk or visit www.Menards.com.

MENARDS®

STONEFIELD

Plan #M06-007D-0216

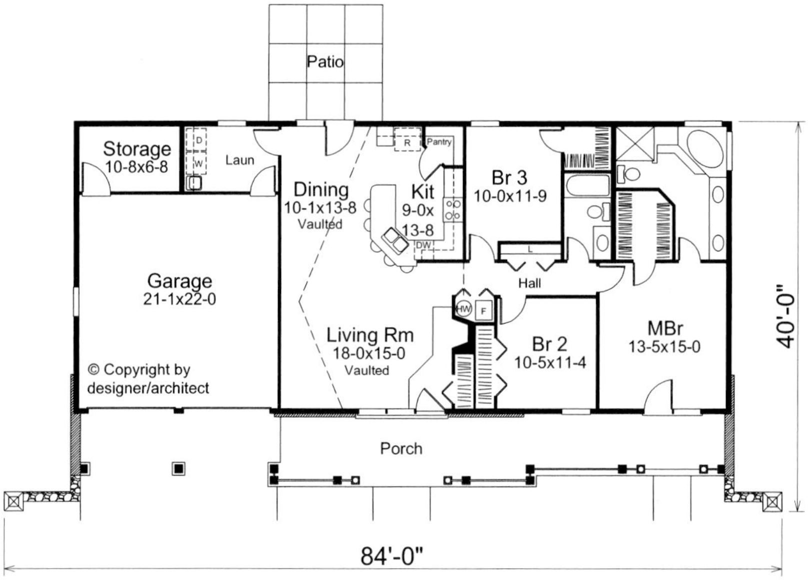

Patio
Storage 10-8x6-8
Laun
Dining 10-1x13-8 Vaulted
Kit 9-0x 13-8
Pantry
Br 3 10-0x11-9
Garage 21-1x22-0
Hall
Living Rm 18-0x15-0 Vaulted
Br 2 10-5x11-4
MBr 13-5x15-0
© Copyright by designer/architect
Porch
40'-0"
84'-0"

COUNTRY RANCH HOME

1,510 total square feet of living area

3 bedrooms, 2 baths

2-car garage

Slab foundation, drawings also include crawl space foundation

SPECIAL FEATURES

Energy efficient home with 2" x 6" exterior walls

The decorative porch arches, wood columns and stone walls combine to create an exterior that demands attention

Open living room and dining area feature vaulted ceilings, a fireplace and French doors to the rear patio

The well-planned kitchen has a large built-in corner pantry and a snack counter, all open to the living room

Convenient to the kitchen is a nice-sized laundry room with sink

PRICE CODE A

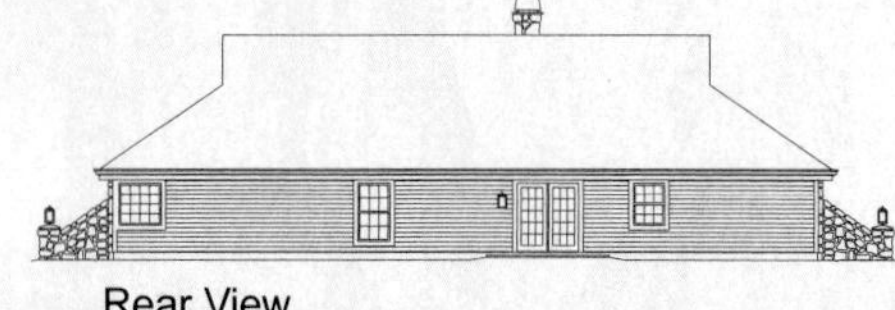

Rear View

To order plans, visit the Menards Building Materials Desk or visit www.Menards.com.

MANOR GROVE

MENARDS®

Plan #M06-007D-0120

A DESIGN FOR PRIVACY AND FLEXIBILITY

1,914 total square feet of living area

4 bedrooms, 3 baths

2-car garage

Basement foundation

SPECIAL FEATURES

The vaulted great room features a dining area, entry, corner fireplace and 9' wide sliding doors to the rear patio

The secondary bedrooms offer walk-in closets and share a Jack and Jill bath

A multi-purpose room has a laundry alcove and can easily be used as a hobby room, sewing room or small office

The bedroom #4/study can be open to the master bedroom suite and utilized as a private home office or nursery

PRICE CODE C

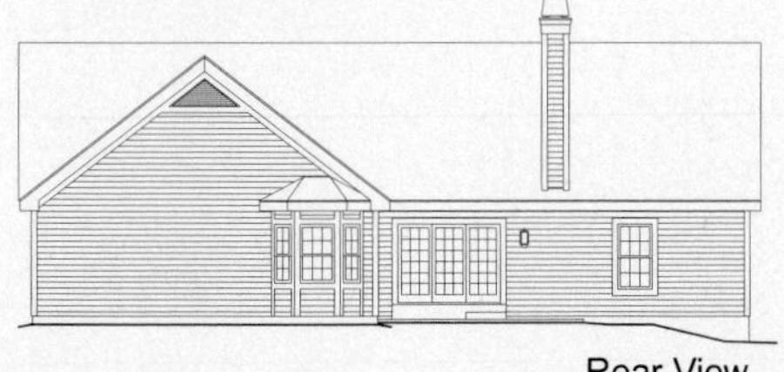

Rear View

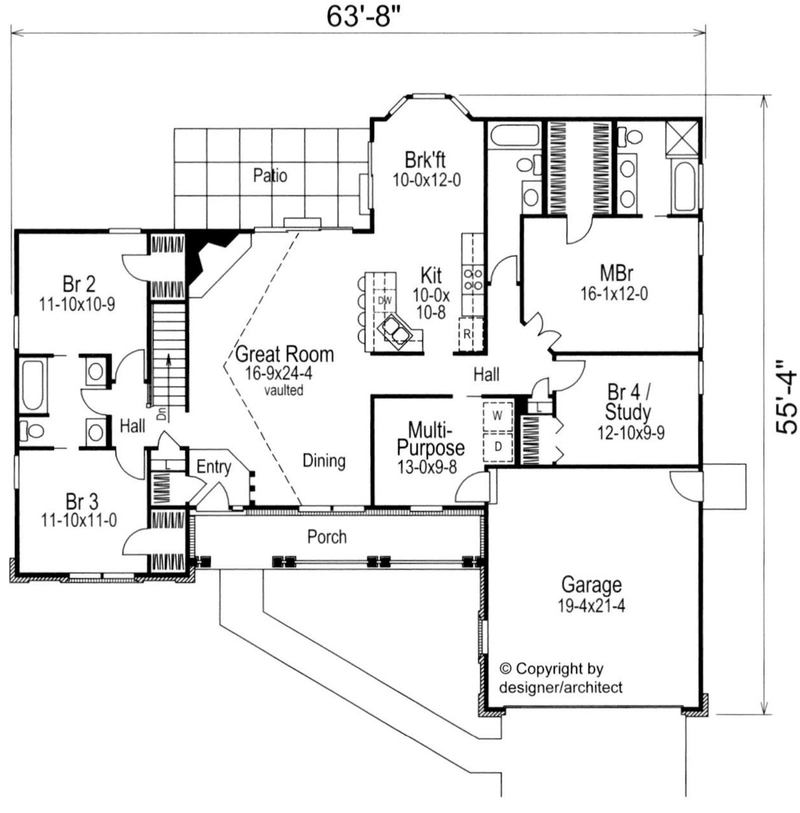

63'-8"
55'-4"
Patio
Brk'ft
10-0x12-0
Br 2
11-10x10-9
Kit
10-0x
10-8
DW
R
MBr
16-1x12-0
Great Room
16-9x24-4
vaulted
Hall
Br 4 /
Study
12-10x9-9
Dn
Hall
Multi-
Purpose
13-0x9-8
W
D
Entry
Dining
Br 3
11-10x11-0
Porch
Garage
19-4x21-4
© Copyright by
designer/architect

To order plans, visit the Menards Building Materials Desk or visit www.Menards.com.

MENARDS®

GRANDTREE

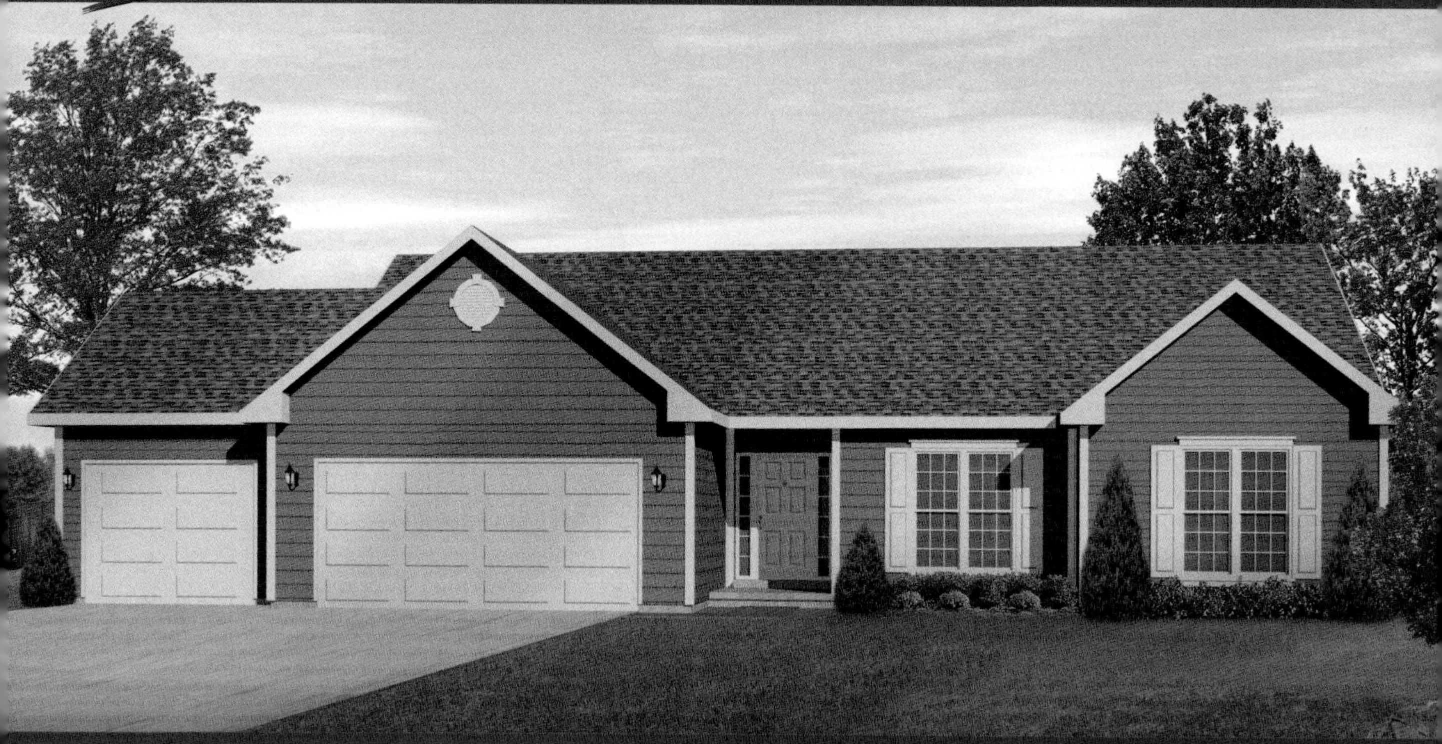

Plan #M06-058D-0061

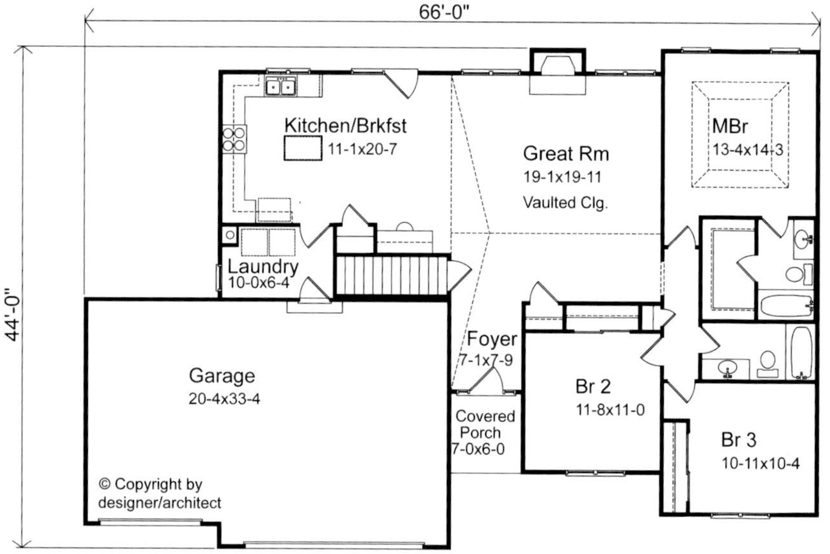

OPEN LIVING AREAS

1,642 total square feet of living area

3 bedrooms, 2 baths

3-car garage

Basement foundation

SPECIAL FEATURES

The bedrooms are separated from the main living areas for privacy

The vaulted great room is warmed by a grand fireplace

Family activities are sure to be a breeze with this spacious floor plan

A convenient laundry area is located at the garage entrance

PRICE CODE B

66'-0"

44'-0"

Kitchen/Brkfst
11-1x20-7

Great Rm
19-1x19-11
Vaulted Clg.

MBr
13-4x14-3

Laundry
10-0x6-4

Foyer
7-1x7-9

Garage
20-4x33-4

Br 2
11-8x11-0

Covered Porch
7-0x6-0

Br 3
10-11x10-4

Rear View

To order plans, visit the Menards Building Materials Desk or visit www.Menards.com.

PIEDMONT PARK

MENARDS

Plan #M06-077L-0065

INVITING FRONT PORCH

2,138 total square feet of living area

3 bedrooms, 3 baths

2-car garage

Basement, crawl space or slab foundation, please specify when ordering

SPECIAL FEATURES

The vaulted sunroom is an enchanting space to dine and accesses two covered porches

The master bedroom enjoys his and her baths and walk-in closets as well as access to one rear porch and an optional storage, lounge or office space

The bonus room on the second floor has an additional 302 square feet of living space

PRICE CODE E

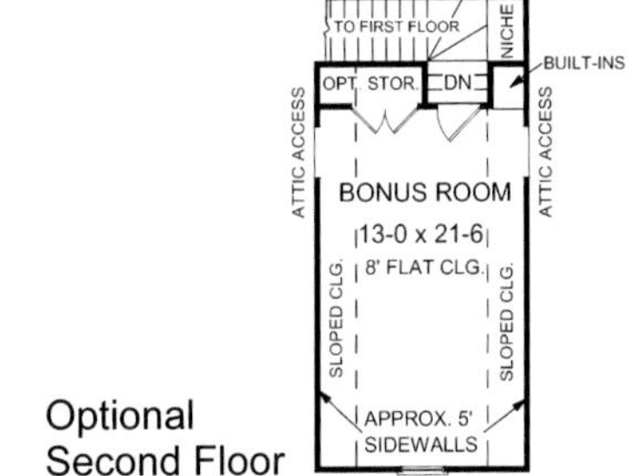

TO FIRST FLOOR
NICHE
OPT. STOR.
DN
BUILT-INS
ATTIC ACCESS
ATTIC ACCESS
BONUS ROOM
13-0 x 21-6
8' FLAT CLG.
SLOPED CLG.
SLOPED CLG.
APPROX. 5' SIDEWALLS

Optional
Second Floor

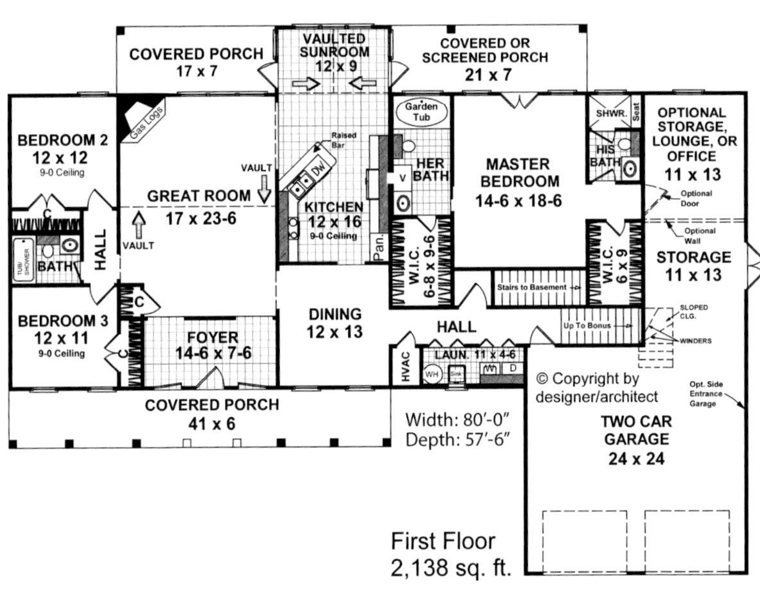

COVERED PORCH
17 x 7
VAULTED SUNROOM
12 x 9
COVERED OR SCREENED PORCH
21 x 7
BEDROOM 2
12 x 12
9-0 Ceiling
Gas Logs
GREAT ROOM
17 x 23-6
VAULT
VAULT
Raised Bar
DW
KITCHEN
12 x 16
9-0 Ceiling
Pan.
Garden Tub
HER BATH
MASTER BEDROOM
14-6 x 18-6
SHWR.
Seat
HIS BATH
OPTIONAL STORAGE, LOUNGE, OR OFFICE
11 x 13
Optional Door
Optional Wall
STORAGE
11 x 13
BATH
HALL
W.I.C.
6-8 x 9-6
W.I.C.
6 x 9
Stairs to Basement
BEDROOM 3
12 x 11
9-0 Ceiling
FOYER
14-6 x 7-6
DINING
12 x 13
HALL
Up To Bonus
SLOPED CLG.
WINDERS
HVAC
LAUN. 11 x 4-6
WH
D
© Copyright by designer/architect
Opt. Side Entrance Garage
COVERED PORCH
41 x 6
Width: 80'-0"
Depth: 57'-6"
TWO CAR GARAGE
24 x 24

First Floor
2,138 sq. ft.

To order plans, visit the Menards Building Materials Desk or visit www.Menards.com.

MENARDS

ADRIANNA

Plan #M06-055L-0210

ENCHANTING RANCH

2,624 total square feet of living area

4 bedrooms, 3 baths

2-car side entry garage

Slab or crawl space foundation, please specify when ordering

SPECIAL FEATURES

Bedroom #2 is secluded and includes a private bath making it ideal for a guest suite

The master suite features a 10' ceiling, porch access and a deluxe bath with two vanities and an extra-large walk-in closet

The large laundry room has a separate entrance

The optional second floor has an additional 561 square feet of living space

PRICE CODE F

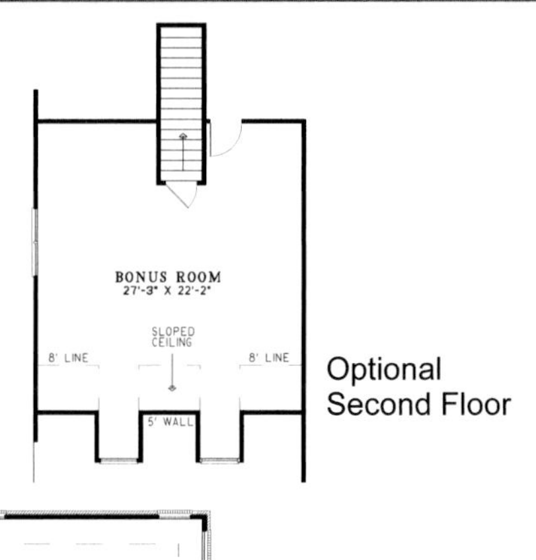

BONUS ROOM
27'-3" X 22'-2"
SLOPED CEILING
8' LINE
8' LINE
5' WALL

Optional Second Floor

MASTER SUITE
20'-0" X 13'-4"
10' BOXED CEILING
GRILLING PORCH
32'-8" X 9'-0"
BEDROOM 2
12'-0" X 13'-4"
M.BATH
16'-6" X 15'-2"
WHP TUB
GLASS SHOWER
LIN
BONUS AREA ABOVE
8" COLUMNS
BRKFAST / HEARTH
13'-4" X 20'-0"
LIVING RM.
16'-4" X 24'-0"
BATH
BEDROOM 3
12'-0" X 11'-0"
LAU.
KID'S NOOK
PASS-THRU
KITCHEN
12'-0" X 16'-6"
PAN
REF
OVEN
DW
FOYER
11'-6" X 9'-4"
FRENCH DOORS
STUDY / BEDROOM 4
11'-0" X 12'-0"
BATH
GARAGE
22'-2" X 21'-0"
© Copyright by designer/architect
DINING
12'-0" X 15'-4"
11' CEILING
COVERED PORCH
19'-2" X 10'-4"
W: 66' - 4"
D: 64' - 0"

First Floor
2,624 sq. ft.

To order plans, visit the Menards Building Materials Desk or visit www.Menards.com.

CRANDALL CLIFF

MENARDS®

Plan #M06-013L-0130

EXCITING ONE-LEVEL HOME

1,798 total square feet of living area

3 bedrooms, 2 1/2 baths

2-car side entry garage

Slab foundation

SPECIAL FEATURES

A gourmet kitchen, casual dining room and a rear covered porch overlooking the pool make this home a delight for entertaining

The generous master suite features a sitting area and large walk-in closet with separate his and her sections

The front home office can easily become a guest bedroom with its walk-in closet and private bath access

The bonus room above the garage has an additional 328 square feet of living area

PRICE CODE E

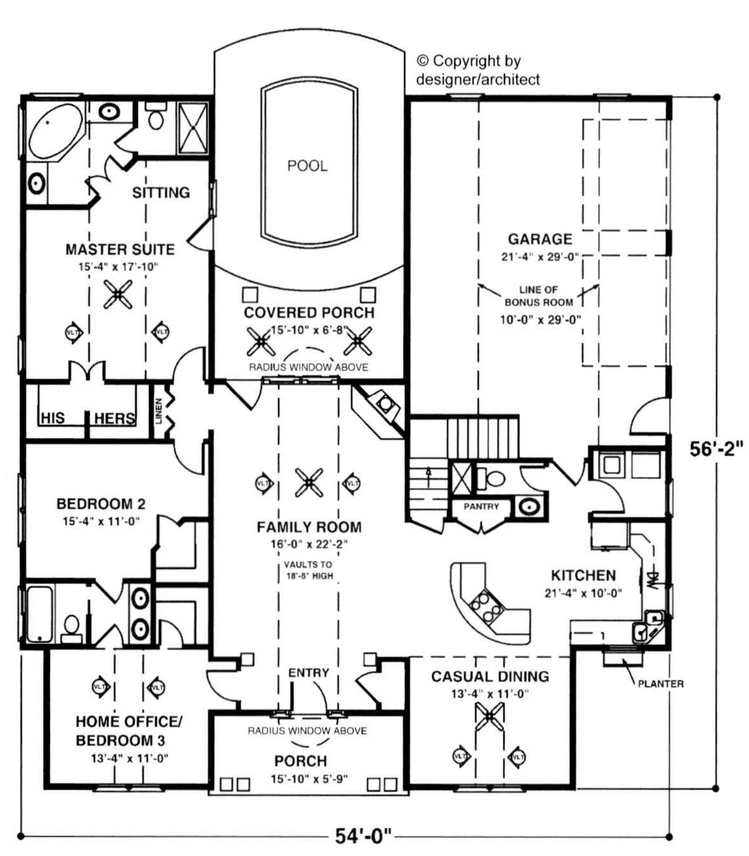

© Copyright by designer/architect
POOL
SITTING
MASTER SUITE
15'-4" x 17'-10"
COVERED PORCH
15'-10" x 6'-8"
RADIUS WINDOW ABOVE
GARAGE
21'-4" x 29'-0"
LINE OF BONUS ROOM
10'-0" x 29'-0"
HIS
HERS
LINEN
56'-2"
BEDROOM 2
15'-4" x 11'-0"
FAMILY ROOM
16'-0" x 22'-2"
VAULTS TO 18'-6" HIGH
PANTRY
KITCHEN
21'-4" x 10'-0"
ENTRY
CASUAL DINING
13'-4" x 11'-0"
PLANTER
HOME OFFICE/
BEDROOM 3
13'-4" x 11'-0"
RADIUS WINDOW ABOVE
PORCH
15'-10" x 5'-9"
54'-0"

To order plans, visit the Menards Building Materials Desk or visit www.Menards.com.

MENARDS®

BETHANY

Plan #M06-068D-0007

COLOSSAL GREAT ROOM

1,599 total square feet of living area

4 bedrooms, 2 baths

2-car garage

Basement foundation, drawings also include crawl space and slab foundations

SPECIAL FEATURES

The kitchen is designed for efficiency with a large pantry and easy access to the laundry room

Bedroom #3 has a charming window seat

The master bedroom has a full bath and large walk-in closet

PRICE CODE B

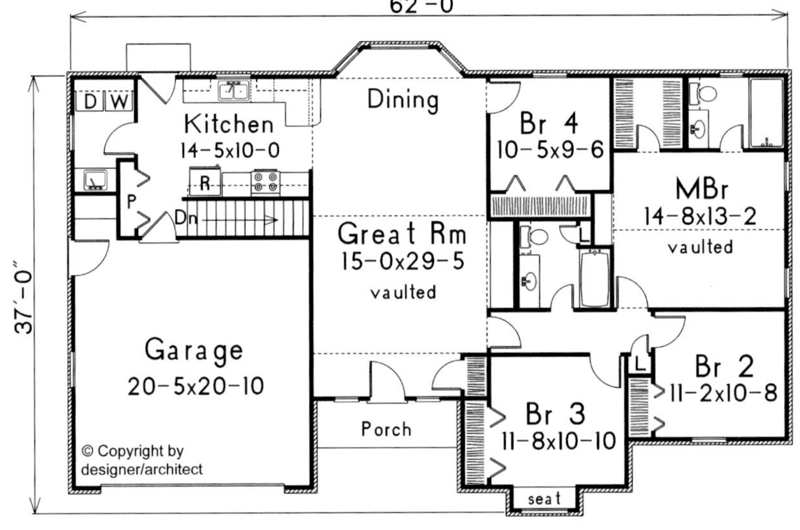

62'-0"
37'-0"
D W
Kitchen
14-5x10-0
R
P
Dn
Dining
Great Rm
15-0x29-5
vaulted
Br 4
10-5x9-6
MBr
14-8x13-2
vaulted
L
Br 2
11-2x10-8
Br 3
11-8x10-10
seat
Porch
Garage
20-5x20-10
© Copyright by
designer/architect

To order plans, visit the Menards Building Materials Desk
or visit www.Menards.com.

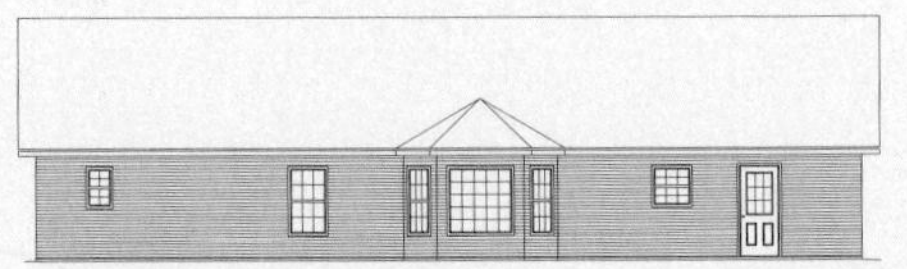

Rear View

MOSS LANDING

MENARDS®

Plan #M06-039L-0007

PRIVATE BEDROOM AREA

1,550 total square feet of living area

3 bedrooms, 2 baths

2-car detached side entry garage

Slab or crawl space foundation, please specify when ordering

SPECIAL FEATURES

The wrap-around front porch is an ideal gathering place

A handy snack bar is positioned so the kitchen flows into the family room

The master bedroom has many amenities including a private bath and spacious walk-in closet

PRICE CODE B

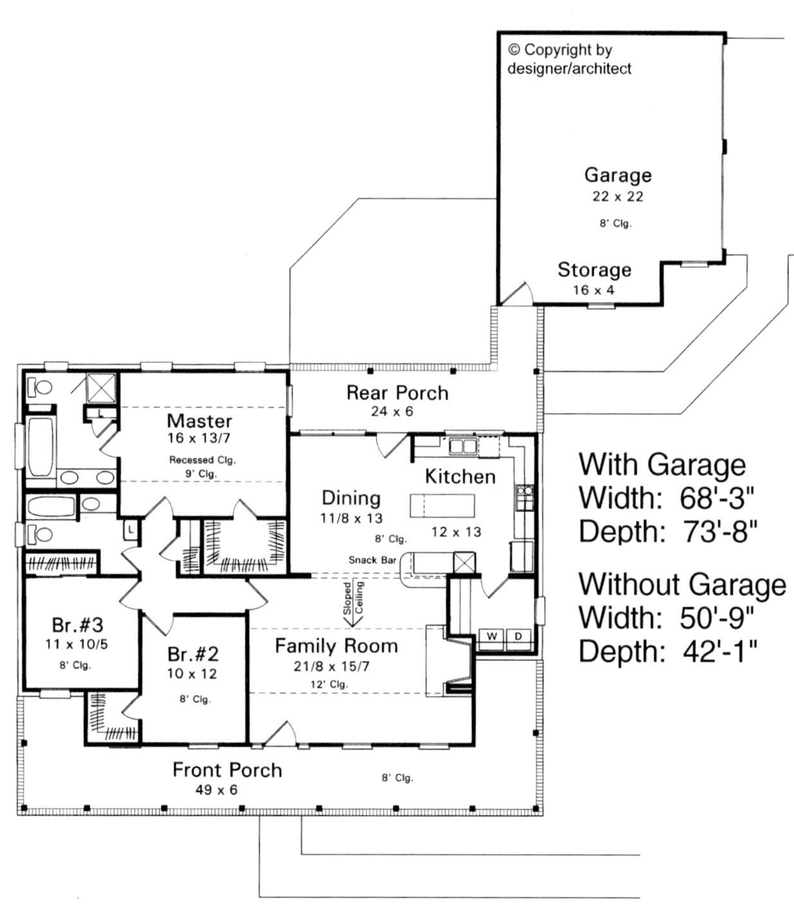

© Copyright by designer/architect
Garage
22 x 22
8' Clg.
Storage
16 x 4
Rear Porch
24 x 6
Master
16 x 13/7
Recessed Clg.
9' Clg.
Dining
11/8 x 13
8' Clg.
Kitchen
12 x 13
Snack Bar
Sloped Ceiling
Br.#3
11 x 10/5
8' Clg.
Br.#2
10 x 12
8' Clg.
Family Room
21/8 x 15/7
12' Clg.
W
D
L
Front Porch
49 x 6
8' Clg.
With Garage
Width: 68'-3"
Depth: 73'-8"
Without Garage
Width: 50'-9"
Depth: 42'-1"

To order plans, visit the Menards Building Materials Desk or visit www.Menards.com.

MENARDS

WELSBERG

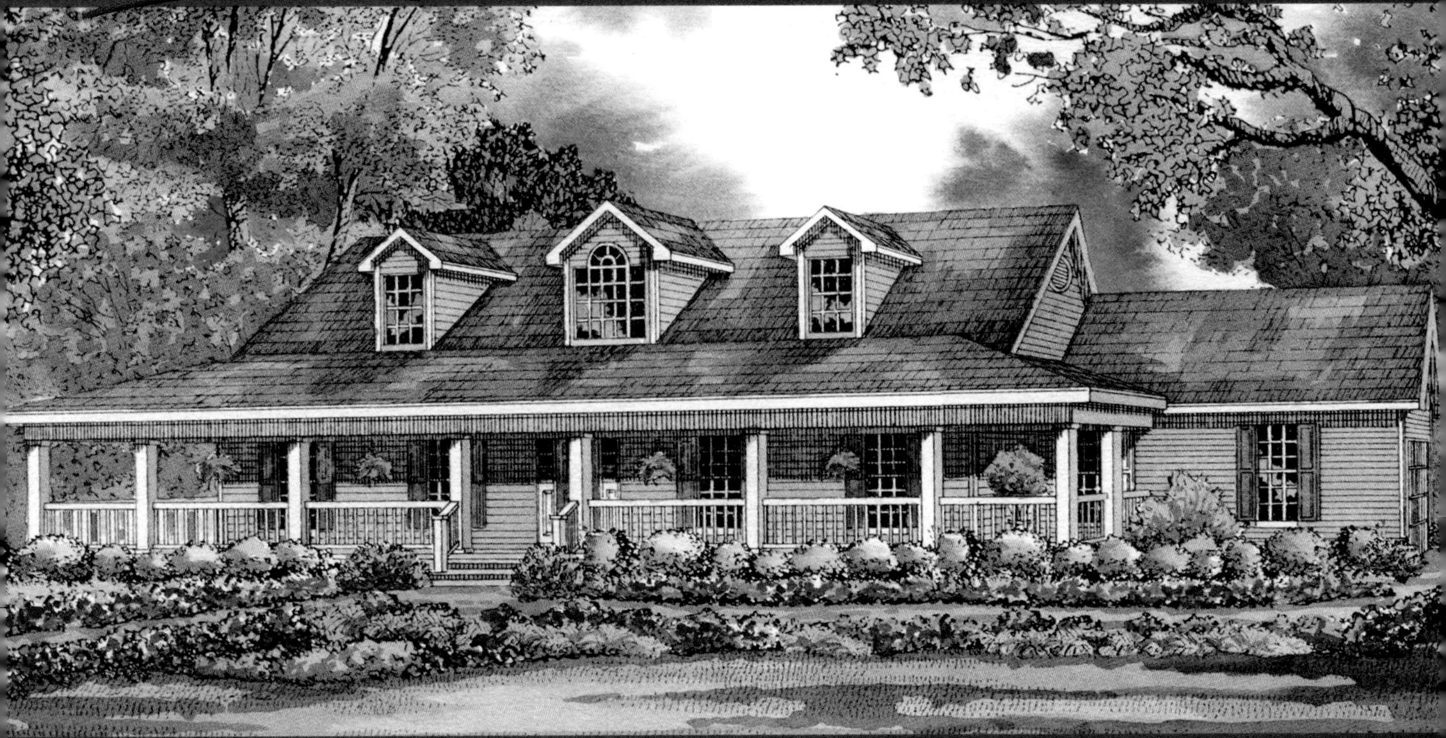

Plan #M06-055L-0213

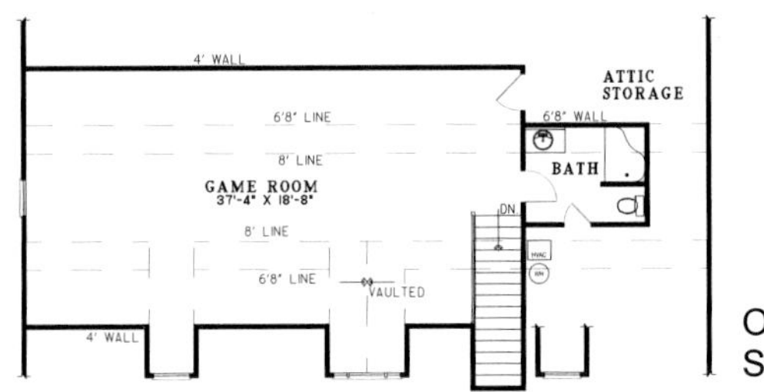

4' WALL
ATTIC STORAGE
6'8" LINE
8' LINE
GAME ROOM
37'-4" X 18'-8"
BATH
DN
VAULTED

Optional
Second Floor

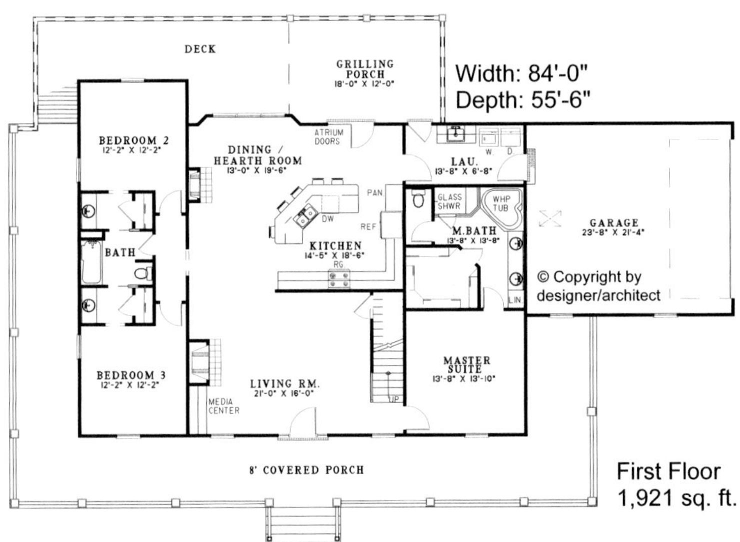

DECK
GRILLING PORCH
18'-0" X 12'-0"
BEDROOM 2
12'-2" X 12'-2"
DINING / HEARTH ROOM
13'-0" X 19'-6"
ATRIUM DOORS
LAU.
13'-8" X 6'-8"
GARAGE
23'-8" X 21'-4"
KITCHEN
14'-5" X 18'-6"
M.BATH
13'-8" X 13'-8"
BATH
BEDROOM 3
12'-2" X 12'-2"
LIVING RM.
21'-0" X 16'-0"
MEDIA CENTER
MASTER SUITE
13'-8" X 13'-10"
8' COVERED PORCH
Width: 84'-0"
Depth: 55'-6"
© Copyright by designer/architect

First Floor
1,921 sq. ft.

GRAND PORCH IS INVITING

1,921 total square feet of living area

3 bedrooms, 2 baths

2-car side entry garage

Slab or crawl space foundation, please specify when ordering; walk-out basement and basement foundations are available for an additional fee

SPECIAL FEATURES

The secondary bedrooms share a Jack and Jill bath

A massive living room is warmed by a fireplace and includes a built-in media center

The wrap-around kitchen counter with seating opens to the dining/hearth room

The optional second floor has an additional 812 square feet of living space

PRICE CODE C

To order plans, visit the Menards Building Materials Desk or visit www.Menards.com.

KAITLYN

MENARDS®

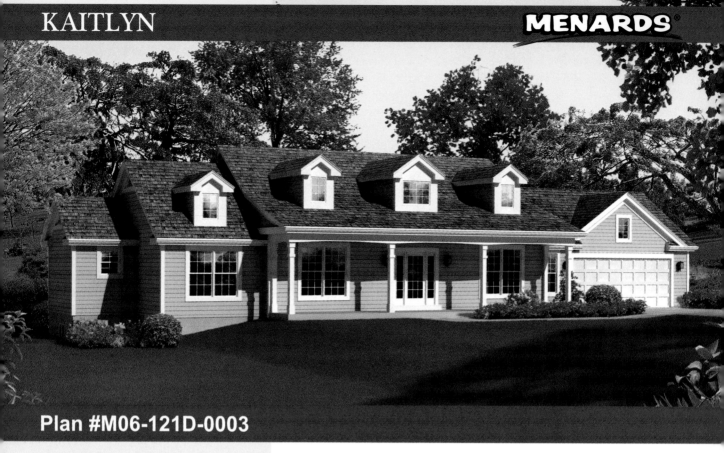

Plan #M06-121D-0003

DORMERS AND PORCH ADD GREAT STRIKING CURB APPEAL

2,215 total square feet of living area

3 bedrooms, 2 1/2 baths

2-car garage

Basement foundation

SPECIAL FEATURES

The stunning great room is topped with an inverted vaulted ceiling and shares a see-through stone surround fireplace with the cheerful vaulted hearth room

The pampering master bedroom features a coffered ceiling for an elegant feel along with a large private bath and walk-in closet

The open and spacious kitchen is outfitted with a large wrap-around counter with enough casual dining space for five people

PRICE CODE C

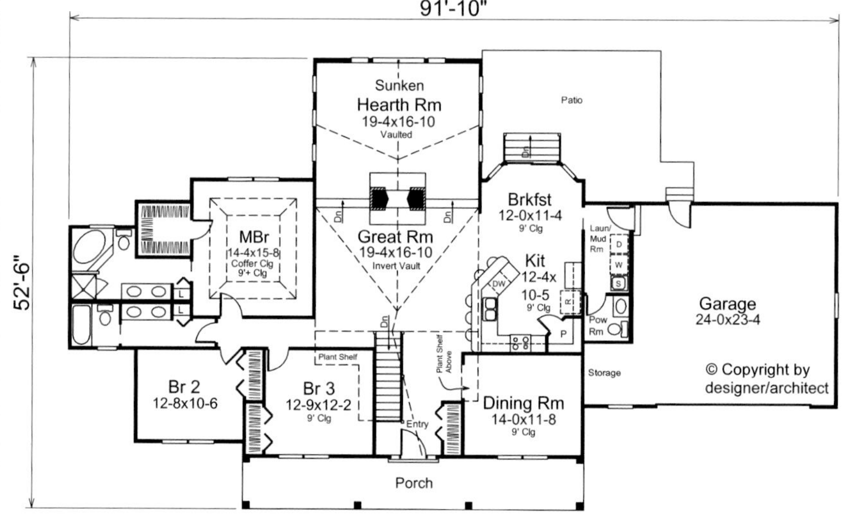

91'-10"
52'-6"
Sunken
Hearth Rm
19-4x16-10
Vaulted
Patio
Brkfst
12-0x11-4
9' Clg
MBr
14-4x15-8
Coffer Clg
9'+ Clg
Great Rm
19-4x16-10
Invert Vault
Kit
12-4x
10-5
9' Clg
Laun/
Mud
Rm
Garage
24-0x23-4
Pow
Rm
Storage
© Copyright by
designer/architect
Plant Shelf
Br 2
12-8x10-6
Br 3
12-9x12-2
9' Clg
Entry
Dining Rm
14-0x11-8
9' Clg
Porch

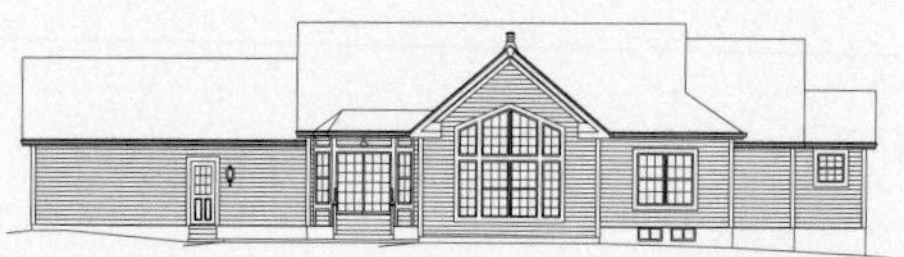

Rear View

To order plans, visit the Menards Building Materials Desk
or visit www.Menards.com.

MENARDS®

MARTIN HOUSE

Plan #M06-013L-0134

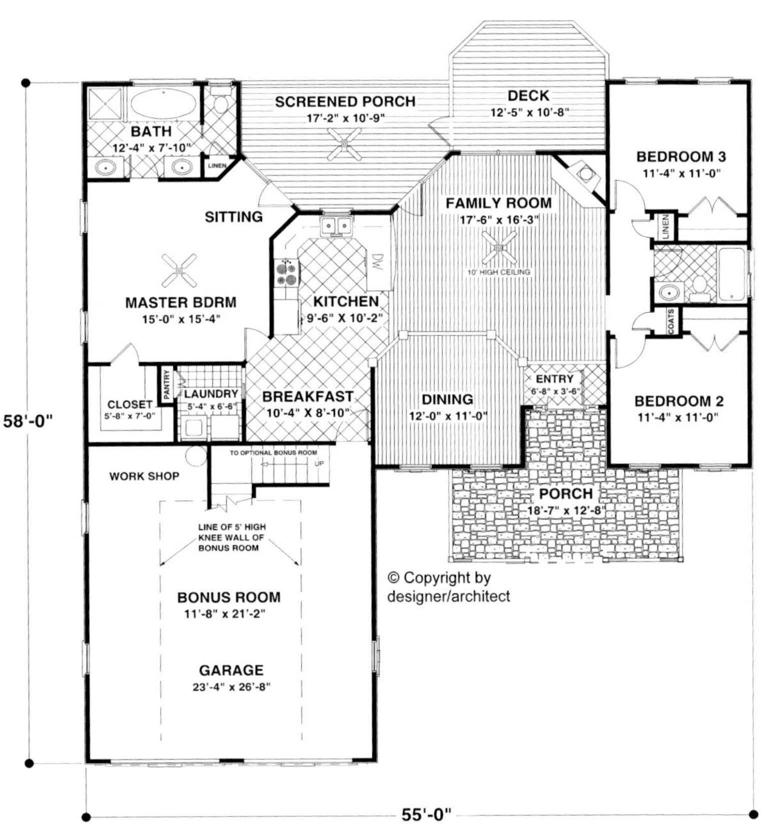

SCREENED PORCH
17'-2" x 10'-9"
DECK
12'-5" x 10'-8"
BATH
12'-4" x 7'-10"
LINEN
BEDROOM 3
11'-4" x 11'-0"
SITTING
FAMILY ROOM
17'-6" x 16'-3"
10' HIGH CEILING
LINEN
DW
MASTER BDRM
15'-0" x 15'-4"
KITCHEN
9'-6" X 10'-2"
COATS
PANTRY
ENTRY
6'-8" x 3'-6"
CLOSET
5'-8" x 7'-0"
LAUNDRY
5'-4" x 6'-6"
BREAKFAST
10'-4" X 8'-10"
DINING
12'-0" x 11'-0"
BEDROOM 2
11'-4" x 11'-0"
58'-0"
TO OPTIONAL BONUS ROOM
UP
WORK SHOP
PORCH
18'-7" x 12'-8"
LINE OF 5' HIGH KNEE WALL OF BONUS ROOM
© Copyright by designer/architect
BONUS ROOM
11'-8" x 21'-2"
GARAGE
23'-4" x 26'-8"
55'-0"

INVITING STONE WALKWAY

1,496 total square feet of living area

3 bedrooms, 2 baths

2-car garage

Slab foundation

SPECIAL FEATURES

This country cottage features spacious open rooms and an easy flow from the welcoming front porch stone walkway to the breezy screened porch off the family room and master bedroom

The family room features a cozy corner fireplace

Isolated from the secondary bedrooms, the master bedroom is an owner's retreat with a sitting area, large walk-in closet and private bath with separate tub and shower

Bonus room above the garage has an additional 301 square feet of living area

PRICE CODE E

To order plans, visit the Menards Building Materials Desk or visit www.Menards.com.

CASTLECLIFF

MENARDS

Plan #M06-039L-0025

BEAUTIFUL LANDSCAPING OPPORTUNITIES

1,430 total square feet of living area

3 bedrooms, 2 baths

2-car detached garage

Crawl space or slab foundation, please specify when ordering

SPECIAL FEATURES

All bedrooms enjoy spacious walk-in closets

A large dining room enjoys close proximity to the kitchen

Varied ceiling heights throughout help add character to the interior

PRICE CODE C

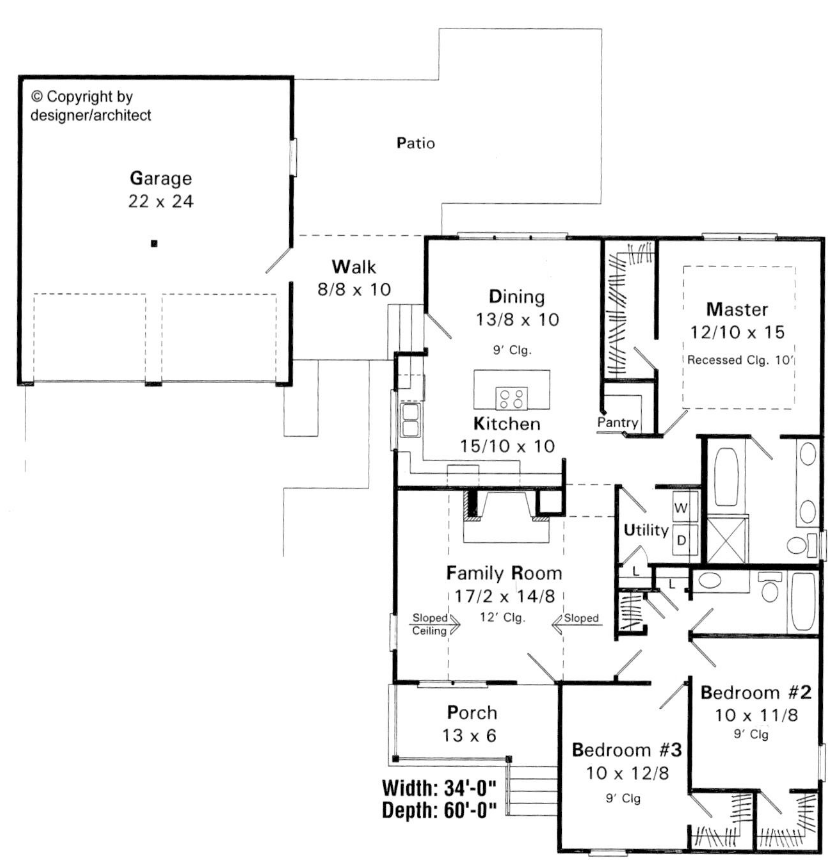

© Copyright by designer/architect
Patio
Garage 22 x 24
Walk 8/8 x 10
Dining 13/8 x 10 9' Clg.
Master 12/10 x 15 Recessed Clg. 10'
Kitchen 15/10 x 10
Pantry
W
D
Utility
L
Family Room 17/2 x 14/8 12' Clg.
Sloped Ceiling
Sloped
Porch 13 x 6
Bedroom #2 10 x 11/8 9' Clg
Bedroom #3 10 x 12/8 9' Clg
Width: 34'-0"
Depth: 60'-0"

To order plans, visit the Menards Building Materials Desk or visit www.Menards.com.

MENARDS

SPENCER

Plan #M06-058D-0169

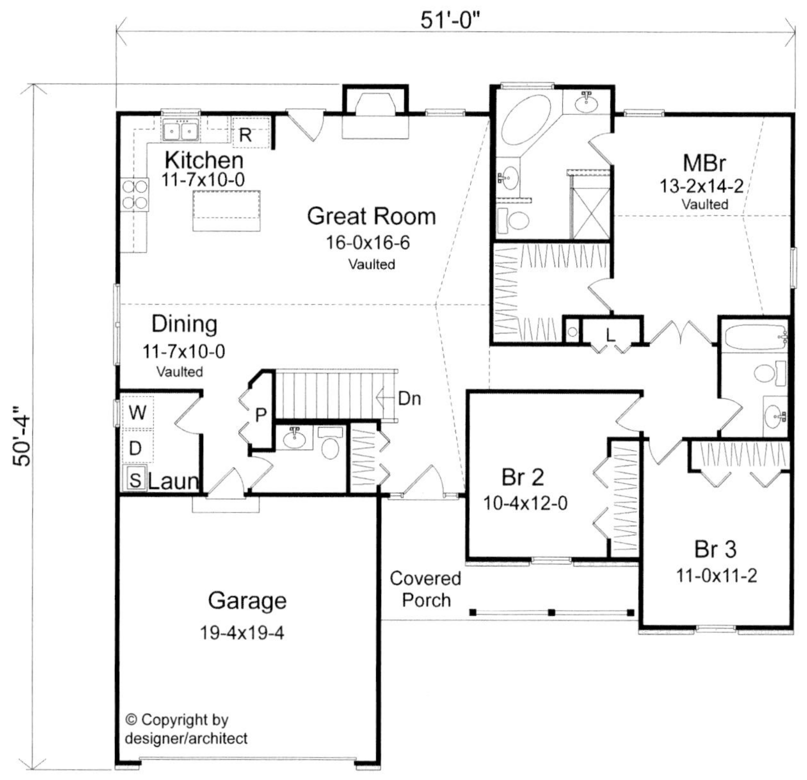

51'-0"
50'-4"
Kitchen
11-7x10-0
R
Great Room
16-0x16-6
Vaulted
MBr
13-2x14-2
Vaulted
Dining
11-7x10-0
Vaulted
L
W
D
S
Laun
P
Dn
Br 2
10-4x12-0
Br 3
11-0x11-2
Covered
Porch
Garage
19-4x19-4
© Copyright by
designer/architect

TWIN DORMERS

1,635 total square feet of living area

3 bedrooms, 2 1/2 baths

2-car garage

Basement foundation

SPECIAL FEATURES

This country-style ranch is sure to please with an open great room and private bedrooms

The great room enjoys the openness to the kitchen and dining area, a grand fireplace and access to the backyard

A walk-in closet, deluxe bath with whirlpool tub and a vaulted ceiling create a luxurious master bedroom

PRICE CODE AA

To order plans, visit the Menards Building Materials Desk or visit www.Menards.com.

MANOR CREEK

MENARDS®

Plan #M06-077L-0140

STYLISH CRAFTSMAN HOME

1,800 total square feet of living area

3 bedrooms, 2 baths

2-car garage

Slab or crawl space foundation, please specify when ordering

SPECIAL FEATURES

A large flex space can easily convert to a home office or formal dining room depending on the owner's needs

A large and spacious kitchen has a center island with eating bar and an attached breakfast room with bay window

The corner jet tub in the master bath pampers the homeowners in their private retreat

The unfinished bonus room has an additional 326 square feet of living area

PRICE CODE D

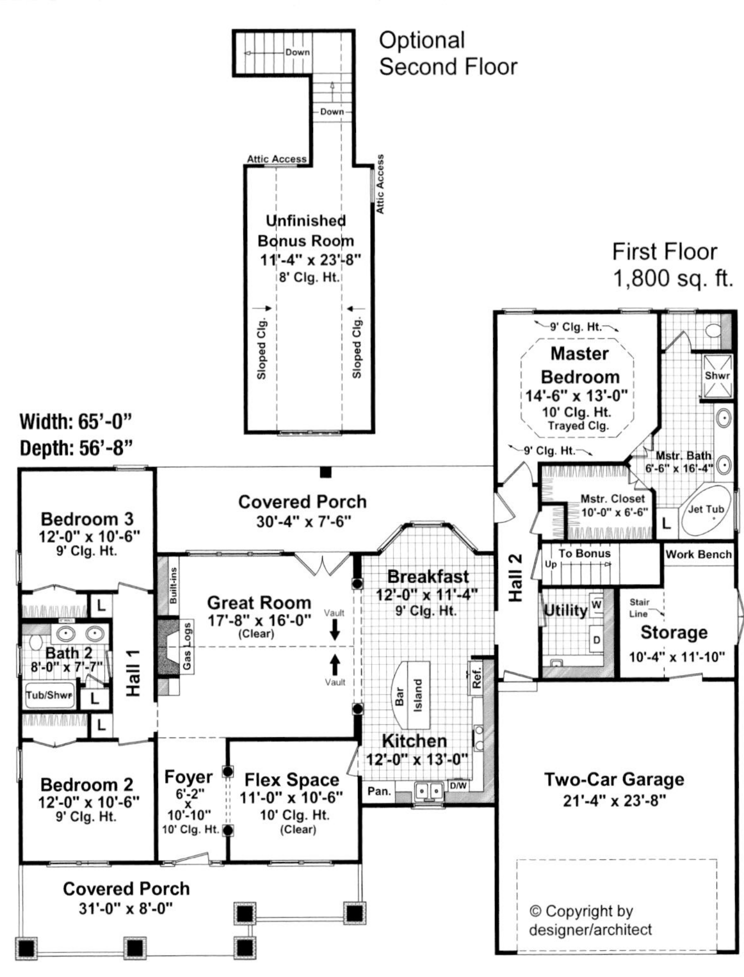

Optional
Second Floor
Down
Down
Attic Access
Attic Access
Unfinished
Bonus Room
11'-4" x 23'-8"
8' Clg. Ht.
Sloped Clg.
Sloped Clg.
First Floor
1,800 sq. ft.
Width: 65'-0"
Depth: 56'-8"
9' Clg. Ht.
Master
Bedroom
14'-6" x 13'-0"
10' Clg. Ht.
Trayed Clg.
9' Clg. Ht.
Shwr
Mstr. Bath
6'-6" x 16'-4"
Mstr. Closet
10'-0" x 6'-6"
Jet Tub
L
Covered Porch
30'-4" x 7'-6"
Bedroom 3
12'-0" x 10'-6"
9' Clg. Ht.
Breakfast
12'-0" x 11'-4"
9' Clg. Ht.
Hall 2
To Bonus
Up
Work Bench
Built-ins
Great Room
17'-8" x 16'-0"
(Clear)
Vault
Vault
Gas Logs
Utility
W
D
Stair
Line
Storage
10'-4" x 11'-10"
L
Bath 2
8'-0" x 7'-7"
Tub/Shwr
L
L
Hall 1
Bar
Island
Ref.
Kitchen
12'-0" x 13'-0"
Pan.
D/W
Bedroom 2
12'-0" x 10'-6"
9' Clg. Ht.
Foyer
6'-2"
x
10'-10"
10' Clg. Ht.
Flex Space
11'-0" x 10'-6"
10' Clg. Ht.
(Clear)
Two-Car Garage
21'-4" x 23'-8"
Covered Porch
31'-0" x 8'-0"
© Copyright by
designer/architect

To order plans, visit the Menards Building Materials Desk or visit www.Menards.com.

MENARDS®

LEWISTON

Plan #M06-053D-0051

FAMILY-SIZED KITCHEN IS CENTRALLY LOCATED

2,731 total square feet of living area

4 bedrooms, 3 1/2 baths

2-car side entry garage

Basement foundation, drawings also include walk-out basement foundation

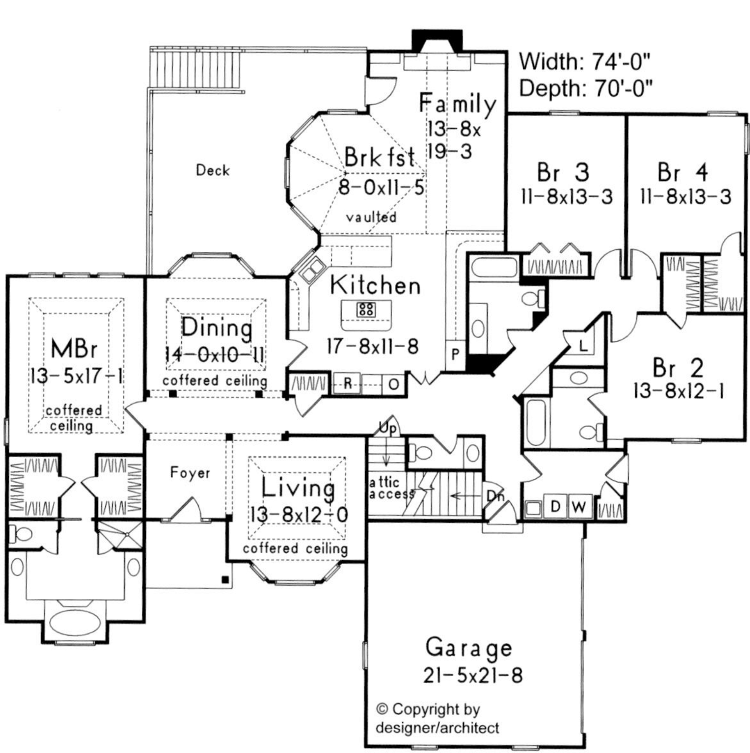

Width: 74'-0"
Depth: 70'-0"
Deck
Family
13-8x
19-3
Brkfst
8-0x11-5
vaulted
Br 3
11-8x13-3
Br 4
11-8x13-3
Kitchen
17-8x11-8
MBr
13-5x17-1
coffered ceiling
Dining
14-0x10-11
coffered ceiling
Br 2
13-8x12-1
Foyer
Living
13-8x12-0
coffered ceiling
attic access
Up
Dn
Garage
21-5x21-8
© Copyright by designer/architect

SPECIAL FEATURES

The master bedroom enjoys double walk-in closets, a coffered ceiling and bath

Both the dining and living rooms feature coffered ceilings and bay windows

The family room features fireplace vaulted ceiling and access to rear deck

The secondary bedrooms are separate from the living areas

PRICE CODE C

Rear View

To order plans, visit the Menards Building Materials Desk or visit www.Menards.com.

HUNTINGTON DOWNS

MENARDS

Plan #M06-077L-0122

DELIGHTFUL COUNTRY HOME

1,888 total square feet of living area

3 bedrooms, 2 1/2 baths

2-car side entry garage

Slab or crawl space foundation, please specify when ordering

SPECIAL FEATURES

The generously sized flex space has a half bath nearby and could easily convert to an ideal guest room in a remote location

The eating bar/island combination in the kitchen provides useful dining space and extra workspace for food preparation

The great room is the focal point of this home with a fireplace flanked by built-in bookcases

The optional second floor has an additional 316 square feet of living space

PRICE CODE D

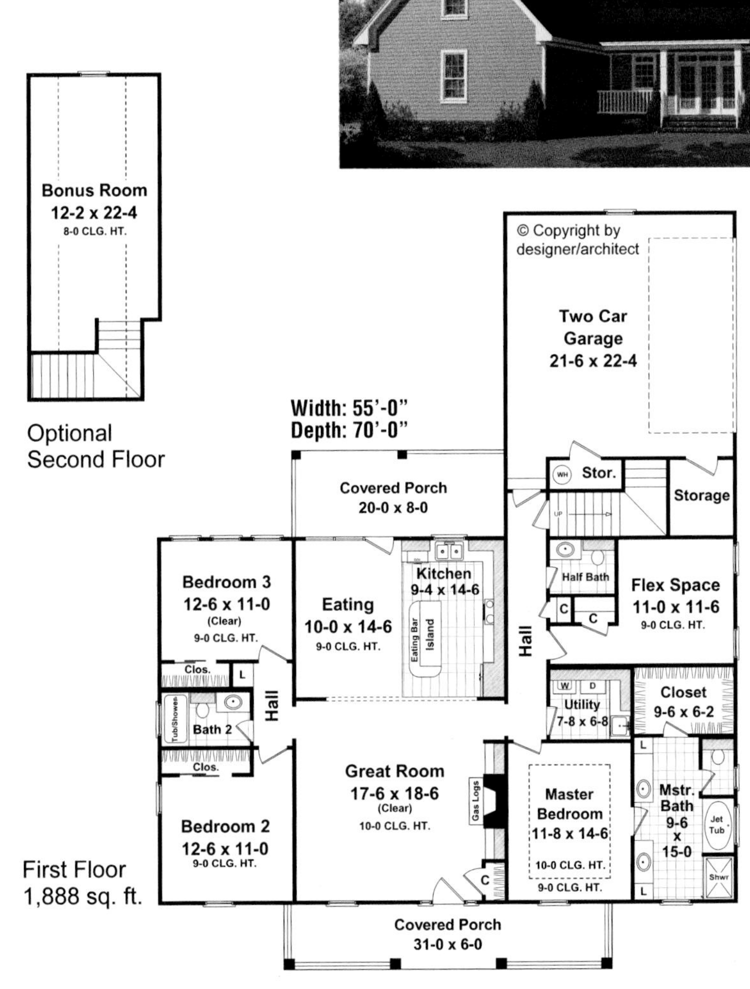

Bonus Room
12-2 x 22-4
8-0 CLG. HT.
Optional Second Floor
© Copyright by designer/architect
Two Car Garage
21-6 x 22-4
Width: 55'-0"
Depth: 70'-0"
Covered Porch
20-0 x 8-0
Stor.
WH
Storage
Bedroom 3
12-6 x 11-0
(Clear)
9-0 CLG. HT.
Eating
10-0 x 14-6
9-0 CLG. HT.
Kitchen
9-4 x 14-6
Eating Bar
Island
Half Bath
Flex Space
11-0 x 11-6
9-0 CLG. HT.
Hall
Clos.
Tub/Shower
Bath 2
Utility
7-8 x 6-8
Closet
9-6 x 6-2
Great Room
17-6 x 18-6
(Clear)
10-0 CLG. HT.
Gas Logs
Master Bedroom
11-8 x 14-6
10-0 CLG. HT.
9-0 CLG. HT.
Mstr. Bath
9-6 x 15-0
Jet Tub
Shwr
Bedroom 2
12-6 x 11-0
9-0 CLG. HT.
First Floor
1,888 sq. ft.
Covered Porch
31-0 x 6-0

To order plans, visit the Menards Building Materials Desk or visit www.Menards.com.

MENARDS®

PARKTOWN

Plan #M06-008D-0122

MULTI-ROOF LEVELS CREATE ATTRACTIVE COLONIAL HOME

1,364 total square feet of living area

3 bedrooms, 2 baths

2-car garage

Basement foundation, drawings also include crawl space and slab foundations

SPECIAL FEATURES

A large porch and entry door with sidelights lead into a generous living room

The well-planned U-shaped kitchen features a laundry closet, built-in pantry and open peninsula

The master bedroom has its own bath with a 4' shower

Convenient to the kitchen is an oversized two-car garage with service door to the rear of the home

PRICE CODE A

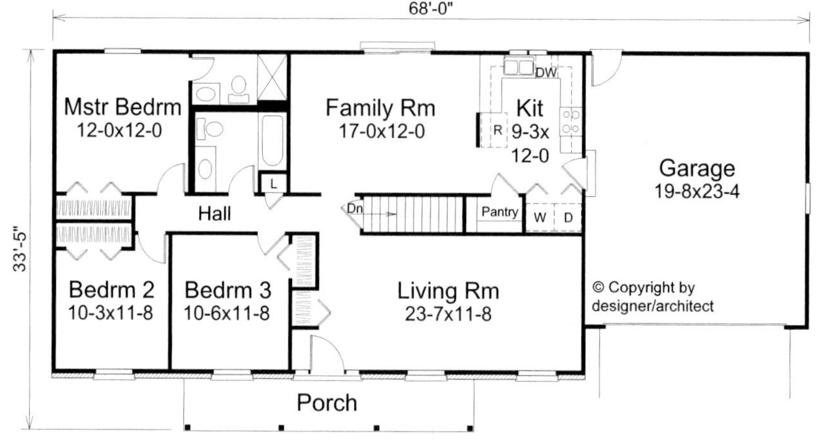
68'-0"
33'-5"
Mstr Bedrm
12-0x12-0
Family Rm
17-0x12-0
DW
Kit
R
9-3x
12-0
Garage
19-8x23-4
L
Hall
Dn
Pantry
W
D
Bedrm 2
10-3x11-8
Bedrm 3
10-6x11-8
Living Rm
23-7x11-8
© Copyright by
designer/architect
Porch

To order plans, visit the Menards Building Materials Desk or visit www.Menards.com.

OAKRIDGE

MENARDS®

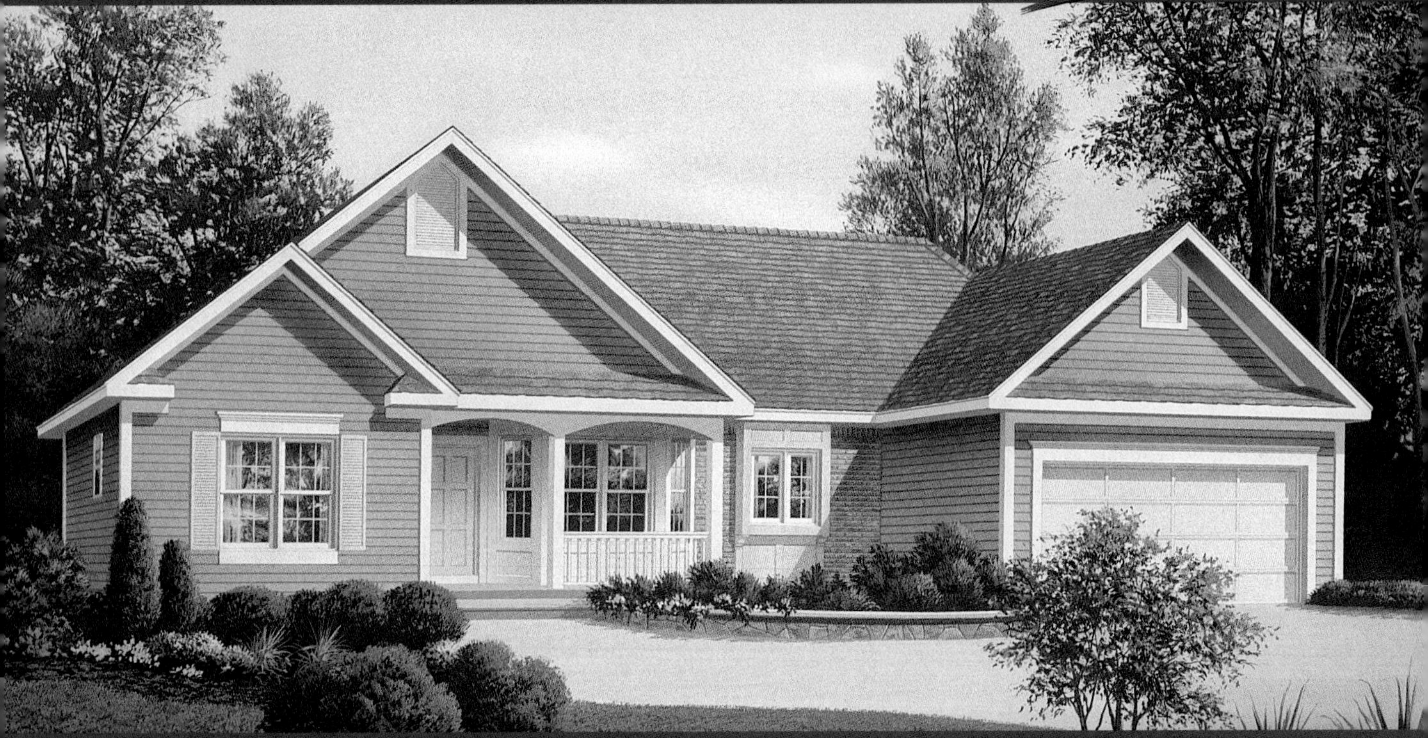

Plan #M06-033D-0012

CENTRAL LIVING AREA KEEPS BEDROOMS PRIVATE

1,546 total square feet of living area

3 bedrooms, 2 baths

2-car garage

Basement foundation

SPECIAL FEATURES

Spacious, open rooms create a casual atmosphere

Master bedroom is secluded for privacy

Dining room features a large bay window

Kitchen and dinette combine for added space and include access to the outdoors

Large laundry room includes a convenient sink

PRICE CODE C

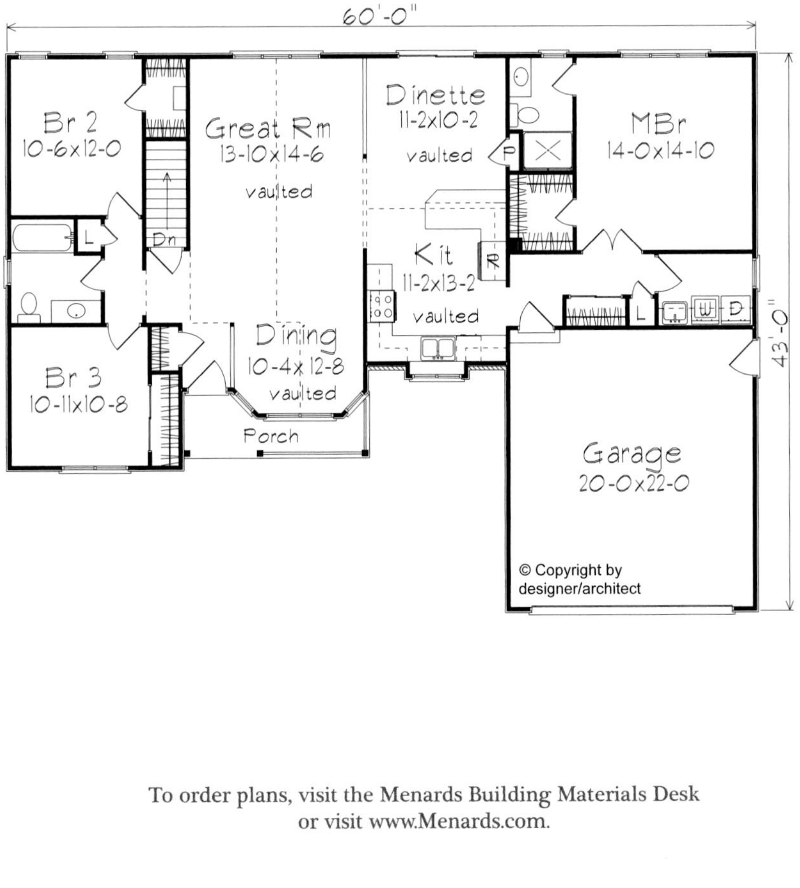

60'-0"

43'-0"

Br 2
10-6x12-0

Great Rm
13-10x14-6
vaulted

Dinette
11-2x10-2
vaulted

MBr
14-0x14-10

Kit
11-2x13-2
vaulted

Dining
10-4x12-8
vaulted

Br 3
10-11x10-8

Porch

Garage
20-0x22-0

Rear View

To order plans, visit the Menards Building Materials Desk or visit www.Menards.com.

MENARDS®

GEORGIA MANOR

Plan #M06-007D-0231

EXTRAORDINARY DESIGN FOR ENTERTAINING

2,312 total square feet of living area

3 bedrooms, 2 1/2 baths

2-car garage

Slab foundation

SPECIAL FEATURES

The open and spacious great room with fireplace has an ideal sitting or piano room that extends into the covered patio areas while the adjacent dining room extends into the front porch area, both with five large windows for lots of light

A breakfast room and curved snack bar adorn the smartly designed kitchen all with splendid views to the rear covered patio through 9' wide sliding glass doors

Double entry doors from the breakfast room invite you into a large screened porch

PRICE CODE E

77'-0"

55'-6"

Covered Patio

Covered Patio

Screened Porch 20-0x12-4

Sitting Rm 12-0x7-6

MBr 19-0x13-0

Laun

Brkfst 12-6x10-0

Great Rm 24-6x15-0

Br 2 11-10x11-8

Hall

Kitchen 12-1x14-0

Garage 19-4x23-7

Entry

Dining Rm 12-0x16-0

Br 3 13-8x14-0

Porch

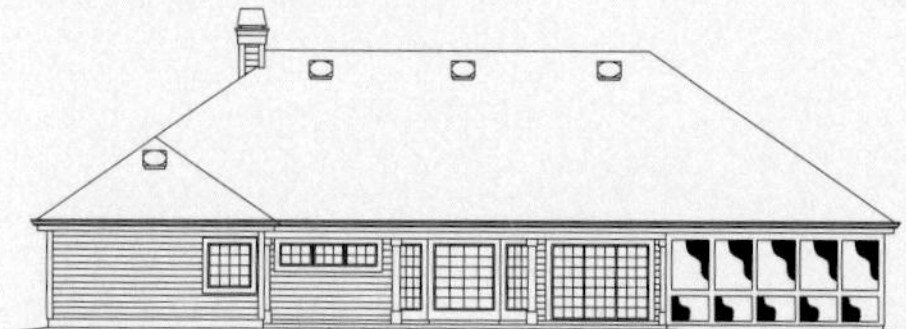

Rear View

To order plans, visit the Menards Building Materials Desk or visit www.Menards.com.

BRAYDEN MANOR

MENARDS

Plan #M06-007D-0151

PERFECT HOME FOR A LARGE FAMILY ON A BUDGET

1,941 total square feet of living area

5 bedrooms, 3 baths

2-car side entry drive under garage

Walk-out basement foundation

SPECIAL FEATURES

Interesting roof lines and a spacious front porch with flanking stonework help to fashion this beautiful country home

The vaulted great room is open to the bayed dining area suitable for friends and a large family

The master bedroom enjoys a big walk-in closet and a gracious bath

Four additional bedrooms complete the home

PRICE CODE C

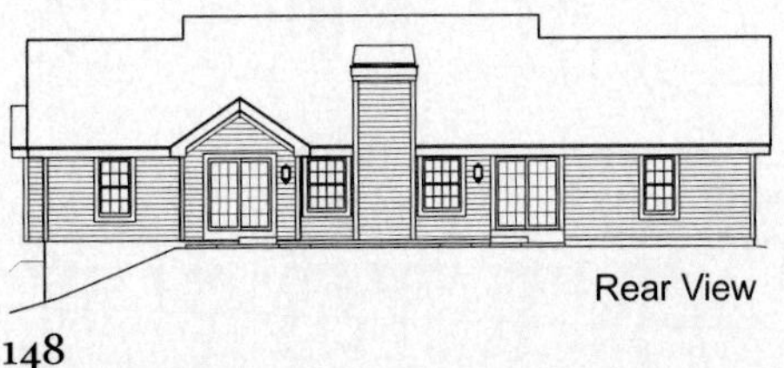

Rear View

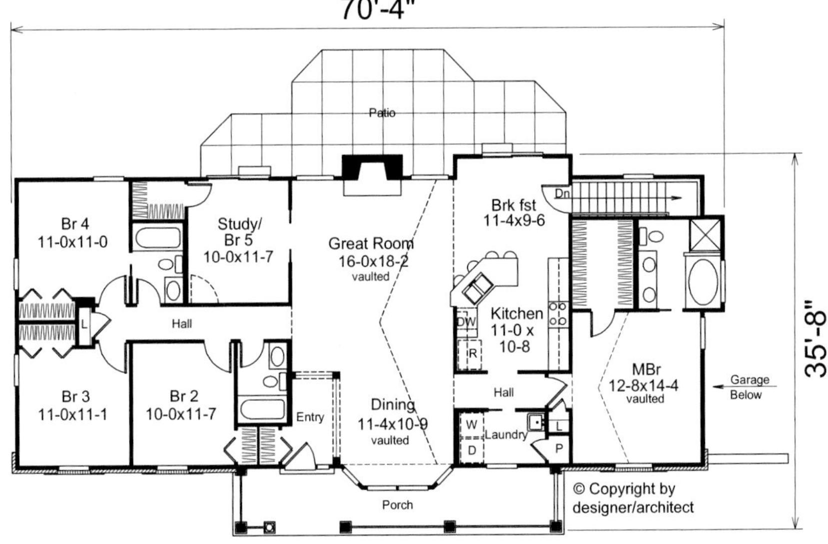

70'-4"
35'-8"
Patio
Br 4
11-0x11-0
Study/
Br 5
10-0x11-7
Great Room
16-0x18-2
vaulted
Brk fst
11-4x9-6
Dn
Kitchen
11-0 x
10-8
DW
R
Hall
Br 3
11-0x11-1
Br 2
10-0x11-7
Entry
Dining
11-4x10-9
vaulted
Hall
W
D
Laundry
L
P
MBr
12-8x14-4
vaulted
Garage
Below
Porch
© Copyright by
designer/architect

To order plans, visit the Menards Building Materials Desk or visit www.Menards.com.

MENARDS

ARBORWAY

Plan #M06-058L-0171

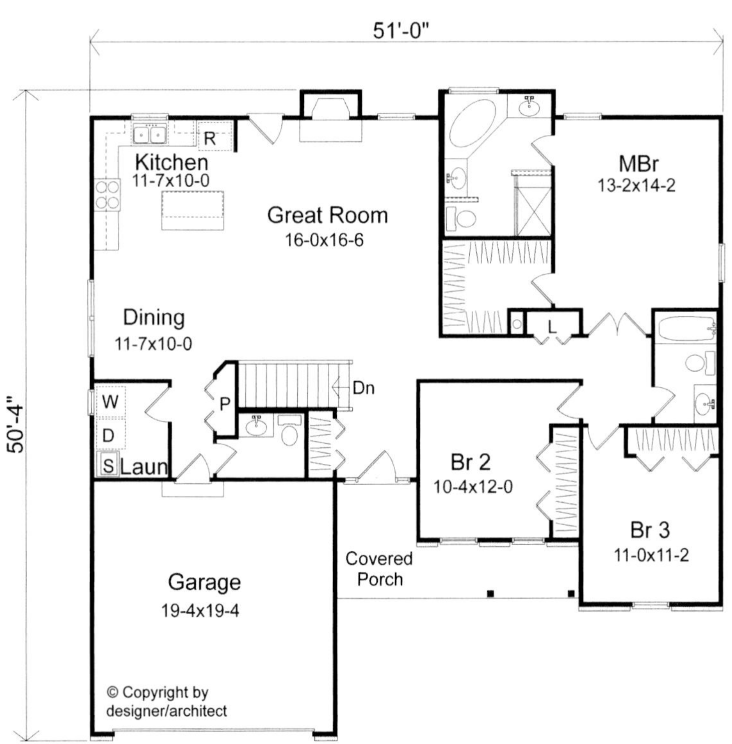

51'-0"
50'-4"
R
Kitchen
11-7x10-0
Great Room
16-0x16-6
MBr
13-2x14-2
Dining
11-7x10-0
L
Dn
P
W
D
S Laun
Br 2
10-4x12-0
Br 3
11-0x11-2
Covered
Porch
Garage
19-4x19-4
© Copyright by
designer/architect

DORMER ADDS CURB APPEAL

1,635 total square feet of living area

3 bedrooms, 2 1/2 baths

2-car garage

Basement foundation

SPECIAL FEATURES

The open atmosphere of the combined kitchen, dining and great rooms makes this a perfect space to gather with family and friends

When it's time to relax, retreat to the luxurious master bedroom equipped with a deluxe bath

A half bath, laundry room and pantry at the garage entrance add function to this family friendly home

PRICE CODE AA

To order plans, visit the Menards Building Materials Desk or visit www.Menards.com.

STONERIDGE

MENARDS®

Plan #M06-007D-0101

COUNTRY FLAVOR WITH ATRIUM

2,317 total square feet of living area

3 bedrooms, 2 1/2 baths

2-car side entry garage

Walk-out basement foundation

SPECIAL FEATURES

Bracketed box windows create an exterior with country charm

Massive-sized great room features a majestic atrium, fireplace, box window wall, dining balcony and a vaulted ceiling

An atrium balcony with large bay window is enjoyed by the spacious breakfast room

1,026 square feet of optional lower level living area with family room, wet bar, bedroom #4 and a bath

PRICE CODE D

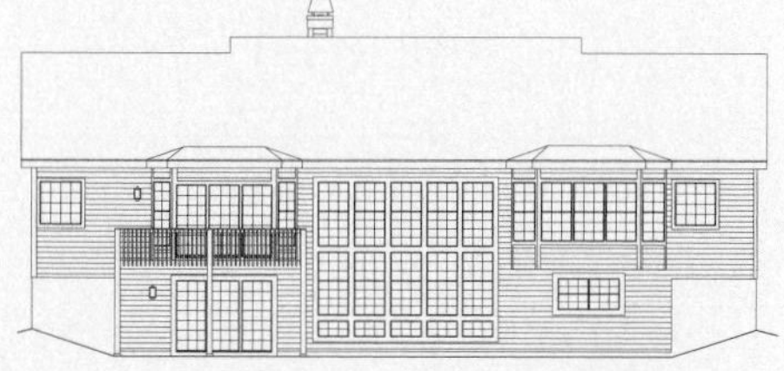

Rear View

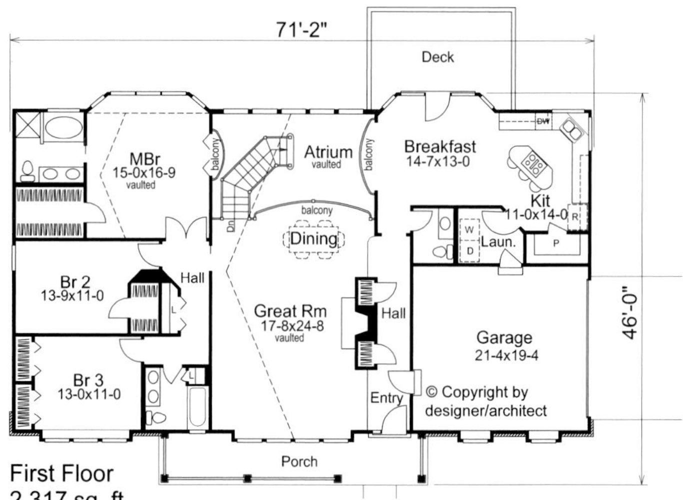

71'-2"
Deck
MBr
15-0x16-9
vaulted
balcony
Atrium
vaulted
balcony
Breakfast
14-7x13-0
Kit
11-0x14-0
balcony
Dn
Dining
W
D
Laun.
P
R
Br 2
13-9x11-0
Hall
Great Rm
17-8x24-8
vaulted
Hall
Garage
21-4x19-4
46'-0"
Br 3
13-0x11-0
Entry
© Copyright by
designer/architect
Porch

First Floor
2,317 sq. ft.

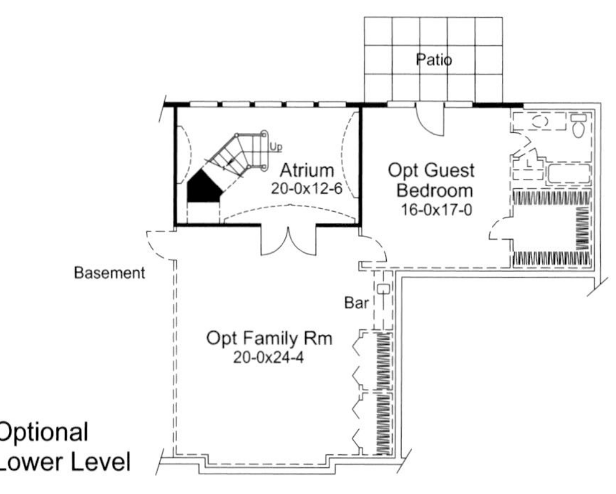

Patio
Up
Atrium
20-0x12-6
Opt Guest
Bedroom
16-0x17-0
Basement
Bar
Opt Family Rm
20-0x24-4

Optional
Lower Level

To order plans, visit the Menards Building Materials Desk or visit www.Menards.com.

Plan #M06-007D-0235

UNIQUE DRIVE-THRU BASEMENT GARAGE

2,213 total square feet of living area

3 bedrooms, 2 baths

8-car drive under side entry garage

Walk-out basement foundation

SPECIAL FEATURES

The spacious great room features a fireplace, wide glass sliding doors to the rear sundeck and a square colonnade

A huge walk-in pantry, large island and generous cabinet space are among the many amenities of the kitchen

The walk-out basement garage offers a convenient drive-thru design, abundant storage area or parking for up to 8 cars, extra wide garage doors and two 9' glass sliding doors for natural light

PRICE CODE E

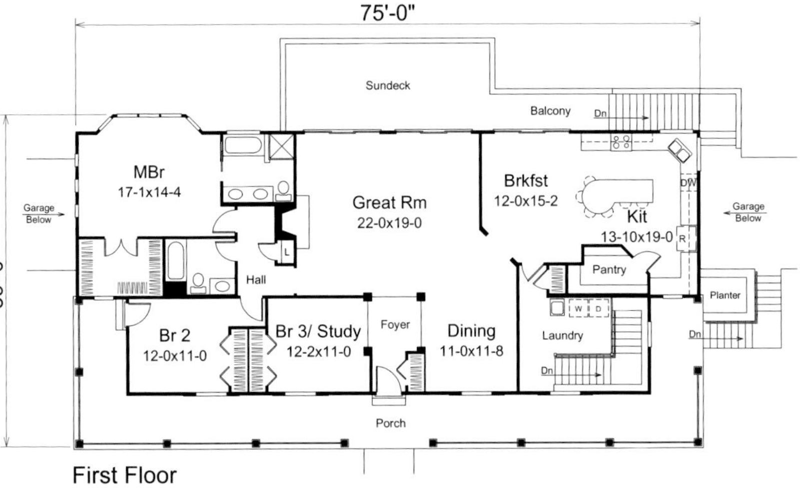

First Floor
2,213 sq. ft.

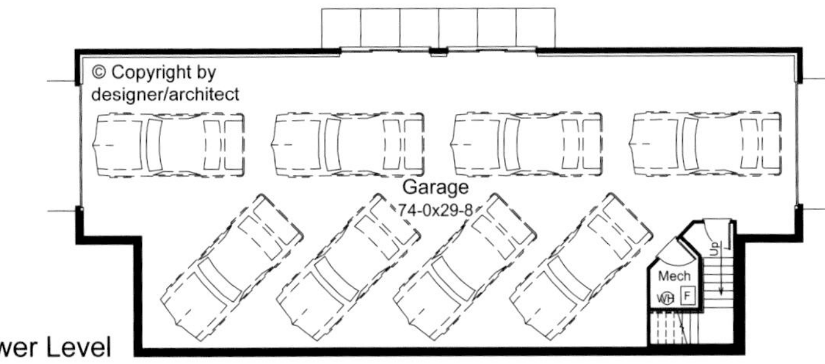
© Copyright by
designer/architect
Garage
74-0x29-8
Mech
Up

Lower Level

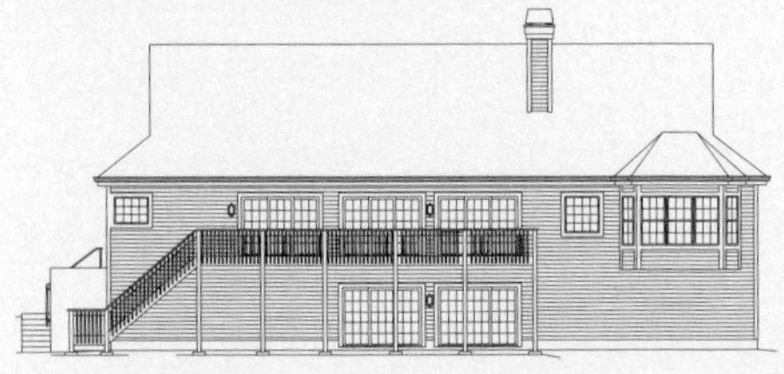

Rear View

To order plans, visit the Menards Building Materials Desk or visit www.Menards.com.

CARROLLSTONE

MENARDS

possible —

Plan #M06-007D-0116

ATRIUM RANCH HOME

3,500 total square feet of living area

3 bedrooms, 3 baths

3-car side entry garage

Walk-out basement foundation

SPECIAL FEATURES

A large courtyard with stone walls, lantern columns and covered porch welcomes you

The great room features a stone fireplace, built-in shelves, vaulted ceiling and atrium with dramatic staircase and a two and a half story window wall

Two walk-in closets, vaulted ceiling with plant shelf and a luxury bath adorn the master bedroom suite

The lower level includes a family room, walk-in bar, sitting area, bedroom #3 and bath

PRICE CODE C

Rear View

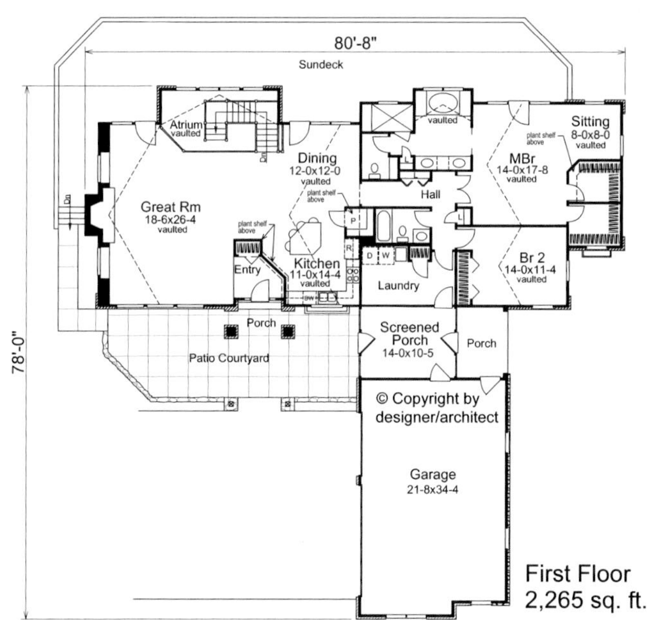
80'-8"
Sundeck
Atrium
vaulted
Dining
12-0x12-0
vaulted
Great Rm
18-6x26-4
vaulted
Kitchen
11-0x14-4
vaulted
Entry
Porch
Patio Courtyard
Laundry
Screened Porch
14-0x10-5
Porch
vaulted
Sitting
8-0x8-0
vaulted
MBr
14-0x17-8
vaulted
Hall
Br 2
14-0x11-4
vaulted
78'-0"
© Copyright by designer/architect
Garage
21-8x34-4

First Floor
2,265 sq. ft.

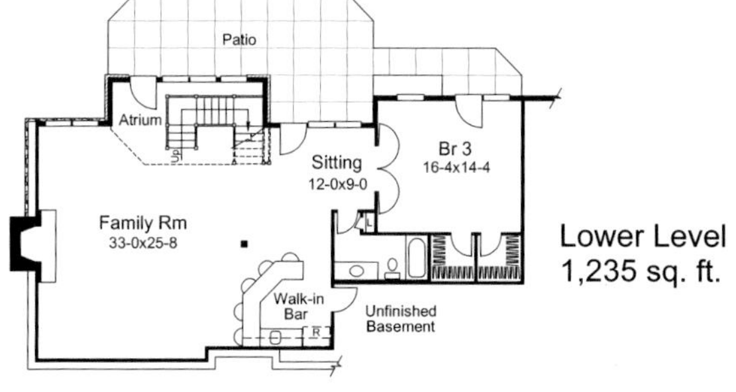
Patio
Atrium
Sitting
12-0x9-0
Br 3
16-4x14-4
Family Rm
33-0x25-8
Walk-in Bar
Unfinished Basement

Lower Level
1,235 sq. ft.

To order plans, visit the Menards Building Materials Desk or visit www.Menards.com.

CASH CANYON

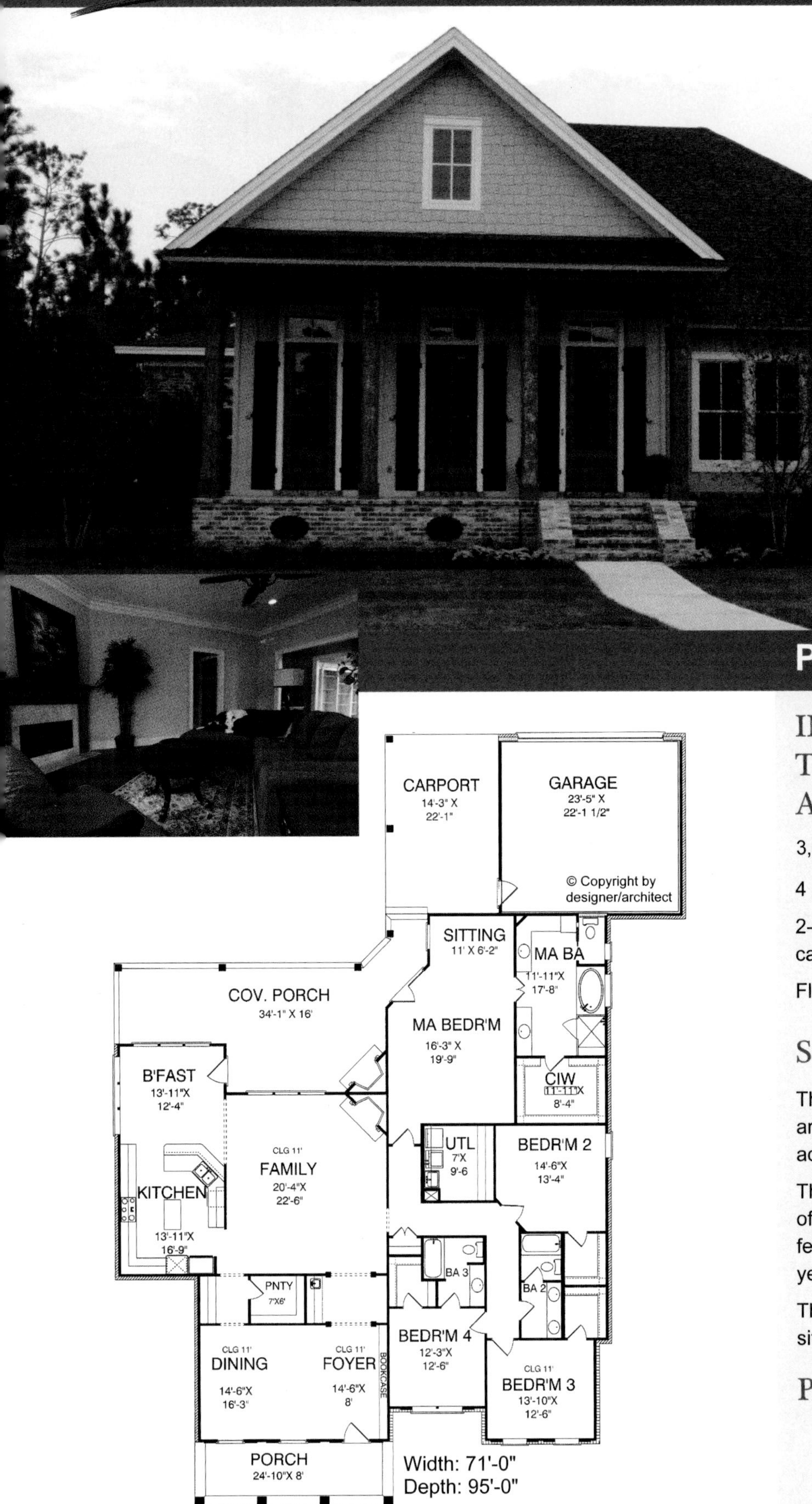
CARPORT
14'-3" X
22'-1"
GARAGE
23'-5" X
22'-1 1/2"
© Copyright by
designer/architect
SITTING
11' X 6'-2"
MA BA
11'-11"X
17'-8"
COV. PORCH
34'-1" X 16'
MA BEDR'M
16'-3" X
19'-9"
B'FAST
13'-11"X
12'-4"
CIW
11'-11"X
8'-4"
CLG 11'
FAMILY
20'-4"X
22'-6"
UTL
7'X
9'-6
BEDR'M 2
14'-6"X
13'-4"
KITCHEN
13'-11"X
16'-9"
PNTY
7'X6'
BA 3
BA 2
CLG 11'
DINING
14'-6"X
16'-3"
CLG 11'
FOYER
14'-6"X
8'
BOOKCASE
BEDR'M 4
12'-3"X
12'-6"
CLG 11'
BEDR'M 3
13'-10"X
12'-6"
PORCH
24'-10"X 8'
Width: 71'-0"
Depth: 95'-0"

Plan #M06-024L-0795

INTERESTING TRIPLE DOORS ACROSS THE FACADE

3,076 total square feet of living area

4 bedrooms, 3 baths

2-car rear entry garage, 1-car rear entry carport

Floating slab foundation

SPECIAL FEATURES

This unique home features all of the living areas near each other for ease with family activities

The cheerful breakfast room enjoys views of the enormous covered rear porch featuring a corner outdoor fireplace for year-round enjoyment

The elegant master bedroom has its own sitting area and pampering spa style bath

PRICE CODE K

To order plans, visit the Menards Building Materials Desk or visit www.Menards.com.

BOLSA KNOLL

MENARDS®

Plan #M06-039L-0014

VAULTED REAR PORCH

1,849 total square feet of living area

3 bedrooms, 2 baths

2-car garage

Crawl space or slab foundation, please specify when ordering

SPECIAL FEATURES

An open floor plan creates an airy feeling

The kitchen and breakfast area include a center island, pantry and built-in desk

The master bedroom has a private entrance off the breakfast area and a view of the vaulted porch

PRICE CODE C

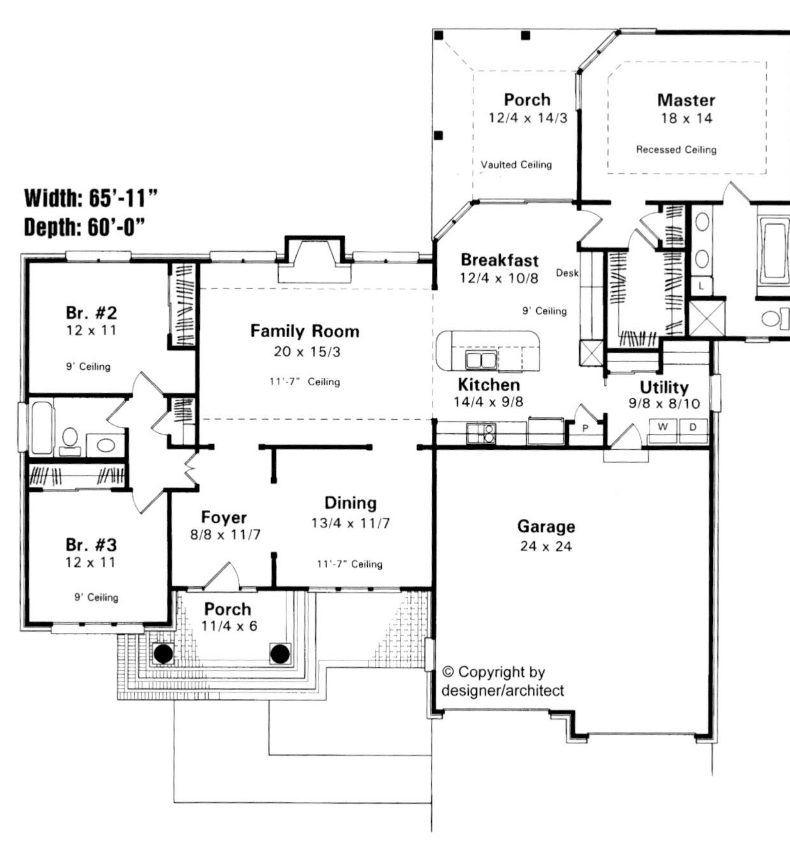

Width: 65'-11"
Depth: 60'-0"
Porch
12/4 x 14/3
Vaulted Ceiling
Master
18 x 14
Recessed Ceiling
Breakfast
12/4 x 10/8
Desk
9' Ceiling
Br. #2
12 x 11
9' Ceiling
Family Room
20 x 15/3
11'-7" Ceiling
Kitchen
14/4 x 9/8
Utility
9/8 x 8/10
W
D
P
L
Foyer
8/8 x 11/7
Dining
13/4 x 11/7
11'-7" Ceiling
Garage
24 x 24
Br. #3
12 x 11
9' Ceiling
Porch
11/4 x 6
© Copyright by designer/architect

To order plans, visit the Menards Building Materials Desk or visit www.Menards.com.

MENARDS®

HAVERSHAM

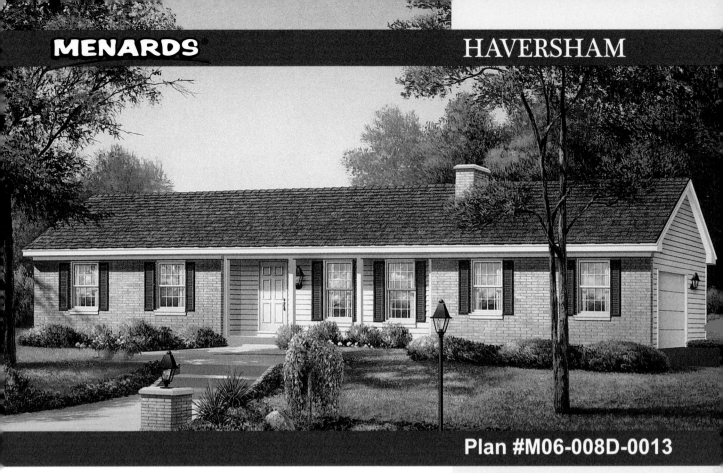

Plan #M06-008D-0013

TERRIFIC DESIGN FOR FAMILY LIVING

1,345 total square feet of living area

3 bedrooms, 2 baths

2-car side entry garage

Basement foundation, drawings also include crawl space and slab foundations

SPECIAL FEATURES

Brick front details add a touch of elegance

The master bedroom has a private full bath

The great room combines with the dining area creating a sense of spaciousness

The garage includes a handy storage area that could easily be converted to a workshop space

PRICE CODE A

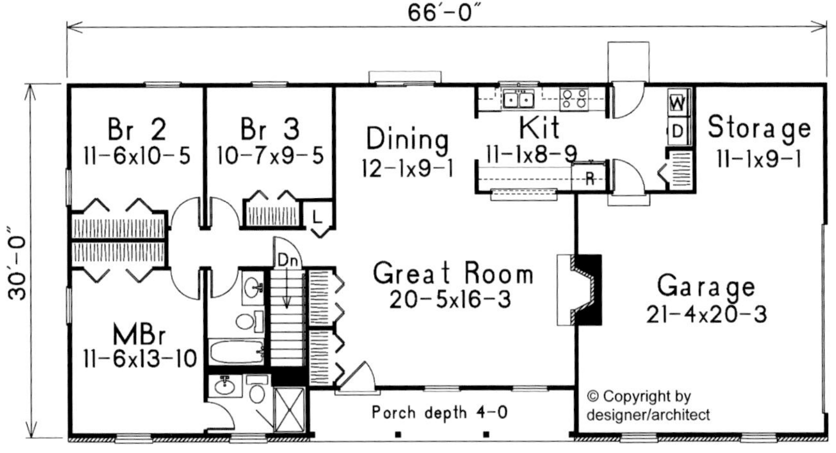

66′-0″
30′-0″
Br 2
11-6x10-5
Br 3
10-7x9-5
Dining
12-1x9-1
Kit
11-1x8-9
W
D
R
Storage
11-1x9-1
L
Dn
Great Room
20-5x16-3
Garage
21-4x20-3
MBr
11-6x13-10
Porch depth 4-0
© Copyright by designer/architect

To order plans, visit the Menards Building Materials Desk or visit www.Menards.com.

WESTMONT MANOR

MENARDS

Plan #M06-007D-0170

CLASSIC EXPRESSION

2,154 total square feet of living area

4 bedrooms, 2 1/2 baths

2-car garage

Basement foundation

SPECIAL FEATURES

Open to a capacious great room is a cheery breakfast room surrounded by three 6' glass sliding doors that lead to the rear and covered side patios

The awesome kitchen features a long angled breakfast counter, walk-in pantry and adjoins a multi-purpose room ideal for a large laundry, study, hobby or exercise room

The vaulted master bedroom has a lavish bath, double walk-in closets and adjoining study/bedroom #4 with an attractive bay window

PRICE CODE C

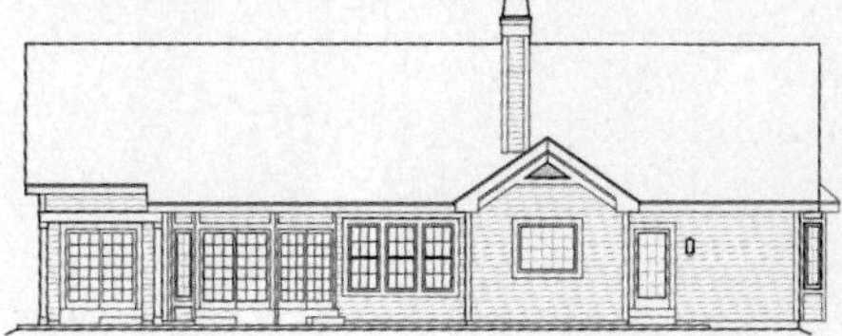

Rear View

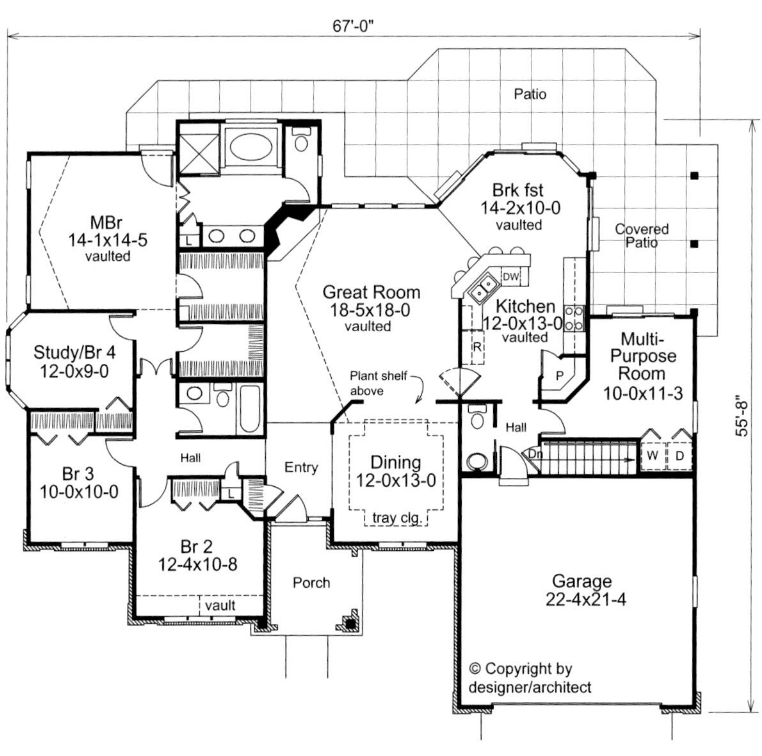
67'-0"
Patio
MBr
14-1x14-5
vaulted
Brk fst
14-2x10-0
vaulted
Covered Patio
Great Room
18-5x18-0
vaulted
DW
Kitchen
12-0x13-0
vaulted
R
P
Study/Br 4
12-0x9-0
Multi-Purpose Room
10-0x11-3
Plant shelf above
55'-8"
Hall
Dn
W
D
Hall
Entry
Dining
12-0x13-0
tray clg.
Br 3
10-0x10-0
Br 2
12-4x10-8
vault
Porch
Garage
22-4x21-4
© Copyright by designer/architect

To order plans, visit the Menards Building Materials Desk or visit www.Menards.com.

MENARDS

FAIRFIELD LAKE

Plan #M06-055L-0192

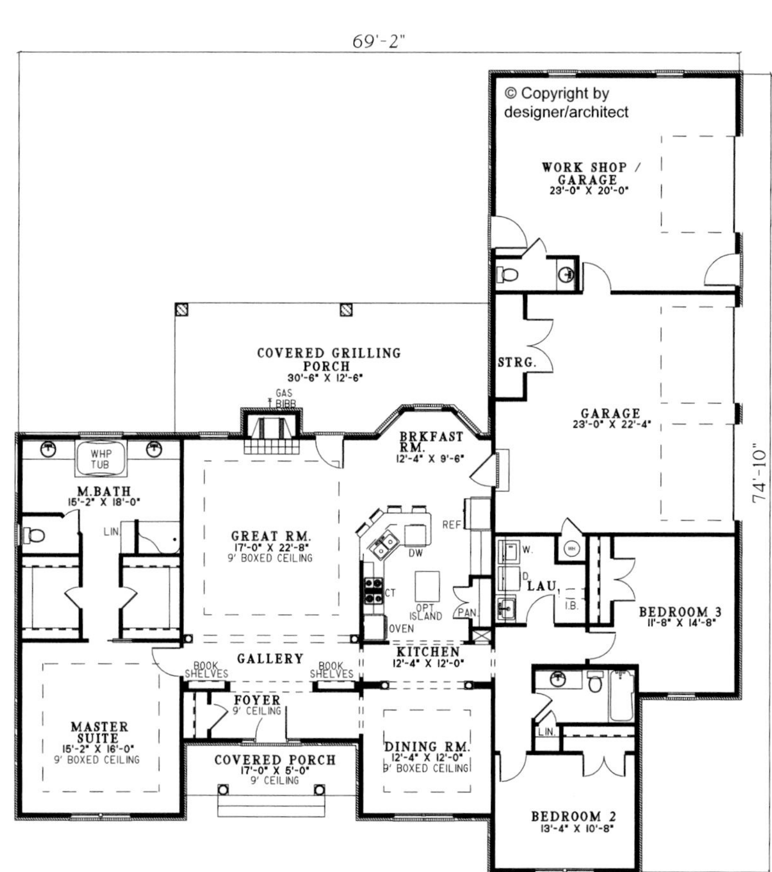

69'-2"
74'-10"
© Copyright by designer/architect
WORK SHOP / GARAGE 23'-0" X 20'-0"
COVERED GRILLING PORCH 30'-6" X 12'-6"
GAS BIBB
STRG.
GARAGE 23'-0" X 22'-4"
BRKFAST RM. 12'-4" X 9'-6"
WHP TUB
M.BATH 15'-2" X 18'-0"
LIN
GREAT RM. 17'-0" X 22'-8" 9' BOXED CEILING
REF
DW
CT
OPT ISLAND
OVEN
PAN
W.
D.
LAU.
I.B.
BEDROOM 3 11'-8" X 14'-8"
GALLERY
BOOK SHELVES
BOOK SHELVES
KITCHEN 12'-4" X 12'-0"
MASTER SUITE 15'-2" X 16'-0" 9' BOXED CEILING
FOYER 9' CEILING
COVERED PORCH 17'-0" X 5'-0" 9' CEILING
DINING RM. 12'-4" X 12'-0" 9' BOXED CEILING
LIN.
BEDROOM 2 13'-4" X 10'-8"

FORMAL DINING ROOM

2,096 total square feet of living area

3 bedrooms, 2 1/2 baths

3-car side entry garage

Slab, crawl space, basement or walk-out basement foundation, please specify when ordering

SPECIAL FEATURES

The foyer opens to the great room that features a fireplace and built-in bookshelves

The secondary bedrooms are secluded with a central bath and laundry room

The grand kitchen has an eating counter, pantry, optional island and connects to the bayed breakfast room

PRICE CODE E

To order plans, visit the Menards Building Materials Desk or visit www.Menards.com.

WELLSHIRE

MENARDS®

Plan #M06-077L-0156

GRAND ONE-LEVEL

2,200 total square feet of living area

4 bedrooms, 2 1/2 baths

2-car side entry garage

Crawl space or slab foundation, please specify when ordering

SPECIAL FEATURES

Step inside this inviting home to find an exquisite great room topped with a tray ceiling and featuring a gas fireplace flanked by built-in shelves

The nearby kitchen is centrally located, offering a walk-in pantry and raised snack bar, and easily serves both the formal dining room and the casual breakfast area

The master bedroom pampers with two walk-in closets and a compartmented bath equipped with a jet tub and twin vanity

The optional second floor has an additional 371 square feet of living area

PRICE CODE E

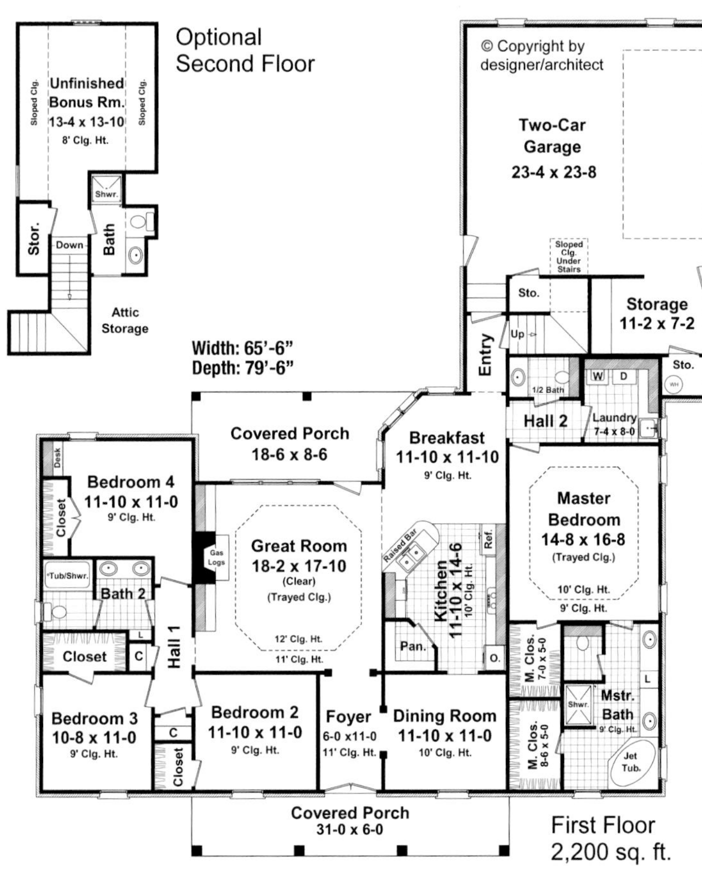

Optional
Second Floor
Unfinished Bonus Rm. 13-4 x 13-10 8' Clg. Ht.
Sloped Clg.
Sloped Clg.
Shwr.
Stor.
Down
Bath
Attic Storage
Width: 65'-6"
Depth: 79'-6"
© Copyright by designer/architect
Two-Car Garage 23-4 x 23-8
Sloped Clg. Under Stairs
Sto.
Storage 11-2 x 7-2
Up
Entry
Sto.
1/2 Bath
W
D
WH
Hall 2
Laundry 7-4 x 8-0
Covered Porch 18-6 x 8-6
Breakfast 11-10 x 11-10 9' Clg. Ht.
Desk
Bedroom 4 11-10 x 11-0 9' Clg. Ht.
Closet
Gas Logs
Great Room 18-2 x 17-10 (Clear) (Trayed Clg.)
12' Clg. Ht.
11' Clg. Ht.
Raised Bar
Kitchen 11-10 x 14-6 10' Clg. Ht.
Ref.
Pan.
O.
Master Bedroom 14-8 x 16-8 (Trayed Clg.)
10' Clg. Ht.
9' Clg. Ht.
Tub/Shwr.
Bath 2
L
Closet
C
Hall 1
M. Clos. 7-0 x 5-0
Shwr.
Mstr. Bath 9' Clg. Ht.
L
M. Clos. 8-6 x 5-0
Jet Tub.
Bedroom 3 10-8 x 11-0 9' Clg. Ht.
C
Closet
Bedroom 2 11-10 x 11-0 9' Clg. Ht.
Foyer 6-0 x11-0 11' Clg. Ht.
Dining Room 11-10 x 11-0 10' Clg. Ht.
Covered Porch 31-0 x 6-0
First Floor
2,200 sq. ft.

To order plans, visit the Menards Building Materials Desk or visit www.Menards.com.

MENARDS®

LYNNEWOOD PLACE

Plan #M06-007D-0239

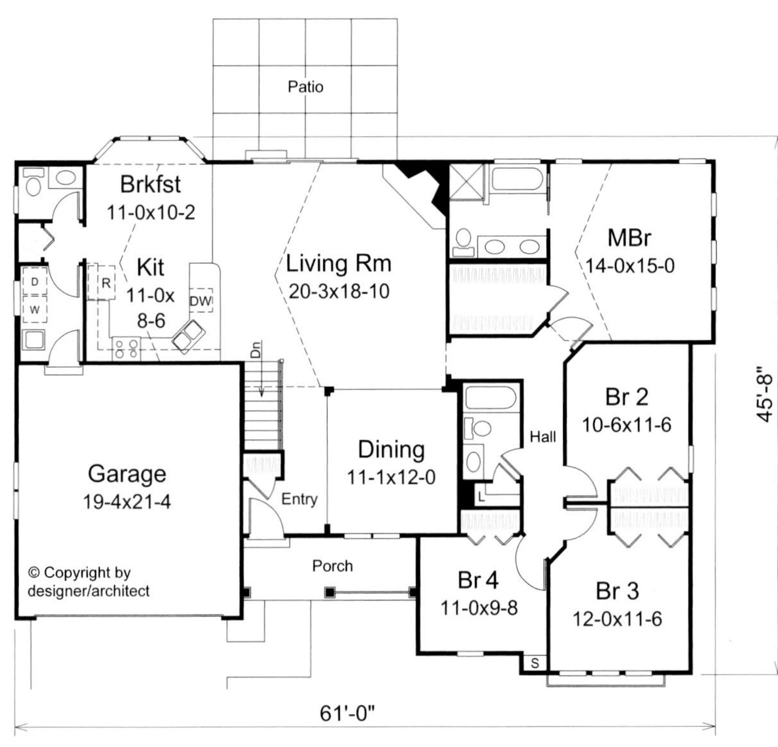

Patio
Brkfst
11-0x10-2
Kit
11-0x
8-6
R
DW
D
W
Living Rm
20-3x18-10
MBr
14-0x15-0
Dn
Br 2
10-6x11-6
Hall
Dining
11-1x12-0
Garage
19-4x21-4
Entry
Porch
Br 4
11-0x9-8
Br 3
12-0x11-6
S
45'-8"
61'-0"
© Copyright by
designer/architect

SMARTLY DESIGNED FOUR BEDROOM RANCH

1,912 total square feet of living area

4 bedrooms, 2 1/2 baths

2-car garage

Basement foundation

SPECIAL FEATURES

The living room, with fireplace and 9' glass sliding doors to rear patio, is open to the kitchen and bayed breakfast area, all with dramatic vaulted ceilings

Adjacent to the kitchen is a convenient laundry room, coat closet and half bath

The master bedroom offers a vaulted ceiling, showcase windows, walk-in closet and luxury bath with separate shower

PRICE CODE C

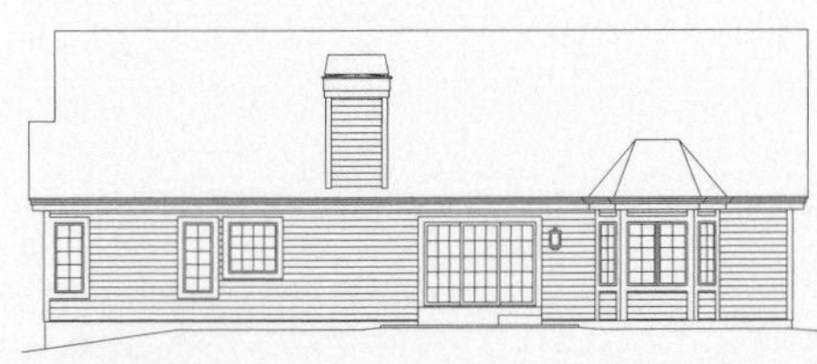

Rear View

To order plans, visit the Menards Building Materials Desk
or visit www.Menards.com.

HILLSBOROUGH

MENARDS®

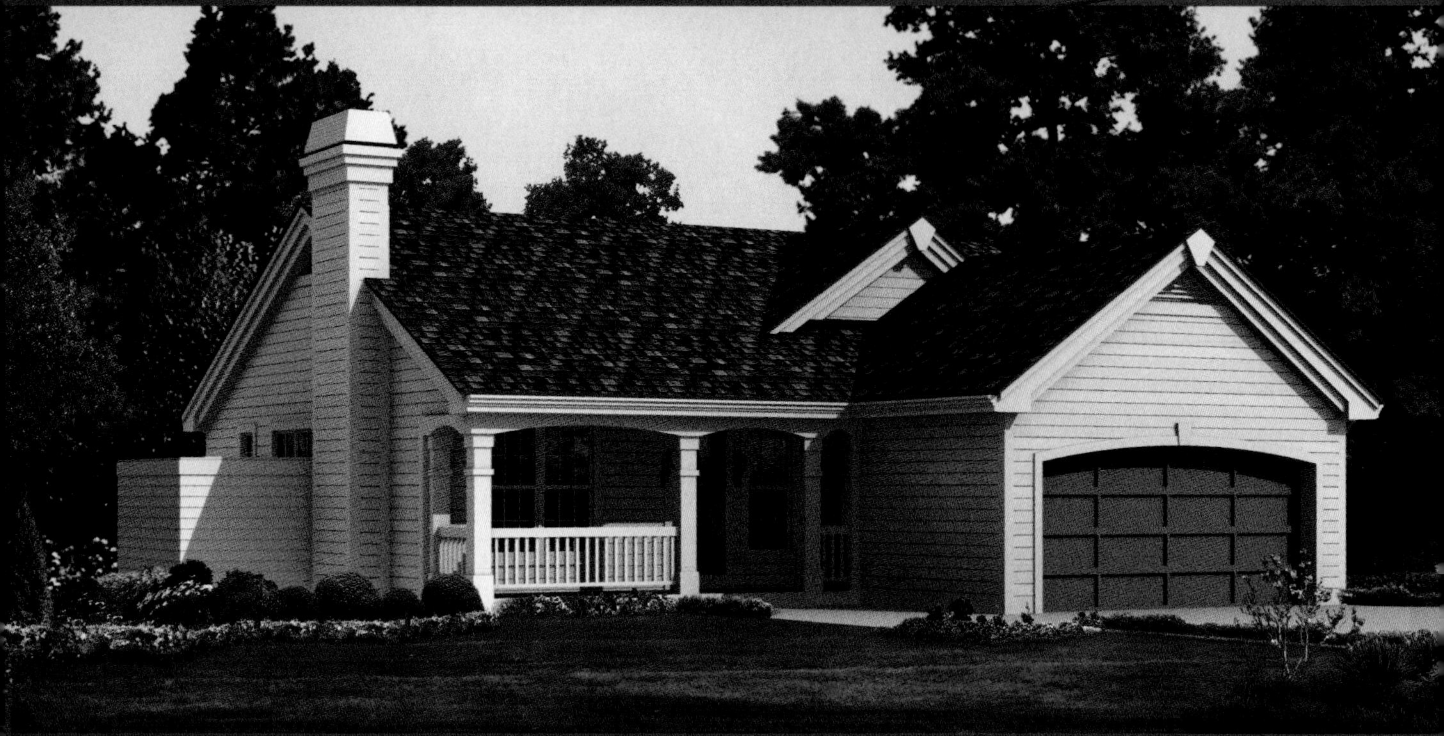

Plan #M06-007D-0178

AFFORDABLE FOUR BEDROOM RANCH

1,203 total square feet of living area

4 bedrooms, 2 1/2 baths

2-car garage

Basement foundation, drawings also include slab and crawl space foundations

SPECIAL FEATURES

Large porch for quiet evening relaxation

The living room features a vaulted ceiling, fireplace and dining area with patio views

The kitchen includes an abundance of cabinet storage, a large walk-in pantry and door to the rear yard

The master bedroom has a vaulted ceiling, private bath with built-in linen storage and a walk-in closet

PRICE CODE A

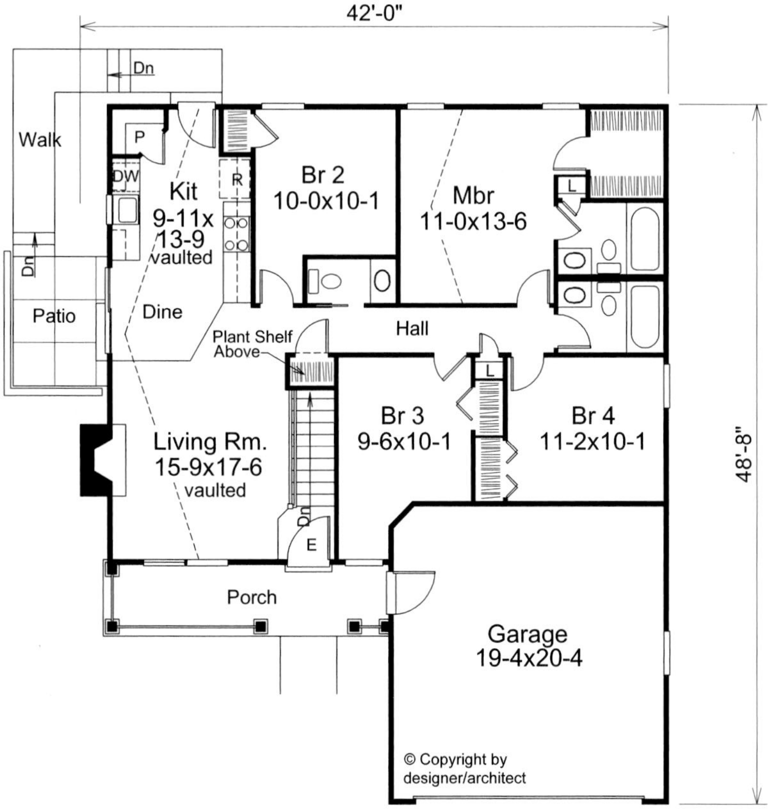

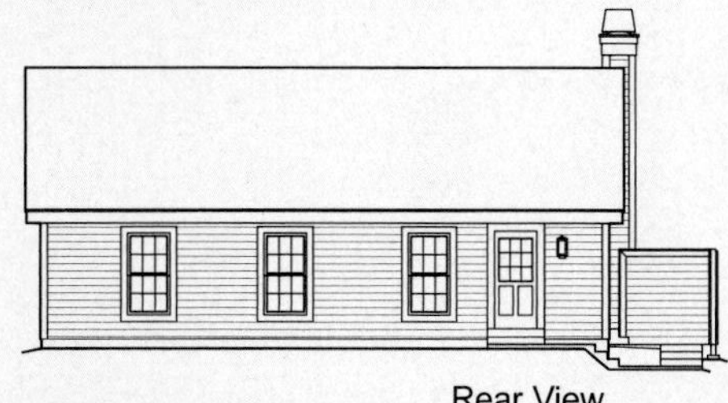

Rear View

42'-0"

48'-8"

Walk

Dn

Patio

Dn

P

DW

R

Kit
9-11x
13-9
vaulted

Dine

Br 2
10-0x10-1

Mbr
11-0x13-6

L

Plant Shelf
Above

Hall

L

Br 3
9-6x10-1

Br 4
11-2x10-1

Living Rm.
15-9x17-6
vaulted

Dn

E

Porch

Garage
19-4x20-4

To order plans, visit the Menards Building Materials Desk or visit www.Menards.com.

MENARDS®

FOXTON

Plan #M06-008D-0027

ENERGY EFFICIENT RANCH

1,176 total square feet of living area

3 bedrooms, 1 1/2 baths

Optional 2-car garage

Basement foundation, drawings also include crawl space and slab foundations

SPECIAL FEATURES

The living room features an entry area with large coat closet and box-bay window

The kitchen has an eating area and adjoins a very spacious family area

The master bedroom has a huge walk-in closet and shares a compartmented bath with two secondary bedrooms

PRICE CODE AA

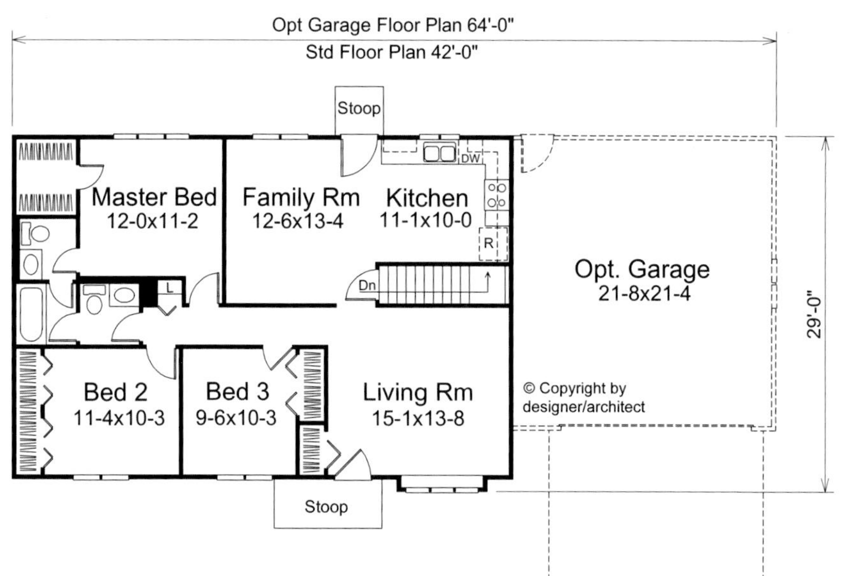

Opt Garage Floor Plan 64'-0"
Std Floor Plan 42'-0"
Stoop
Master Bed
12-0x11-2
Family Rm
12-6x13-4
Kitchen
11-1x10-0
DW
R
L
Dn
Opt. Garage
21-8x21-4
29'-0"
Bed 2
11-4x10-3
Bed 3
9-6x10-3
Living Rm
15-1x13-8
© Copyright by designer/architect
Stoop

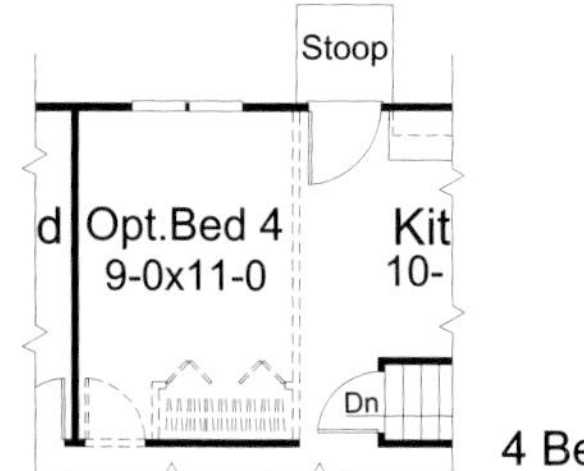

Stoop
d
Opt.Bed 4
9-0x11-0
Kit
10-
Dn

4 Bedroom Option

To order plans, visit the Menards Building Materials Desk or visit www.Menards.com.

EMILIA

MENARDS®

Plan #M06-121D-0006

EXTERIOR ACCENTS CREATE TIMELESS CURB APPEAL

2,241 total square feet of living area

4 bedrooms, 2 1/2 baths

2-car side entry garage

Basement foundation

SPECIAL FEATURES

11' ceilings in the entry, great room, kitchen and dining room for added spaciousness

Joining the kitchen and great room is a see-through fireplace with convenient built-in shelving units on both sides

The kitchen features an amazing amount of dining space including a large island with breakfast table extension that has enough space for seven people

PRICE CODE C

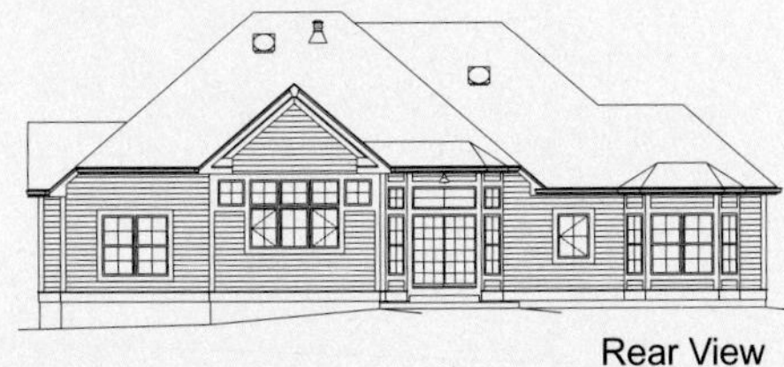

Rear View

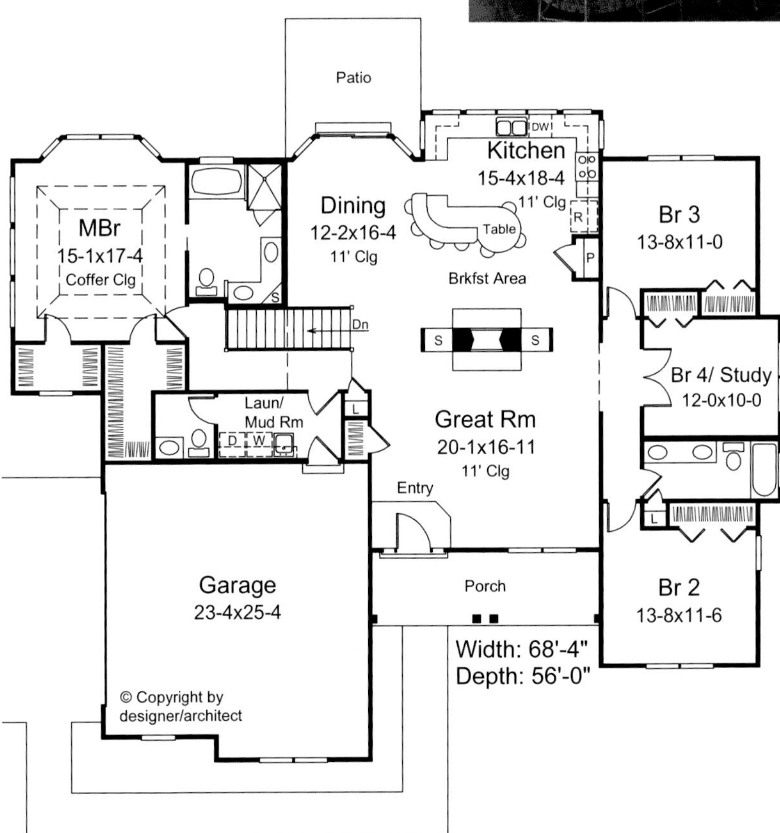
Patio
Kitchen
15-4x18-4
11' Clg
DW
R
P
Dining
12-2x16-4
11' Clg
Table
Brkfst Area
MBr
15-1x17-4
Coffer Clg
S
Dn
Br 3
13-8x11-0
Br 4/ Study
12-0x10-0
Great Rm
20-1x16-11
11' Clg
Laun/
Mud Rm
D
W
L
Entry
Porch
Br 2
13-8x11-6
Garage
23-4x25-4
Width: 68'-4"
Depth: 56'-0"
© Copyright by
designer/architect

To order plans, visit the Menards Building Materials Desk or visit www.Menards.com.

MENARDS

CHADBOURNE

Plan #M06-024L-0048

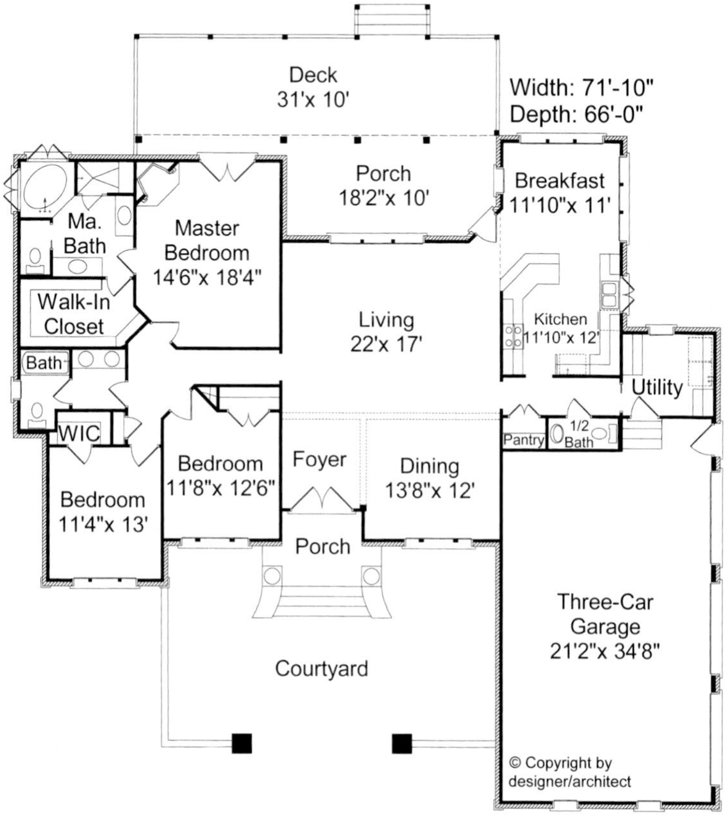

Deck
31'x 10'
Width: 71'-10"
Depth: 66'-0"
Porch
18'2"x 10'
Breakfast
11'10"x 11'
Ma.
Bath
Master
Bedroom
14'6"x 18'4"
Walk-In
Closet
Living
22'x 17'
Kitchen
11'10"x 12'
Bath
Utility
WIC
Pantry
1/2
Bath
Bedroom
11'8"x 12'6"
Foyer
Dining
13'8"x 12'
Bedroom
11'4"x 13'
Porch
Three-Car
Garage
21'2"x 34'8"
Courtyard
© Copyright by
designer/architect

To order plans, visit the Menards Building Materials Desk
or visit www.Menards.com.

COURTYARD OFFERS LANDSCAPING OPPORTUNITIES

2,240 total square feet of living area

3 bedrooms, 2 1/2 baths

3-car side entry garage

Crawl space or basement foundation, please specify when ordering

SPECIAL FEATURES

All of the bedrooms are located on the left side of the home remaining private from the more active living areas

The breakfast area is bright and cheery with an abundance of windows

Access the porch and deck from the master bedroom and living area for outdoor relaxation

Optional bonus space above the garage has an additional 519 square feet of living area

PRICE CODE H

SHILOH VALLEY

MENARDS

Plan #M06-007D-0168

LUXURY LIVING IN A COUNTRY HOME

1,814 total square feet of living area

3 bedrooms, 2 baths

3-car side entry garage

Basement foundation

SPECIAL FEATURES

This home enjoys a large country porch for a perfect leisurely living area

The vaulted great room, sunny breakfast area and kitchen with snack bar are all open to one another to create a very open sense of spaciousness

A sensational lavish bath is the highlight of the master bedroom suite that features double vanities with a makeup counter, a 5' x 5' shower with seat, separate toilet and a step-up whirlpool-in-a-sunroom

PRICE CODE C

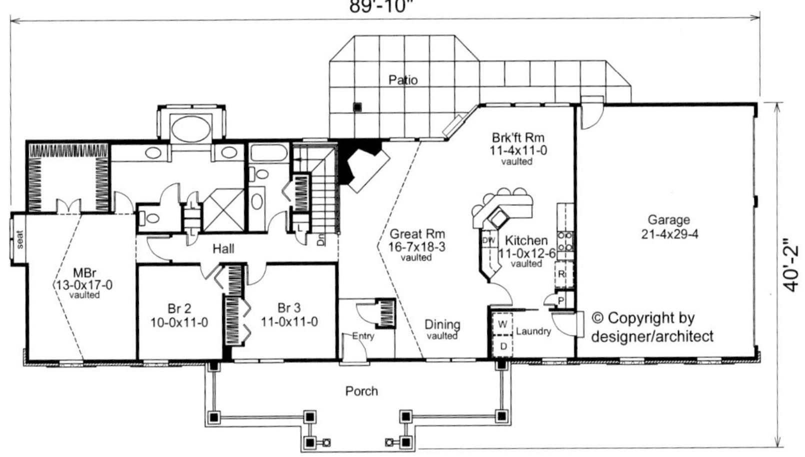

89'-10"
40'-2"
Patio
Brk'ft Rm
11-4x11-0
vaulted
Garage
21-4x29-4
Great Rm
16-7x18-3
vaulted
Kitchen
11-0x12-6
vaulted
seat
MBr
13-0x17-0
vaulted
Hall
Br 2
10-0x11-0
Br 3
11-0x11-0
Entry
Dining
vaulted
Laundry
W
D
DW
R
P
Porch
© Copyright by
designer/architect

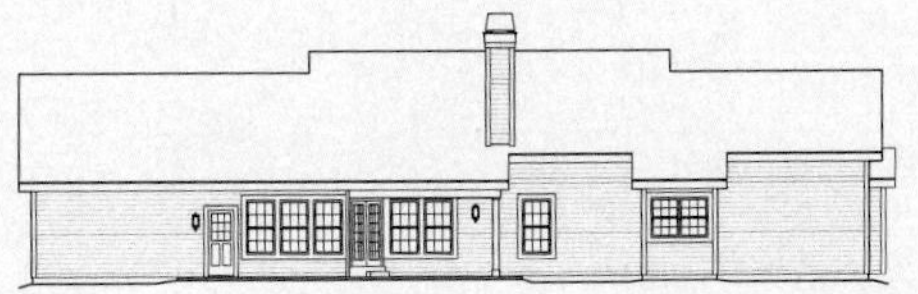

Rear View

To order plans, visit the Menards Building Materials Desk or visit www.Menards.com.

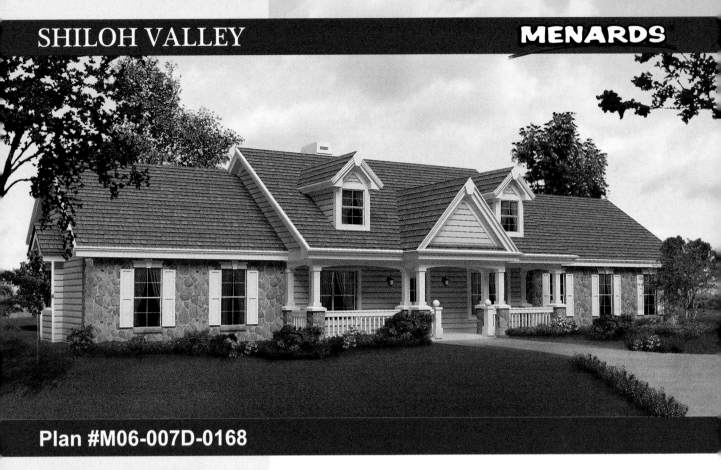

MENARDS

CHATHAM PLACE

Plan #M06-024L-0022

IMPRESSIVE CENTRAL LIVING ROOM

2,400 total square feet of living area

4 bedrooms, 2 baths

2-car side entry garage

Slab or crawl space foundation, please specify when ordering

SPECIAL FEATURES

The fantastic bay-shaped kitchen is loaded with space and includes a large utility room and breakfast room nearby

A corner fireplace enhances the living area

The master bedroom includes all the luxuries such as a step-up tub, double walk-in closets, and direct access to the patio

The optional second floor has an additional 747 square feet of living area

PRICE CODE D

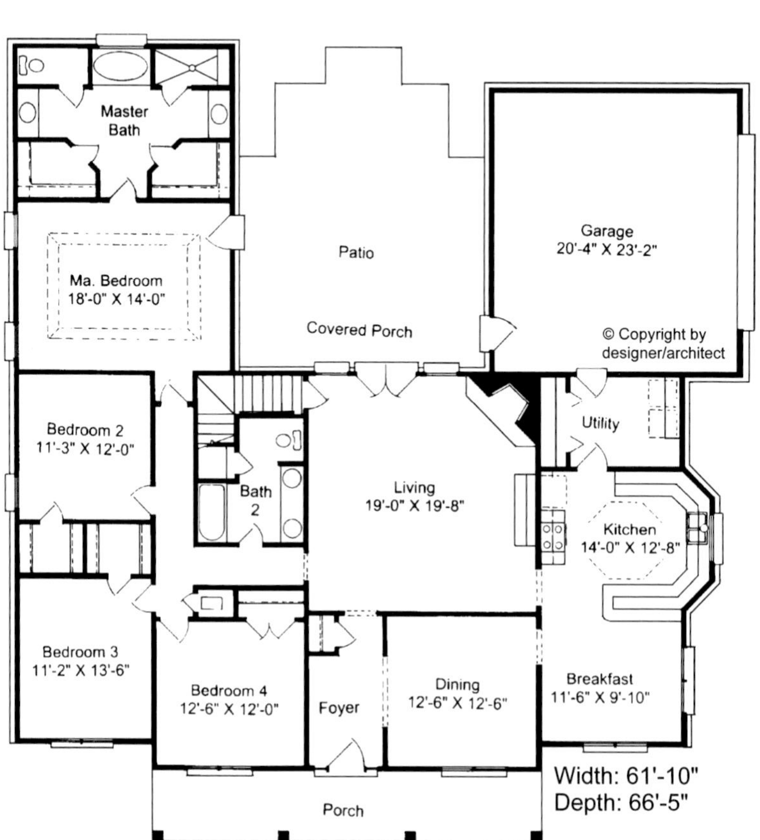

Master Bath
Patio
Garage 20'-4" X 23'-2"
Ma. Bedroom 18'-0" X 14'-0"
Covered Porch
© Copyright by designer/architect
Bedroom 2 11'-3" X 12'-0"
Utility
Bath 2
Living 19'-0" X 19'-8"
Kitchen 14'-0" X 12'-8"
Bedroom 3 11'-2" X 13'-6"
Bedroom 4 12'-6" X 12'-0"
Foyer
Dining 12'-6" X 12'-6"
Breakfast 11'-6" X 9'-10"
Porch
Width: 61'-10"
Depth: 66'-5"

To order plans, visit the Menards Building Materials Desk or visit www.Menards.com.

PRAIRIE LAKE

MENARDS®

Plan #M06-007D-0248

IDEAL LAKE HOME

1,763 total square feet of living area

3 bedrooms, 2 1/2 baths

2-car side entry garage

Slab foundation, drawings also include crawl space and basement foundations

SPECIAL FEATURES

The entry with glass double doors and a 10' volume ceiling has a convenient guest closet

A corner fireplace and 9' glass sliding doors to the rear patio make the huge great room very inviting

The L-shaped kitchen features a snack bar, menu desk, cabinet pantry and adjacent breakfast room, laundry room and half bath

Double-entry doors, a luxury bath, large walk-in closet and glass door to a second private patio are a few of the amenities of the master bedroom

PRICE CODE C

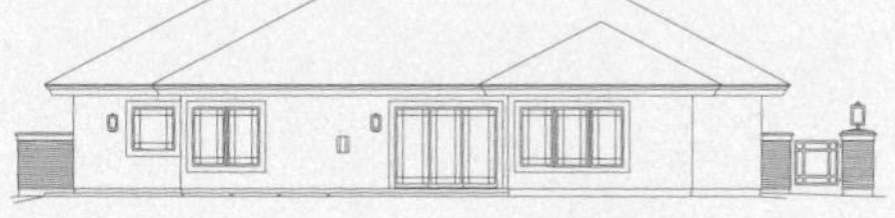

Rear View

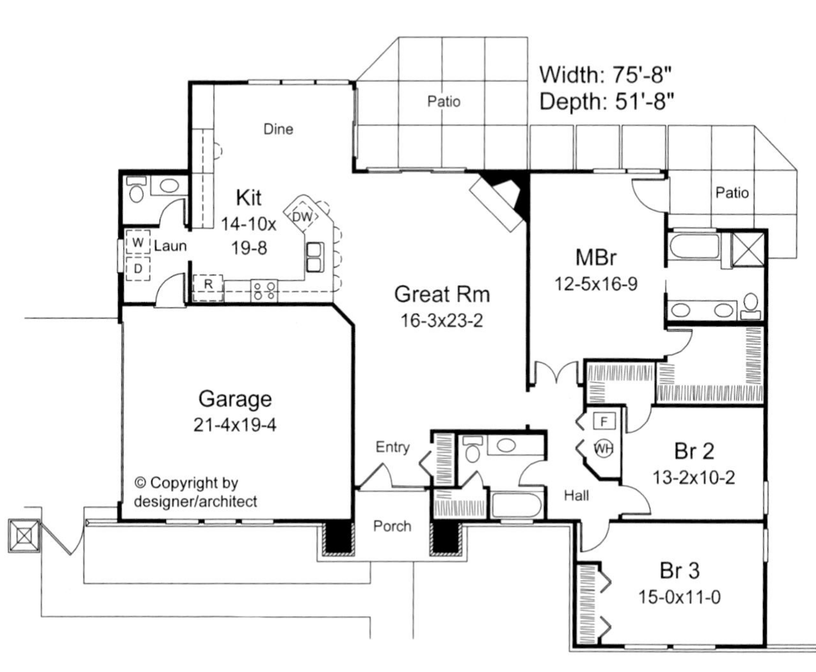
Width: 75'-8"
Depth: 51'-8"
Patio
Dine
Kit
14-10x
19-8
DW
W
D
Laun
R
Great Rm
16-3x23-2
MBr
12-5x16-9
Patio
Garage
21-4x19-4
© Copyright by
designer/architect
Entry
Porch
F
WH
Hall
Br 2
13-2x10-2
Br 3
15-0x11-0

To order plans, visit the Menards Building Materials Desk or visit www.Menards.com.

MENARDS®

WHEELERSCREST

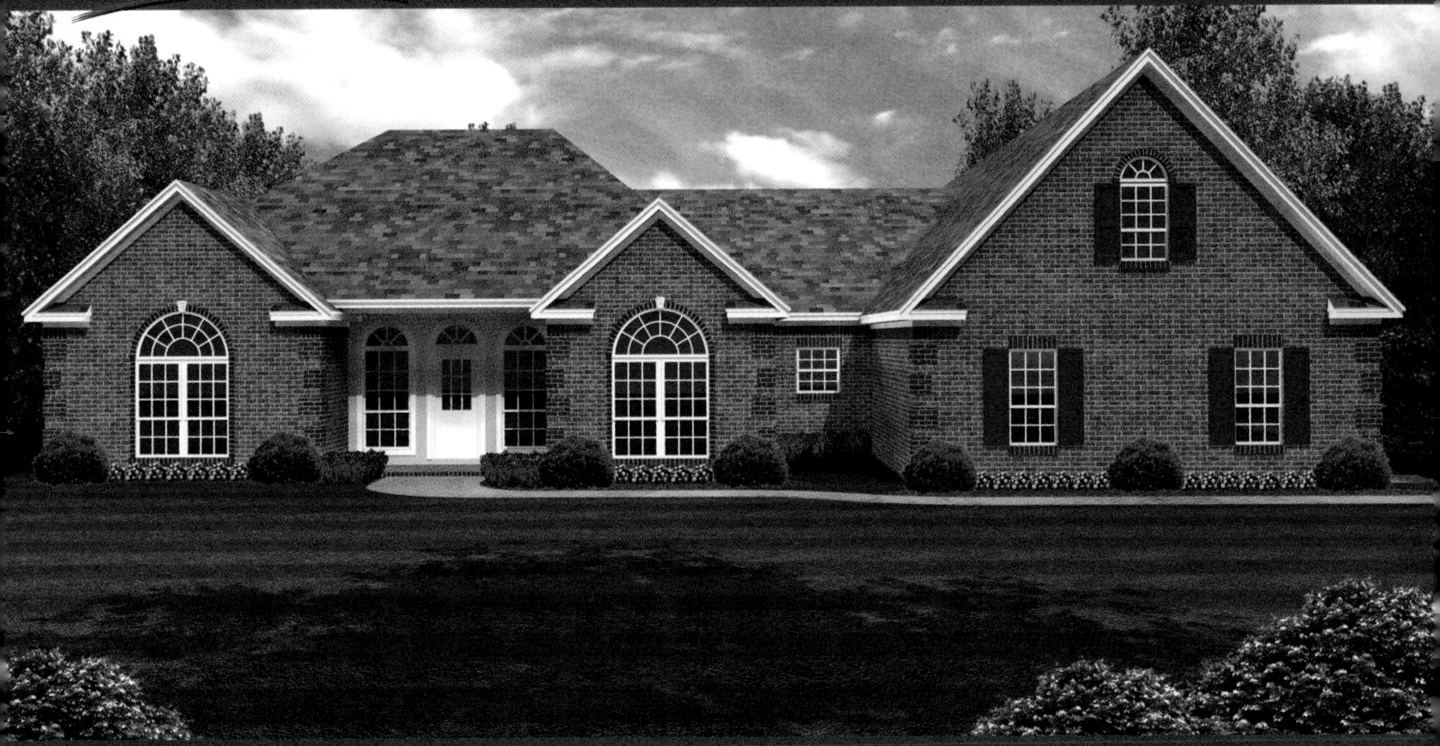

Plan #M06-077L-0067

GRACEFUL WINDOWS

2,251 total square feet of living area

3 bedrooms, 2 1/2 baths

3-car side entry garage

Basement, crawl space or slab foundation, please specify when ordering

SPECIAL FEATURES

The highly functional kitchen has ample counterspace, a corner pantry and a raised bar

The breakfast room overlooks both rear porches

The second floor bonus room features an additional 501 square feet of living space with the option of a bath

PRICE CODE E

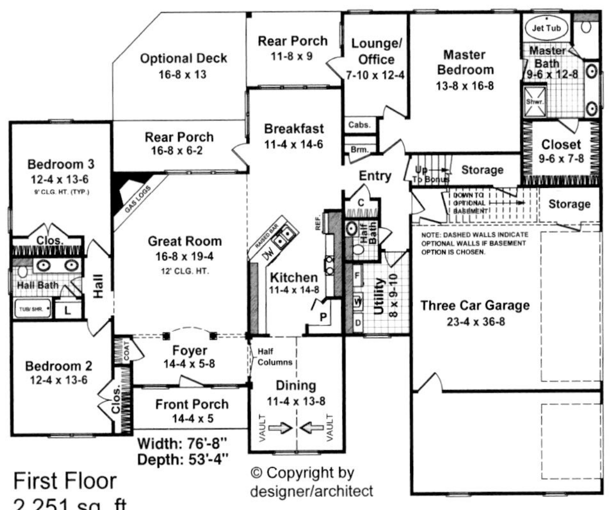

Optional Deck 16-8 x 13
Rear Porch 11-8 x 9
Lounge/ Office 7-10 x 12-4
Master Bedroom 13-8 x 16-8
Jet Tub
Master Bath 9-6 x 12-8
Rear Porch 16-8 x 6-2
Breakfast 11-4 x 14-6
Cabs.
Brm.
Closet 9-6 x 7-8
Bedroom 3 12-4 x 13-6
Entry
Up To Bonus
Storage
Storage
Great Room 16-8 x 19-4 12' CLG. HT.
Clos.
Kitchen 11-4 x 14-8
Half Bath
Utility 8 x 9-10
NOTE: DASHED WALLS INDICATE OPTIONAL WALLS IF BASEMENT OPTION IS CHOSEN.
Three Car Garage 23-4 x 36-8
Hall Bath
Hall
Foyer 14-4 x 5-8
Half Columns
Bedroom 2 12-4 x 13-6
Dining 11-4 x 13-8
Clos.
Front Porch 14-4 x 5
Width: 76'-8"
Depth: 53'-4"

First Floor
2,251 sq. ft.

© Copyright by designer/architect

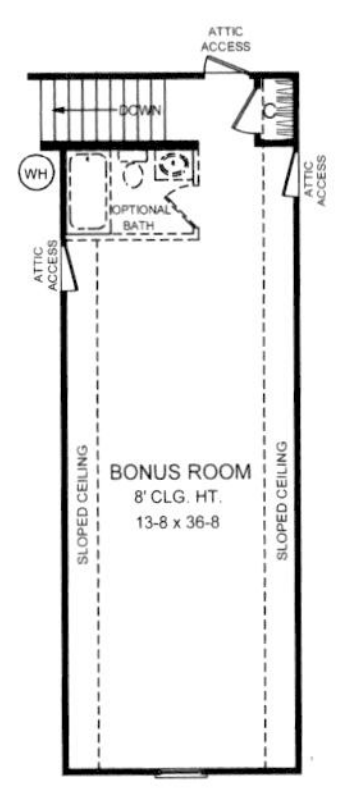

ATTIC ACCESS
DOWN
OPTIONAL BATH
BONUS ROOM 8' CLG. HT. 13-8 x 36-8
SLOPED CEILING
SLOPED CEILING

Optional
Second Floor

To order plans, visit the Menards Building Materials Desk or visit www.Menards.com.

DURAND

MENARDS

Plan #M06-013L-0037

GRAND ARCHED ENTRY

2,564 total square feet of living area

3 bedrooms, 2 1/2 baths

2-car side entry garage

Basement, crawl space or slab foundation, please specify when ordering

SPECIAL FEATURES

The hearth room is surrounded by the kitchen, dining and breakfast rooms making it the focal point of those living areas

Escape to the master bedroom featuring a luxurious private bath and a sitting area leading to the deck outdoors

The secondary bedrooms share a Jack and Jill bath and both have a walk-in closet

The bonus room above the garage has an additional 302 square feet of living area

PRICE CODE E

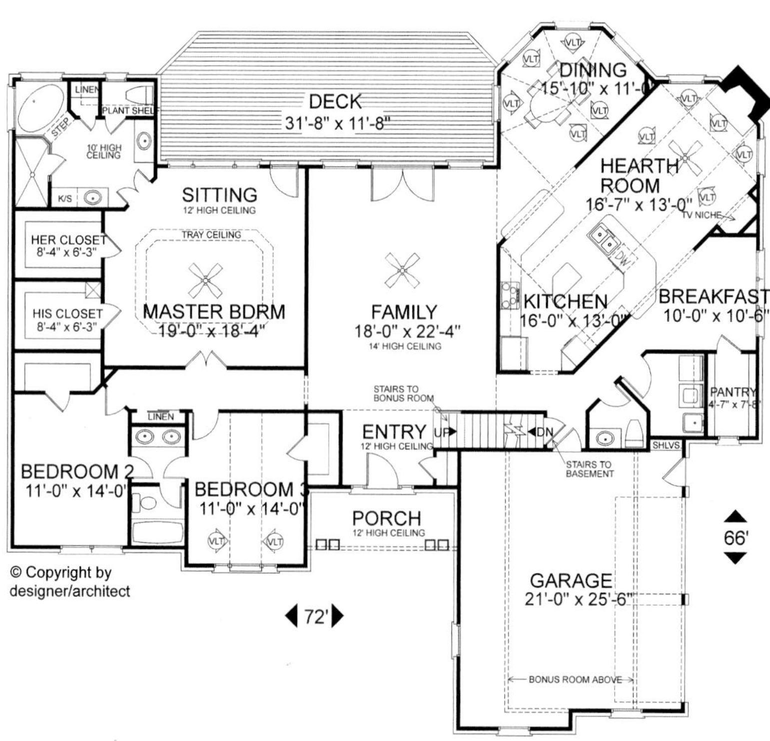

DECK
31'-8" x 11'-8"
DINING
15'-10" x 11'-0"
HEARTH ROOM
16'-7" x 13'-0"
TV NICHE
LINEN
PLANT SHELF
STEP
10' HIGH CEILING
K/S
SITTING
12' HIGH CEILING
TRAY CEILING
HER CLOSET
8'-4" x 6'-3"
HIS CLOSET
8'-4" x 6'-3"
MASTER BDRM
19'-0" x 18'-4"
FAMILY
18'-0" x 22'-4"
14' HIGH CEILING
KITCHEN
16'-0" x 13'-0"
DW
BREAKFAST
10'-0" x 10'-6"
PANTRY
4'-7" x 7'-8"
STAIRS TO BONUS ROOM
ENTRY
12' HIGH CEILING
UP
DN
STAIRS TO BASEMENT
SHLVS
LINEN
BEDROOM 2
11'-0" x 14'-0"
BEDROOM 3
11'-0" x 14'-0"
VLT
PORCH
12' HIGH CEILING
66'
GARAGE
21'-0" x 25'-6"
BONUS ROOM ABOVE
72'
© Copyright by designer/architect

To order plans, visit the Menards Building Materials Desk or visit www.Menards.com.

MENARDS

REGINA

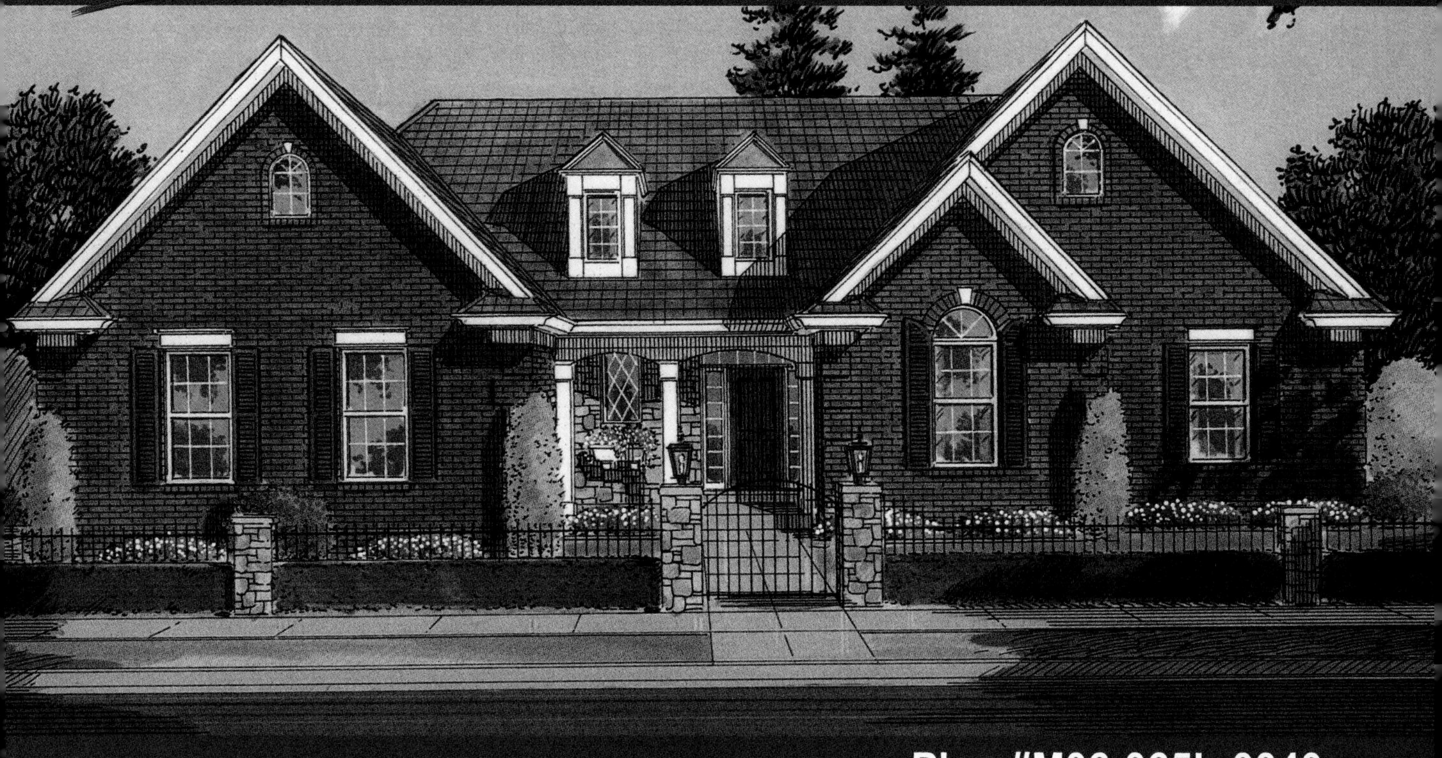

Plan #M06-065L-0040

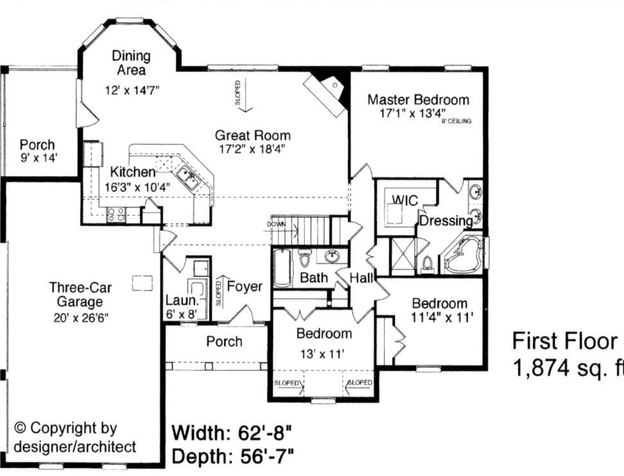

Dining Area
12' x 14'7"
Great Room
17'2" x 18'4"
Master Bedroom
17'1" x 13'4"
Porch
9' x 14'
Kitchen
16'3" x 10'4"
WIC
Dressing
Three-Car Garage
20' x 26'6"
Laun.
6' x 8'
Foyer
Bath
Hall
Bedroom
11'4" x 11'
Porch
Bedroom
13' x 11'
© Copyright by designer/architect
Width: 62'-8"
Depth: 56'-7"

First Floor
1,874 sq. ft.

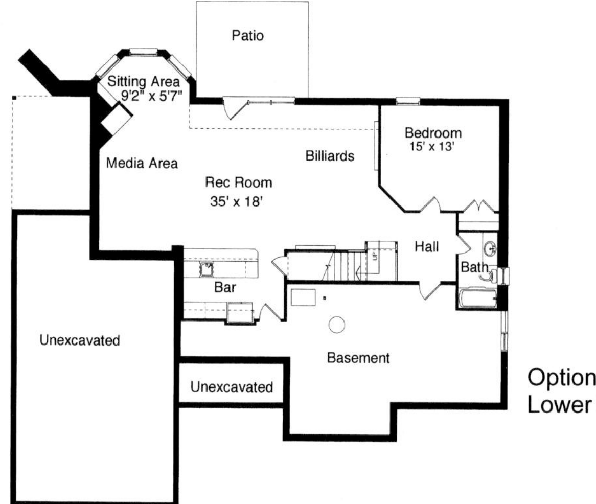

Patio
Sitting Area
9'2" x 5'7"
Media Area
Billiards
Rec Room
35' x 18'
Bedroom
15' x 13'
Hall
Bath
Bar
Unexcavated
Basement
Unexcavated

Optional
Lower Level

To order plans, visit the Menards Building Materials Desk or visit www.Menards.com.

WARM AND INVITING RANCH

1,874 total square feet of living area

3 bedrooms, 2 baths

3-car side entry garage

Walk-out basement foundation

SPECIAL FEATURES

The bayed dining area, kitchen and great room with a fireplace combine for an open living area

The master bedroom pampers with a corner whirlpool tub, double vanity and walk-in closet

9' ceilings throughout this home add to the spaciousness

Optional lower level has an additional 1,175 square feet of living area

PRICE CODE C

BROOKMONT

MENARDS®

Plan #M06-007D-0067

SMALL RANCH FOR A PERFECT COUNTRY HAVEN

1,761 total square feet of living area

4 bedrooms, 2 baths

2-car side entry garage

Basement foundation

SPECIAL FEATURES

Exterior window dressing, roof dormers and planter boxes provide visual warmth and charm

The great room, that opens to a pass-through kitchen, boasts a vaulted ceiling and a fireplace

The vaulted master bedroom includes a luxury bath and walk-in closet

Home features an abundance of storage

PRICE CODE B

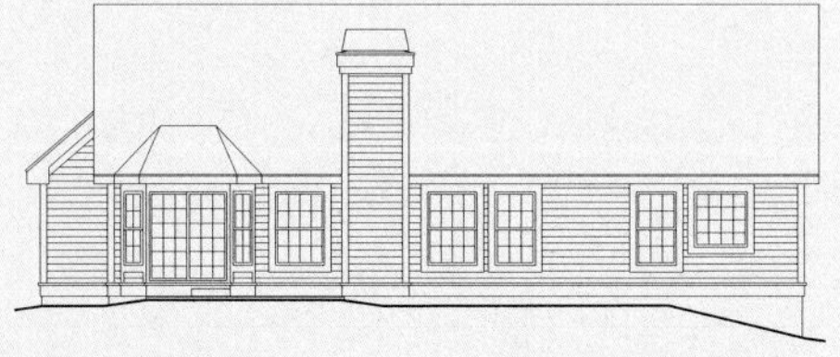

Rear View

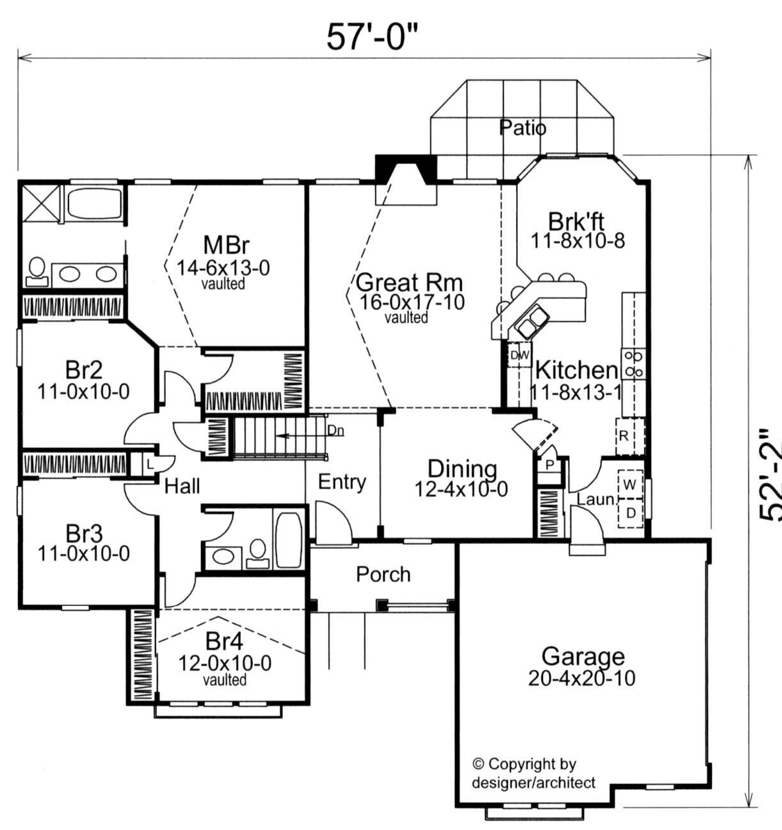
57'-0"
52'-2"
Patio
MBr
14-6x13-0
vaulted
Great Rm
16-0x17-10
vaulted
Brk'ft
11-8x10-8
Kitchen
11-8x13-1
DW
R
P
W
D
Laun.
Br2
11-0x10-0
Dn
Hall
L
Entry
Dining
12-4x10-0
Br3
11-0x10-0
Porch
Br4
12-0x10-0
vaulted
Garage
20-4x20-10
© Copyright by
designer/architect

To order plans, visit the Menards Building Materials Desk or visit www.Menards.com.

NOTTINGHAM HILL

Plan #M06-007D-0215

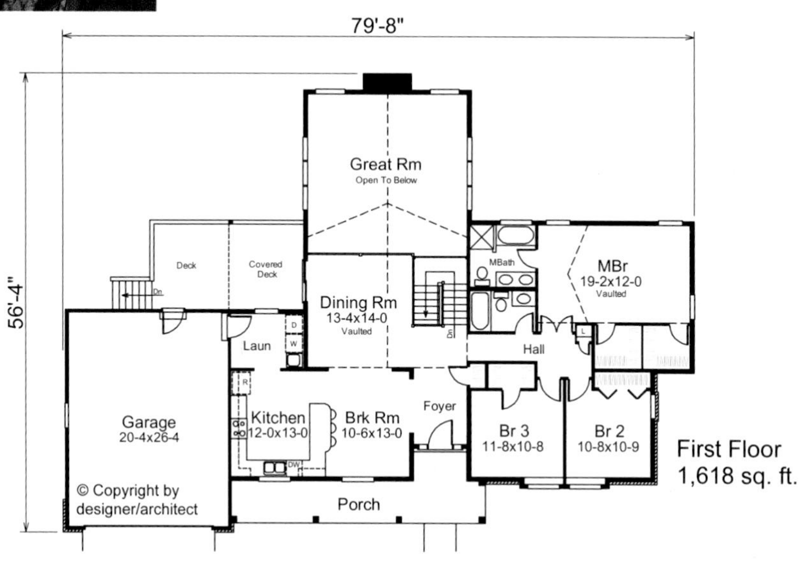

79'-8"
56'-4"
Great Rm
Open To Below
Deck
Covered Deck
Dn
MBath
MBr
19-2x12-0
Vaulted
Dining Rm
13-4x14-0
Vaulted
Laun
D
W
Hall
Kitchen
12-0x13-0
Brk Rm
10-6x13-0
Foyer
Garage
20-4x26-4
Br 3
11-8x10-8
Br 2
10-8x10-9
© Copyright by
designer/architect
Porch

First Floor
1,618 sq. ft.

Patio
Great Rm
20-0x19-10
Vaulted
Opt. WIC
Opt. Br 4/ Theater
18-10x17-4
Game Area
13-0x13-8
Kit/
Bar
8-11x
10-4
Hall
Basement
Up

Lower Level
923 sq. ft.

To order plans, visit the Menards Building Materials Desk
or visit www.Menards.com.

CLASSIC TUDOR HOME

2,541 total square feet of living area

3 bedrooms, 3 baths

2-car garage

Walk-out basement foundation

SPECIAL FEATURES

The sophisticated exterior is complimented by traditional Old English details including stucco, stone, wood trim and decorative lightning rods atop multiple gables

The porch leads to the foyer and into large vaulted living areas with a handcrafted staircase and upper dining overlook

The lower level great room features a two-story vaulted ceiling, stone fireplace, game room, its own kitchen and bar, 9' wide glass doors to patio and lots of windows

PRICE CODE C

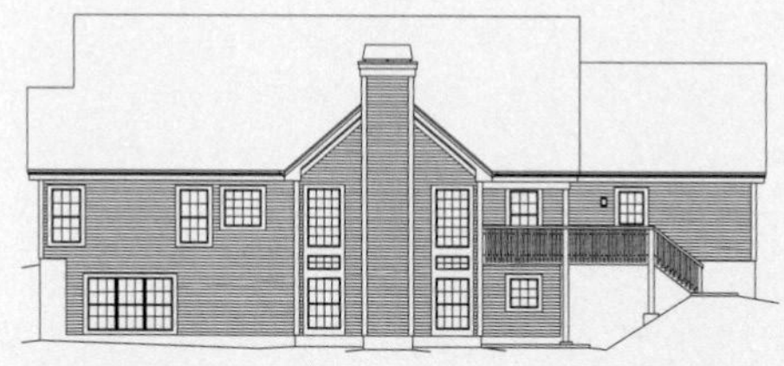

Rear View

SOUTHFIELD

MENARDS

Plan #M06-058D-0021

GRACIOUSLY DESIGNED TRADITIONAL RANCH

1,477 total square feet of living area

3 bedrooms, 2 baths

2-car side entry garage

Basement foundation

SPECIAL FEATURES

Oversized porch provides protection from the elements

Innovative kitchen employs step-saving design

The kitchen has a snack bar that opens to the breakfast area with bay window

2" x 6" exterior walls available, please order plan #M06-058D-0081

PRICE CODE A

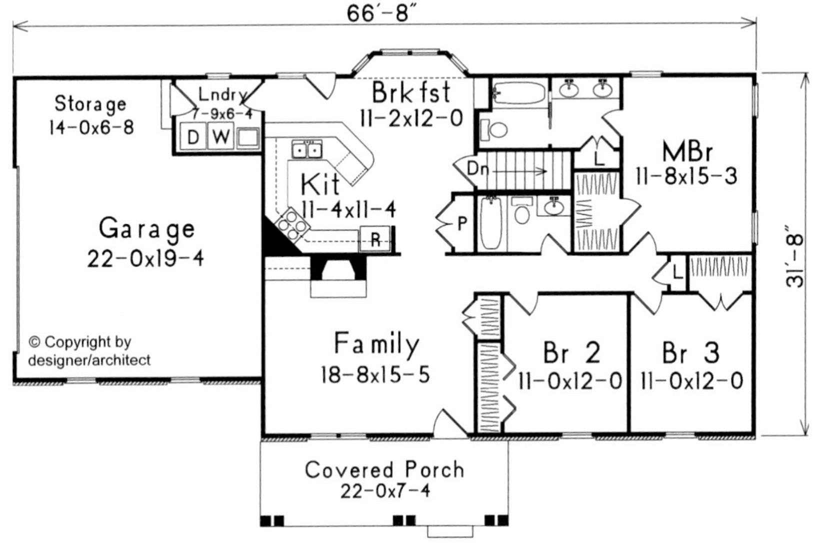

66'-8"
Storage
14-0x6-8
Lndry
7-9x6-4
D W
Brkfst
11-2x12-0
Kit
11-4x11-4
R
Dn
P
L
MBr
11-8x15-3
Garage
22-0x19-4
© Copyright by designer/architect
Family
18-8x15-5
Br 2
11-0x12-0
Br 3
11-0x12-0
L
Covered Porch
22-0x7-4
31'-8"

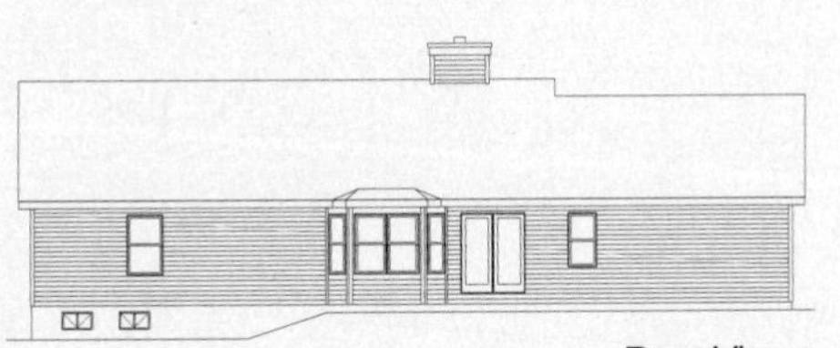

Rear View

To order plans, visit the Menards Building Materials Desk or visit www.Menards.com.

MENARDS
ROWLAND PLACE
Plan #M06-024L-0051
Porch
22'11"x 10'5"
Master
Bedroom
15'x 19'6"
Master
Bath
Walk-In
Closet
Breakfast
13'6"x 12'6"
Living
20'11"x 17'
Bath
Bedroom
12'8"x 11'2"
Hall
Kitchen
11'x 14'
Dining
13'x 13'
Foyer
Bedroom
12'6"x 11'6"
Bedroom
12'8"x 11'
Utility
Porch
Width: 62'-10"
Depth: 75'-3"
Two-Car
Garage
21'2"x 21'8"
© Copyright by
designer/architect

INVITING FAMILY HOME

2,471 total square feet of living area

4 bedrooms, 2 1/2 baths

2-car side entry garage

Slab foundation

SPECIAL FEATURES

Decorative columns define the formal dining room

The spacious living room enjoys a warm fireplace and porch access

The kitchen and breakfast area combine and maintain openness with the living room

The right side of the home is for relaxing with all the bedrooms situated together

PRICE CODE E

To order plans, visit the Menards Building Materials Desk
or visit www.Menards.com.

QUAILCREEK

MENARDS®

Plan #M06-068D-0009

INVITING GABLED ENTRY

2,128 total square feet of living area

4 bedrooms, 2 baths

2-car garage

Slab foundation, drawings also include crawl space foundation

SPECIAL FEATURES

Versatile kitchen has plenty of space for entertaining with a large dining area and counter seating

Luxurious master bedroom has a double-door entry and private bath with whirlpool tub, double sinks and large walk-in closet

Secondary bedrooms include spacious closets

Coat closet in front entry is a nice added feature

PRICE CODE C

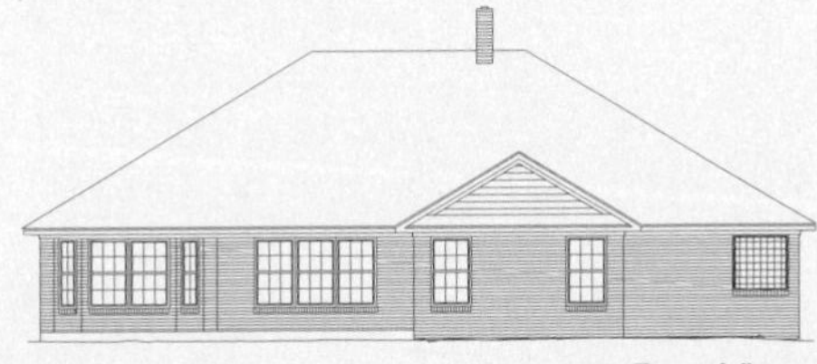

Rear View

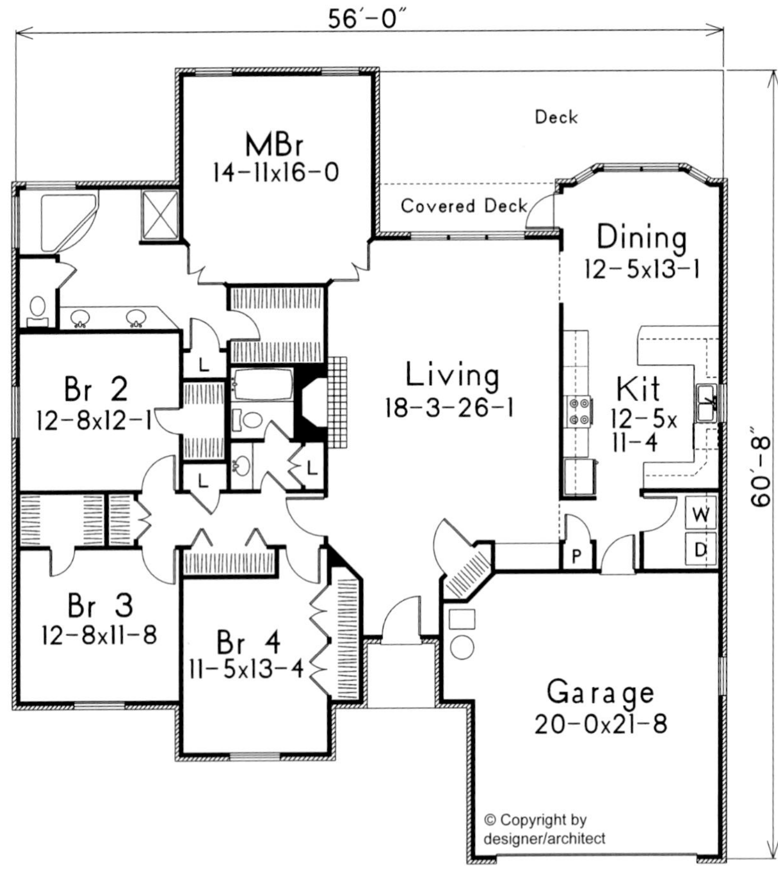
56′-0″
60′-8″
Deck
MBr
14-11x16-0
Covered Deck
Dining
12-5x13-1
Br 2
12-8x12-1
Living
18-3-26-1
Kit
12-5x
11-4
L
L
L
W
D
P
Br 3
12-8x11-8
Br 4
11-5x13-4
Garage
20-0x21-8
© Copyright by
designer/architect

To order plans, visit the Menards Building Materials Desk or visit www.Menards.com.

MENARDS®

KENORA PARK

Plan #M06-055L-0214

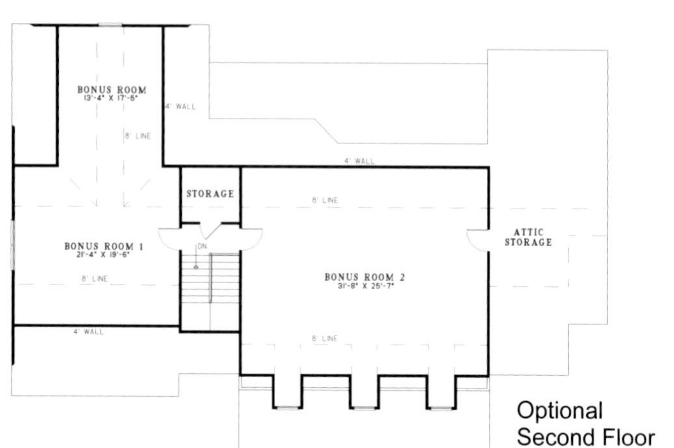
BONUS ROOM
13'-4" X 17'-5"
STORAGE
BONUS ROOM 1
21'-4" X 19'-6"
BONUS ROOM 2
31'-8" X 25'-7"
ATTIC STORAGE

Optional
Second Floor

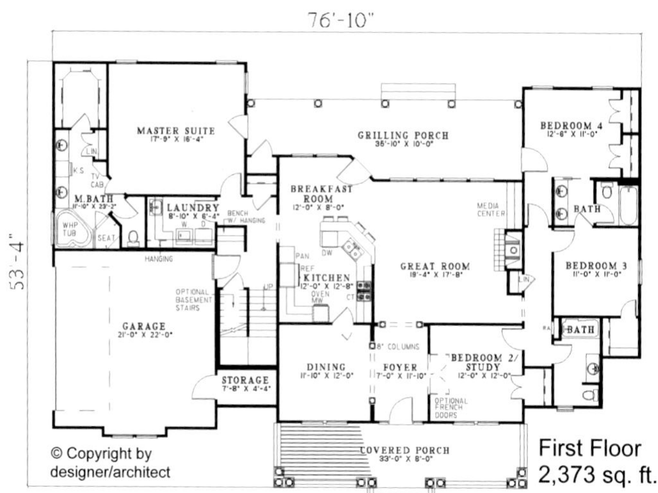
76'-10"
53'-4"
MASTER SUITE
17'-9" X 16'-4"
GRILLING PORCH
36'-10" X 10'-0"
BEDROOM 4
12'-6" X 11'-0"
M.BATH
LAUNDRY
BREAKFAST ROOM
12'-0" X 8'-0"
MEDIA CENTER
BATH
GREAT ROOM
19'-4" X 17'-8"
KITCHEN
12'-0" X 12'-8"
BEDROOM 3
11'-0" X 11'-0"
GARAGE
21'-0" X 22'-0"
OPTIONAL BASEMENT STAIRS
BATH
DINING
11'-10" X 12'-0"
FOYER
BEDROOM 2/ STUDY
12'-0" X 12'-0"
STORAGE
7'-8" X 4'-4"
COVERED PORCH
33'-0" X 8'-0"

First Floor
2,373 sq. ft.

To order plans, visit the Menards Building Materials Desk
or visit www.Menards.com.

PORCH AND DORMERS DECORATE EXTERIOR

2,373 total square feet of living area

4 bedrooms, 3 baths

2-car side entry garage

Slab or crawl space foundation, please specify when ordering

SPECIAL FEATURES

The grilling porch extends dining opportunities to the outdoors

The fireplace in the great room also warms the adjoining kitchen and breakfast room

The relaxing master suite enjoys a deluxe bath with whirlpool tub and walk-in closet

The optional second floor has an additional 1,672 square feet of living area

PRICE CODE E

WHITEFIELD

MENARDS

Plan #M06-008D-0006

UNIQUE SECTIONING FOR ENTERTAINING

1,593 total square feet of living area

3 bedrooms, 2 baths

2-car garage

Basement foundation, drawings also include crawl space and slab foundations

SPECIAL FEATURES

A welcoming porch invites you into a spacious living room

The kitchen and dining room are open to the family room through wood balustrades

The master bedroom offers a private bath and two closets

The laundry room is located directly off the garage with convenient access to the outdoors

PRICE CODE B

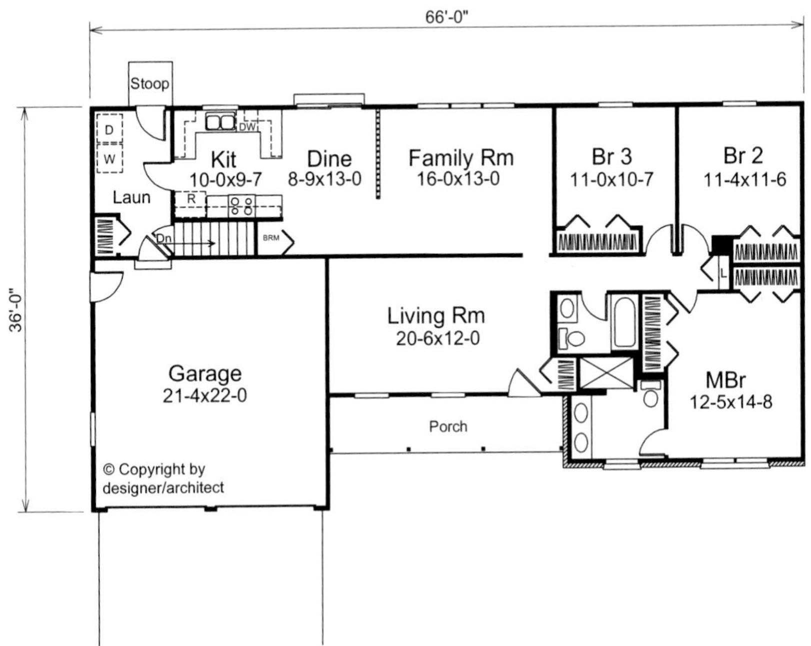

66'-0"
36'-0"
Stoop
D
W
Laun
DW
Kit
10-0x9-7
R
Dn
BRM
Dine
8-9x13-0
Family Rm
16-0x13-0
Br 3
11-0x10-7
Br 2
11-4x11-6
L
Living Rm
20-6x12-0
Garage
21-4x22-0
MBr
12-5x14-8
Porch
© Copyright by designer/architect

To order plans, visit the Menards Building Materials Desk or visit www.Menards.com.

MENARDS

ASHBRIAR

Plan #M06-007D-0077

CLASSIC ATRIUM RANCH

1,978 total square feet of living area

4 bedrooms, 2 1/2 baths

3-car side entry garage

Walk-out basement foundation

SPECIAL FEATURES

Classic traditional exterior is always in style

The spacious great room boasts a vaulted ceiling, dining area, atrium with elegant staircase and feature windows

The lower level has an additional 1,295 square feet of optional living area that consists of a family room, two bedrooms, two baths and a study

2" x 6" exterior walls available, please order plan #M06-007E-0077

PRICE CODE C

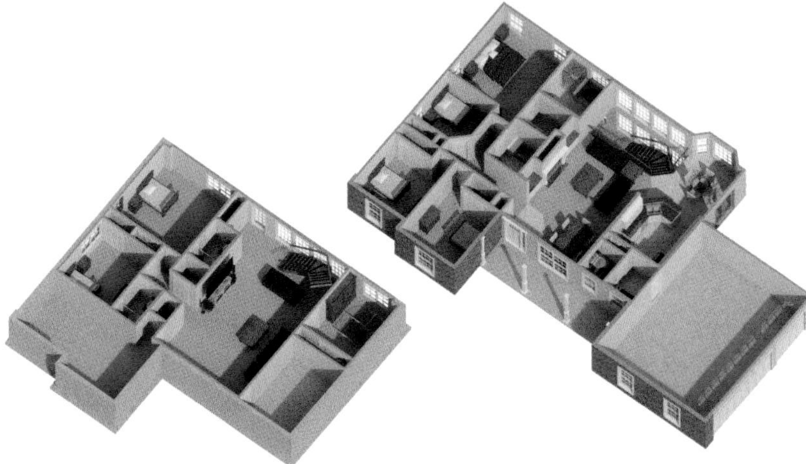

Opt Br 5 15-3x15-6
Atrium
Opt Study 10-9x13-2
Opt Family 18-4x30-6
Storage
Hall
Opt Br 6 11-5x12-7
Storage

Optional Lower Level

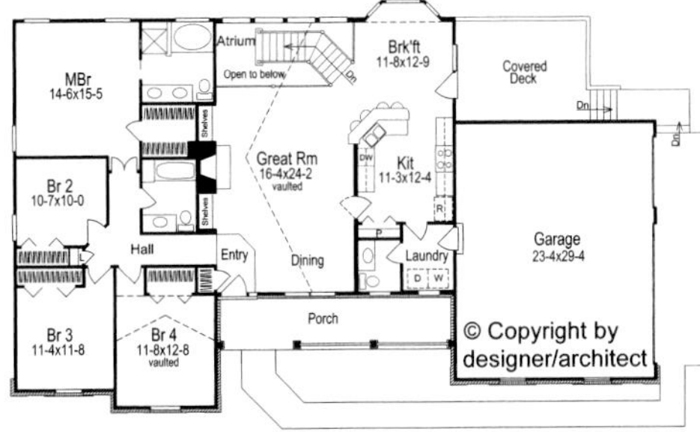
MBr 14-6x15-5
Atrium
Open to below
Brk'ft 11-8x12-9
Covered Deck
Great Rm 16-4x24-2 vaulted
Kit 11-3x12-4
Br 2 10-7x10-0
Hall
Entry
Dining
Laundry
Garage 23-4x29-4
Porch
Br 3 11-4x11-8
Br 4 11-8x12-8 vaulted
© Copyright by designer/architect

First Floor 1,978 sq. ft.

Width: 76'-8"
Depth: 47'-4"

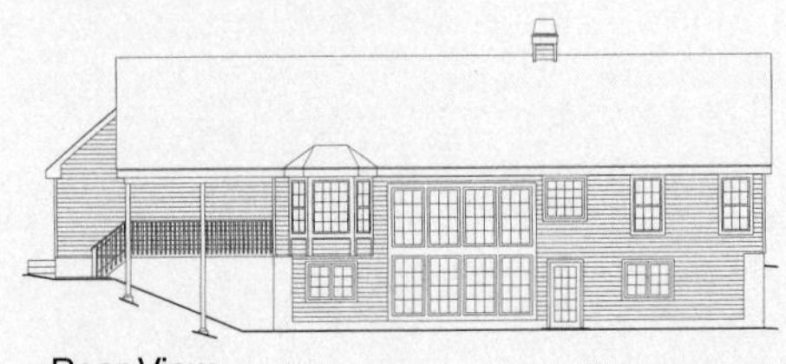

Rear View

To order plans, visit the Menards Building Materials Desk or visit www.Menards.com.

GRANTVILLE

MENARDS®

Plan #M06-058D-0062

PRIVATE BEDROOMS

1,902 total square feet of living area

3 bedrooms, 2 1/2 baths

3-car garage

Basement foundation

SPECIAL FEATURES

The wrap-around kitchen counter plus an island provides plenty of counterspace

The foyer opens into the expansive vaulted great room providing an impressive entrance

The laundry area conveniently includes a half bath and walk-in closet

PRICE CODE C

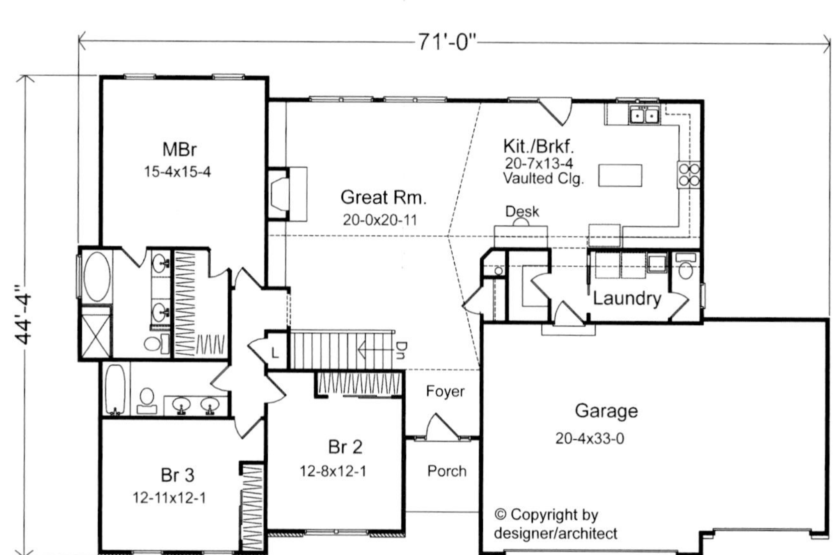
71'-0"
44'-4"
MBr
15-4x15-4
Great Rm.
20-0x20-11
Kit./Brkf.
20-7x13-4
Vaulted Clg.
Desk
Laundry
L
Dn
Foyer
Garage
20-4x33-0
Br 2
12-8x12-1
Br 3
12-11x12-1
Porch
© Copyright by
designer/architect

Rear View

To order plans, visit the Menards Building Materials Desk or visit www.Menards.com.

MENARDS®

SOUTHERN POINT

Plan #M06-024L-0590

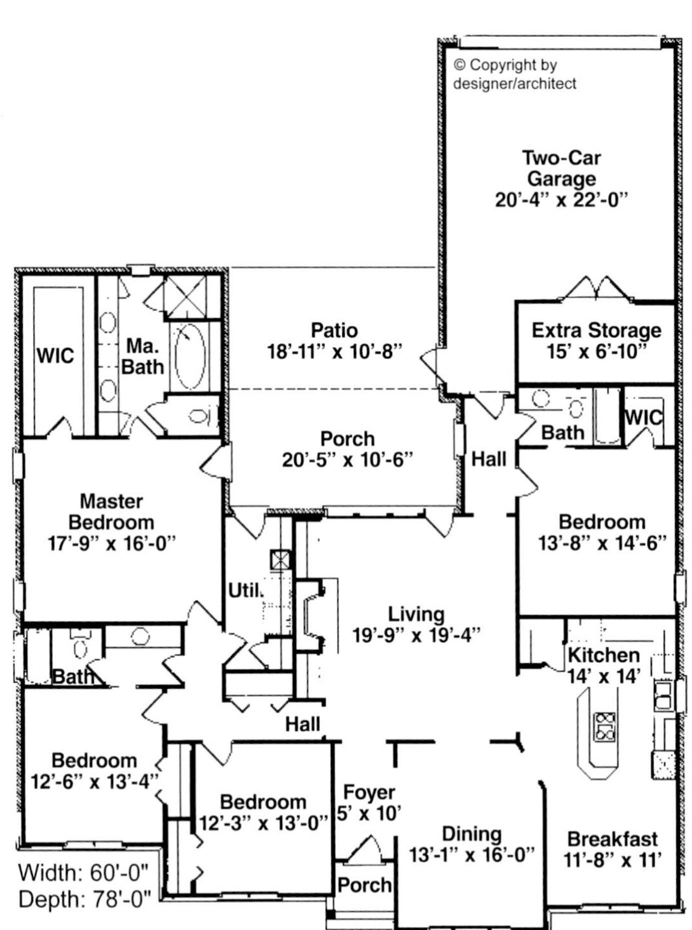
© Copyright by designer/architect
Two-Car Garage 20'-4" x 22'-0"
Extra Storage 15' x 6'-10"
Patio 18'-11" x 10'-8"
WIC
Ma. Bath
Porch 20'-5" x 10'-6"
Hall
Bath
WIC
Master Bedroom 17'-9" x 16'-0"
Bedroom 13'-8" x 14'-6"
Util.
Living 19'-9" x 19'-4"
Kitchen 14' x 14'
Bath
Hall
Bedroom 12'-6" x 13'-4"
Bedroom 12'-3" x 13'-0"
Foyer 5' x 10'
Dining 13'-1" x 16'-0"
Breakfast 11'-8" x 11'
Porch
Width: 60'-0"
Depth: 78'-0"

To order plans, visit the Menards Building Materials Desk or visit www.Menards.com.

STUCCO RANCH HOME HAS GREAT-LOOKING GABLES

2,637 total square feet of living area

4 bedrooms, 3 baths

2-car rear entry garage

Slab foundation

SPECIAL FEATURES

The foyer spills into the formal dining room that easily adjoins the casual kitchen, breakfast nook, and the expansive living room

A gourmet cooktop island with space for seating and a walk-in pantry create a kitchen any family chef will love

Homeowners will find it easy to relax in their master bedroom retreat featuring a walk-in closet, access to the rear porch, and a bath equipped with a whirlpool tub and double-bowl vanity

PRICE CODE E

JEREMY

MENARDS

Plan #M06-077L-0101

DORMERS AND PORCHES OFFER COUNTRY CHARM

2,250 total square feet of living area

4 bedrooms, 3 baths

2-car side entry garage

Slab, crawl space or basement foundation, please specify when ordering

SPECIAL FEATURES

The kitchen easily serves the casual bayed breakfast room or the formal dining room

The master bedroom enjoys a luxurious bath, two walk-in closets, porch access and a nearby office/nursery

A large laundry room complete with a sink and counterspace adds simplicity to the household chore

The unfinished bonus room has an additional 310 square feet of living area

PRICE CODE E

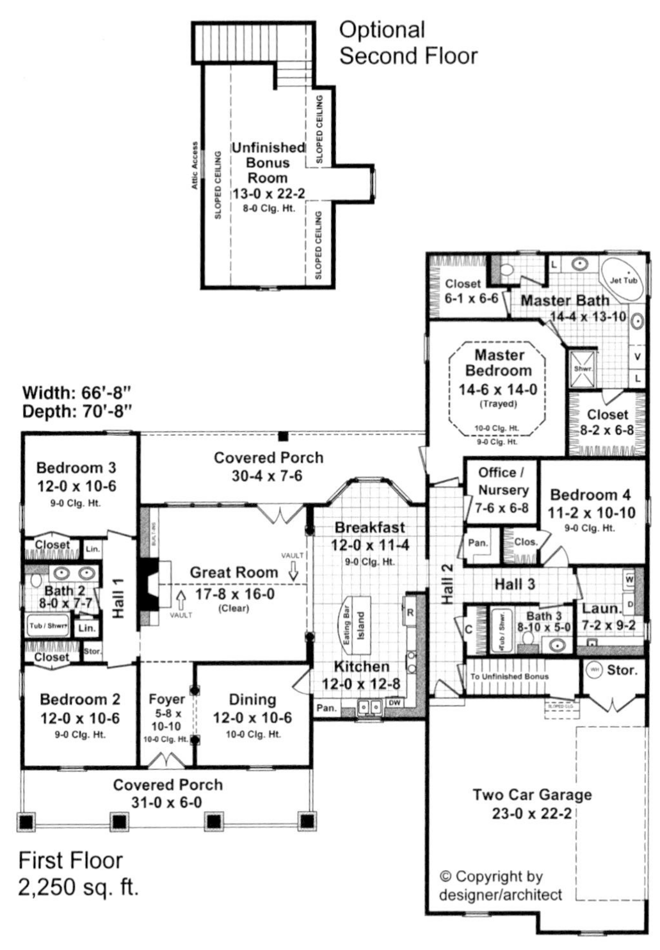

Optional Second Floor
Unfinished Bonus Room 13-0 x 22-2
8-0 Clg. Ht.
SLOPED CEILING
Attic Access
Width: 66'-8"
Depth: 70'-8"
Closet 6-1 x 6-6
Master Bath 14-4 x 13-10
Jet Tub
Master Bedroom 14-6 x 14-0
(Trayed)
Closet 8-2 x 6-8
Bedroom 3 12-0 x 10-6
9-0 Clg. Ht.
Covered Porch 30-4 x 7-6
Office / Nursery 7-6 x 6-8
Bedroom 4 11-2 x 10-10
9-0 Clg. Ht.
Breakfast 12-0 x 11-4
9-0 Clg. Ht.
Closet
Lin.
Great Room 17-8 x 16-0
(Clear)
VAULT
Pan.
Clos.
Bath 2 8-0 x 7-7
Hall 1
Hall 2
Hall 3
Eating Bar
Island
Bath 3 8-10 x 5-0
Laun. 7-2 x 9-2
Tub / Shwr.
Lin.
Closet
Stor.
Kitchen 12-0 x 12-8
Stor.
To Unfinished Bonus
Bedroom 2 12-0 x 10-6
9-0 Clg. Ht.
Foyer 5-8 x 10-10
10-0 Clg. Ht.
Dining 12-0 x 10-6
10-0 Clg. Ht.
Pan.
DW
Covered Porch 31-0 x 6-0
Two Car Garage 23-0 x 22-2
First Floor
2,250 sq. ft.
© Copyright by designer/architect

To order plans, visit the Menards Building Materials Desk or visit www.Menards.com.

MENARDS

EDISON MANOR

Plan #M06-055L-0029

LUXURIOUS ARCH WINDOWS

2,525 total square feet of living area

3 bedrooms, 2 1/2 baths

2-car side entry garage

Basement foundation

SPECIAL FEATURES

A glorious sun room off the great room has French doors leading to the optional grilling porch

The enormous laundry room includes a sink and loads of counterspace to make chores much easier

The formal living/study as well as the dining room are accented with decorative columns

PRICE CODE D

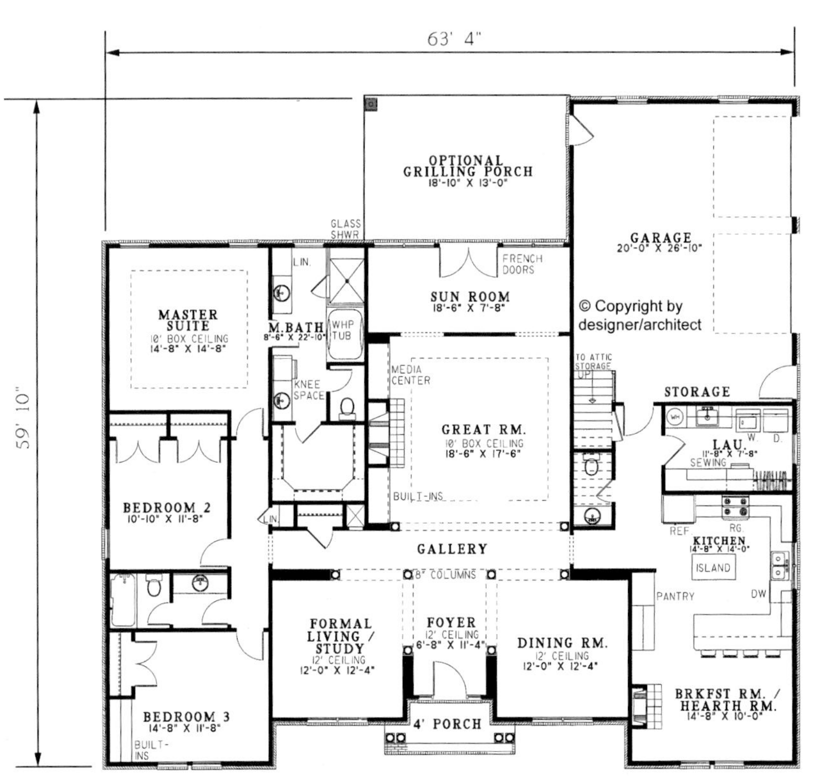

63' 4"
59' 10"
OPTIONAL GRILLING PORCH 18'-10" X 13'-0"
GLASS SHWR
GARAGE 20'-0" X 26'-10"
© Copyright by designer/architect
FRENCH DOORS
SUN ROOM 18'-6" X 7'-8"
MASTER SUITE 10' BOX CEILING 14'-8" X 14'-8"
M.BATH 8'-6" X 22'-10"
LIN
WHP TUB
KNEE SPACE
MEDIA CENTER
GREAT RM. 10' BOX CEILING 18'-6" X 17'-6"
TO ATTIC STORAGE UP
STORAGE
LAU. 11'-8" X 7'-8"
SEWING
W
D
BEDROOM 2 10'-10" X 11'-8"
BUILT-INS
LIN
GALLERY
8" COLUMNS
REF
RG
KITCHEN 14'-8" X 14'-0"
ISLAND
PANTRY
DW
FORMAL LIVING / STUDY 12' CEILING 12'-0" X 12'-4"
FOYER 12' CEILING 6'-8" X 11'-4"
DINING RM. 12' CEILING 12'-0" X 12'-4"
BRKFST RM. / HEARTH RM. 14'-8" X 10'-0"
BEDROOM 3 14'-8" X 11'-8"
BUILT-INS
4' PORCH

To order plans, visit the Menards Building Materials Desk or visit www.Menards.com.

FREEMONT

MENARDS®

Plan #M06-023D-0012

FULLY COLUMNED FRONT ENTRANCE

2,365 total square feet of living area

4 bedrooms, 2 baths

2-car carport

Slab foundation

SPECIAL FEATURES

9' ceilings throughout the home add a spacious feel

The expansive central living room is complemented by a corner fireplace

The breakfast bay overlooks the rear covered porch

The master bedroom features a bath with two walk-in closets, a separate tub and shower as well as a handy linen closet

The peninsula keeps the kitchen private

PRICE CODE D

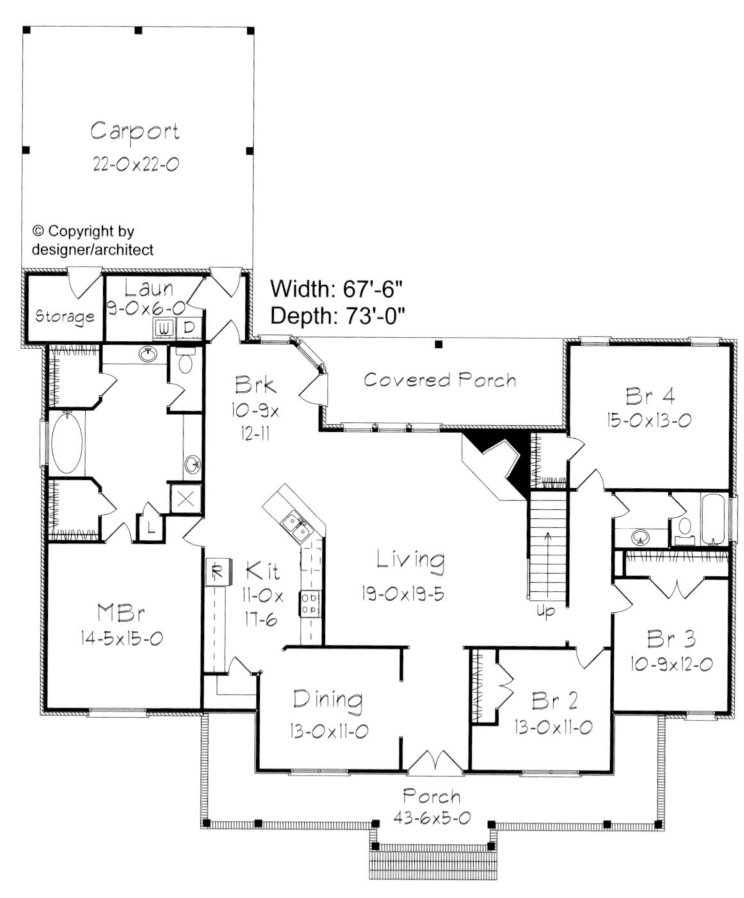

Carport
22-0x22-0
© Copyright by
designer/architect
Storage
Laun
9-0x6-0
W
D
Width: 67'-6"
Depth: 73'-0"
Brk
10-9x
12-11
Covered Porch
Br 4
15-0x13-0
Kit
11-0x
17-6
Living
19-0x19-5
Up
MBr
14-5x15-0
Br 3
10-9x12-0
Dining
13-0x11-0
Br 2
13-0x11-0
Porch
43-6x5-0

To order plans, visit the Menards Building Materials Desk or visit www.Menards.com.

MENARDS
EXCELSIOR

Plan #M06-065L-0061

Dining
11' x 12'
Garage
20'8" x 21'
Great Room
16' x 16'
Master
Bedroom
8'-10" CEILING HGT @ CENTER
11'10" x 14'
WALK IN CLOSET
SLOPE
Kitchen
11' x 13'3"
CLOS.
Dressing
© Copyright by
designer/architect
Foyer
CLOSET
CLOSET
DN 13 R.
Laun.
Bath
LIN.
Bedroom
10'9" x 11'
Porch
Bedroom
10'6" x 10'6"
SLP
SLP
44'10"
66'4"

STEP-SAVING CONVENIENCE

1,498 total square feet of living area

3 bedrooms, 2 baths

2-car garage

Basement, crawl space or slab foundation, please specify when ordering

SPECIAL FEATURES

The great room with fireplace and sloped ceiling is visible from the foyer, dining room and kitchen creating a large, open gathering area

The master bedroom enjoys a luxurious bath, large walk-in closet and raised ceiling

A snack bar, walk-in pantry and nearby laundry room enhance the spacious kitchen

Two generously sized bedrooms share a full bath with convenient linen closet

PRICE CODE A

To order plans, visit the Menards Building Materials Desk
or visit www.Menards.com.

FOXRIDGE

MENARDS

Plan #M06-007D-0136

COUNTRY RANCH WITH DRAMATIC ATRIUM VIEWS

1,532 total square feet of living area

3 bedrooms, 2 baths

2-car garage

Walk-out basement foundation

SPECIAL FEATURES

Multiple gables and stonework deliver a warm and inviting exterior

The vaulted great room has a fireplace and spectacular views accomplished with a two-story atrium window wall

A covered rear deck is easily accessed from the breakfast room or garage

The optional lower level has an additional 740 square feet of living area

PRICE CODE B

Rear View

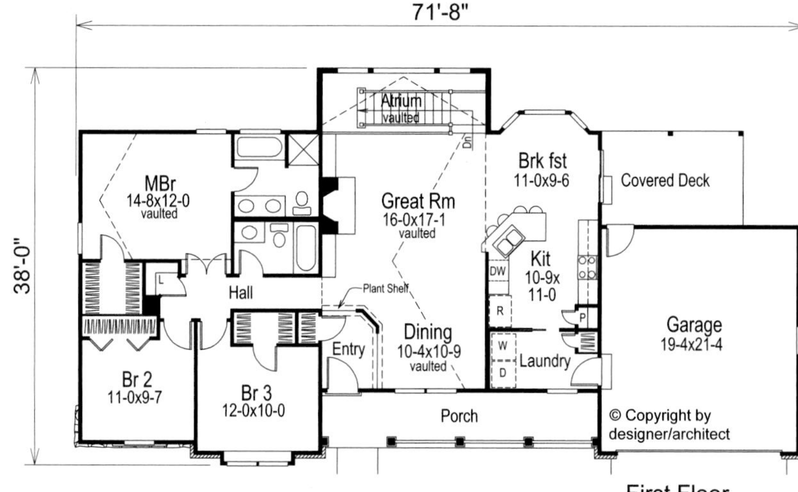
71'-8"
38'-0"
Atrium
vaulted
Dn
MBr
14-8x12-0
vaulted
Great Rm
16-0x17-1
vaulted
Brk fst
11-0x9-6
Covered Deck
Kit
10-9x
11-0
DW
R
P
Hall
L
Plant Shelf
Dining
10-4x10-9
vaulted
Entry
W
D
Laundry
Garage
19-4x21-4
Br 2
11-0x9-7
Br 3
12-0x10-0
Porch
© Copyright by
designer/architect

First Floor
1,532 sq. ft.

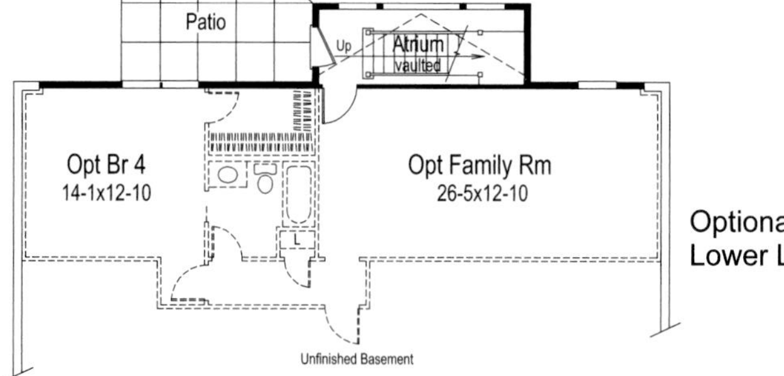
Patio
Up
Atrium
vaulted
Opt Br 4
14-1x12-10
Opt Family Rm
26-5x12-10
L
Unfinished Basement

Optional
Lower Level

To order plans, visit the Menards Building Materials Desk
or visit www.Menards.com.

MENARDS

EXCELSIOR PARK

Plan #M06-051L-0057

NK.
10'4" X 10'4"
DIN.
TRAY CEILING
11'4" X 12'6"
GRT.RM.
CATHEDRAL CEILING
18'6" X 19'0"
MBR.
CATHEDRAL CEILING
18'0" X 13'4"
KIT.
12'8" X 15'8"
E.
11'-1 1/8" CEILING
BR.2
11'2" X 12'8"
BR.3
12'8" X 12'4"
2 CAR GAR.
21'6" X 25'8"
56'0"
65'0"

AMENITY-FULL RANCH

2,229 total square feet of living area

3 bedrooms, 2 baths

2-car side entry garage

Basement foundation

SPECIAL FEATURES

Energy efficient home with 2" x 6" exterior walls

A welcoming and expansive front porch

The dining room has a tray ceiling

A sunny nook with arched soffit creates an inviting entry into this eating space

PRICE CODE D

To order plans, visit the Menards Building Materials Desk
or visit www.Menards.com.

AUBURN

MENARDS

Plan #M06-013L-0148

ENCHANTING SCREEN PORCH

1,800 total square feet of living area

3 bedrooms, 3 baths

2-car detached garage

Crawl space foundation

SPECIAL FEATURES

Entertaining is simple and easy in the roomy kitchen with an eating nook and serving bar

The dining, office or guest room is a flexible space that can adapt to fit your family's needs

Tucked away quietly in a corner of this home is a spacious master suite with a sitting area

The bonus room above the garage has an additional 373 square feet of living area

PRICE CODE C

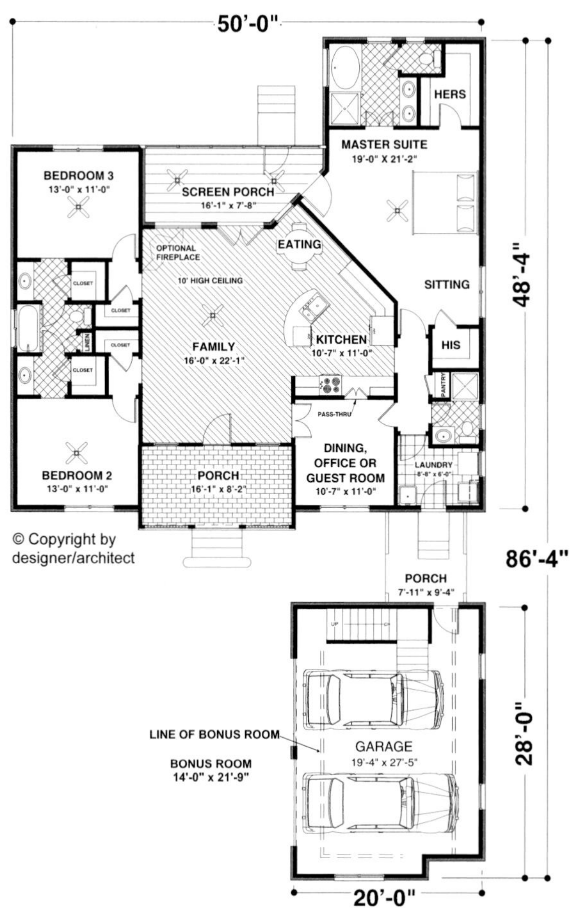

50'-0"
48'-4"
86'-4"
28'-0"
20'-0"
HERS
MASTER SUITE
19'-0" X 21'-2"
BEDROOM 3
13'-0" x 11'-0"
SCREEN PORCH
16'-1" x 7'-8"
EATING
OPTIONAL FIREPLACE
10' HIGH CEILING
SITTING
CLOSET
FAMILY
16'-0" x 22'-1"
KITCHEN
10'-7" x 11'-0"
HIS
PANTRY
PASS-THRU
DINING, OFFICE OR GUEST ROOM
10'-7" x 11'-0"
LAUNDRY
BEDROOM 2
13'-0" x 11'-0"
PORCH
16'-1" x 8'-2"
© Copyright by designer/architect
PORCH
7'-11" x 9'-4"
LINE OF BONUS ROOM
BONUS ROOM
14'-0" x 21'-9"
GARAGE
19'-4" x 27'-5"

To order plans, visit the Menards Building Materials Desk or visit www.Menards.com.

MENARDS®

ASHMONT PARK

Plan #M06-007D-0163

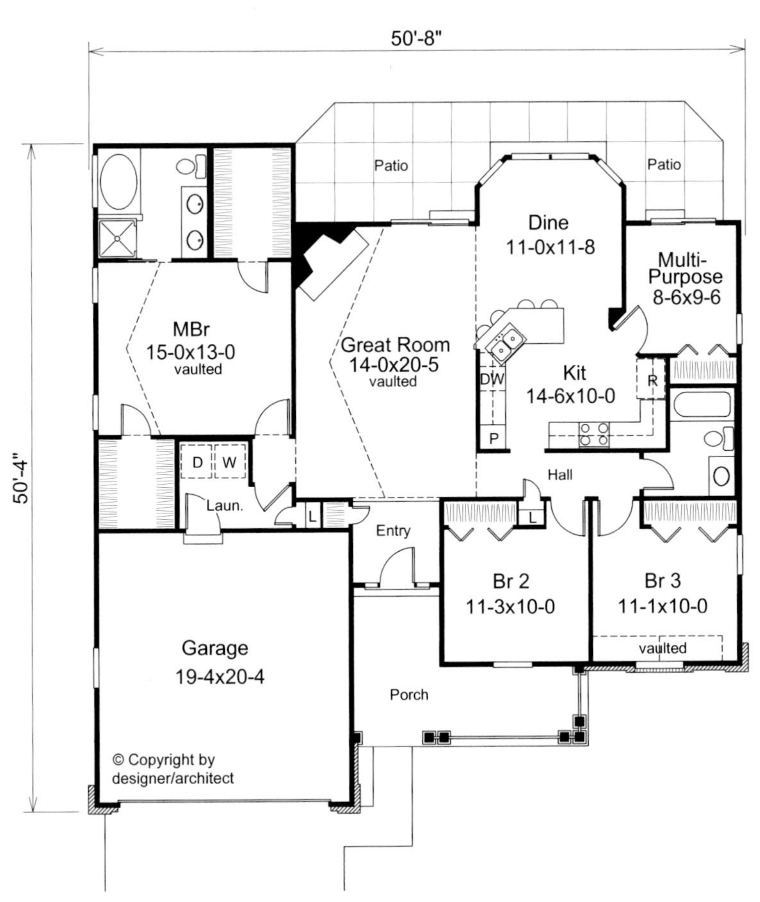

50'-8"
50'-4"
Patio
Patio
Dine
11-0x11-8
Multi-Purpose
8-6x9-6
MBr
15-0x13-0
vaulted
Great Room
14-0x20-5
vaulted
DW
Kit
14-6x10-0
R
P
Hall
D
W
Laun.
L
Entry
L
Br 2
11-3x10-0
Br 3
11-1x10-0
vaulted
Garage
19-4x20-4
Porch
© Copyright by designer/architect

To order plans, visit the Menards Building Materials Desk or visit www.Menards.com.

ELEGANCE WITH EFFICIENCY

1,580 total square feet of living area

3 bedrooms, 2 baths

2-car garage

Crawl space foundation, drawings also include slab and basement foundations

SPECIAL FEATURES

Home offers great looks with an oversized front porch

The large great room features a corner fireplace, vaulted ceiling, access to the patio and is open to the bayed dining area and kitchen breakfast bar

The spacious kitchen enjoys an adjoining multi-purpose room ideal for a study

The master bedroom has a vaulted ceiling, two walk-in closets and a plush bath

PRICE CODE B

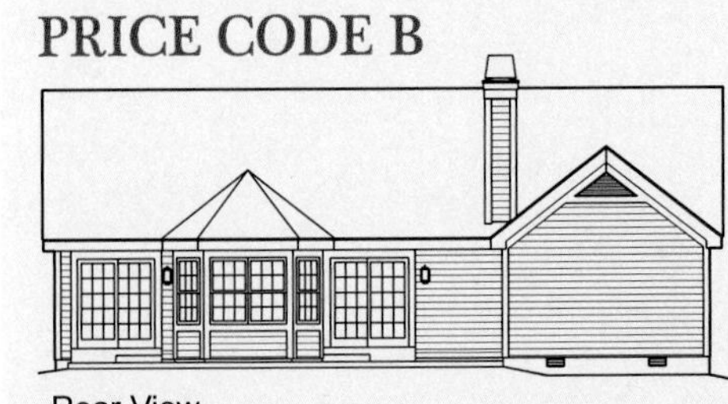

Rear View

SUMMERHOUSE

MENARDS®

Plan #M06-007D-0172

A PORCH LOVER'S DREAM HOME

1,646 total square feet of living area

2 bedrooms, 2 baths

2-car side entry garage

Basement foundation, drawings also include slab and crawl space foundations

SPECIAL FEATURES

The great room includes a corner fireplace and beautiful views provided by ten windows and doors

A U-shaped kitchen with snack counter is open to the breakfast room and enjoys access to both the side and rear porch

The master bedroom has a luxury bath with corner tub, double vanities with makeup counter and a huge walk-in closet

PRICE CODE B

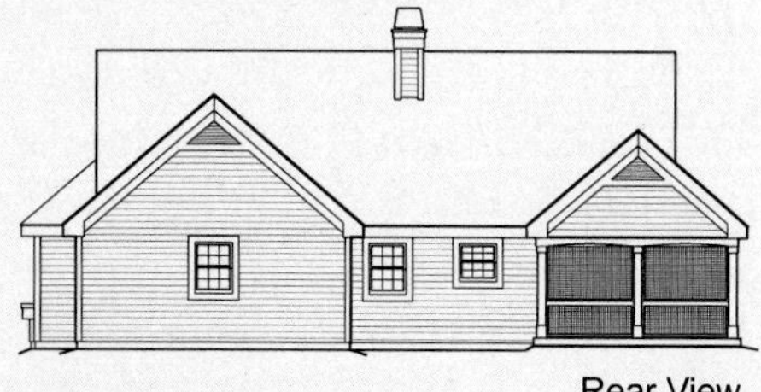

Rear View

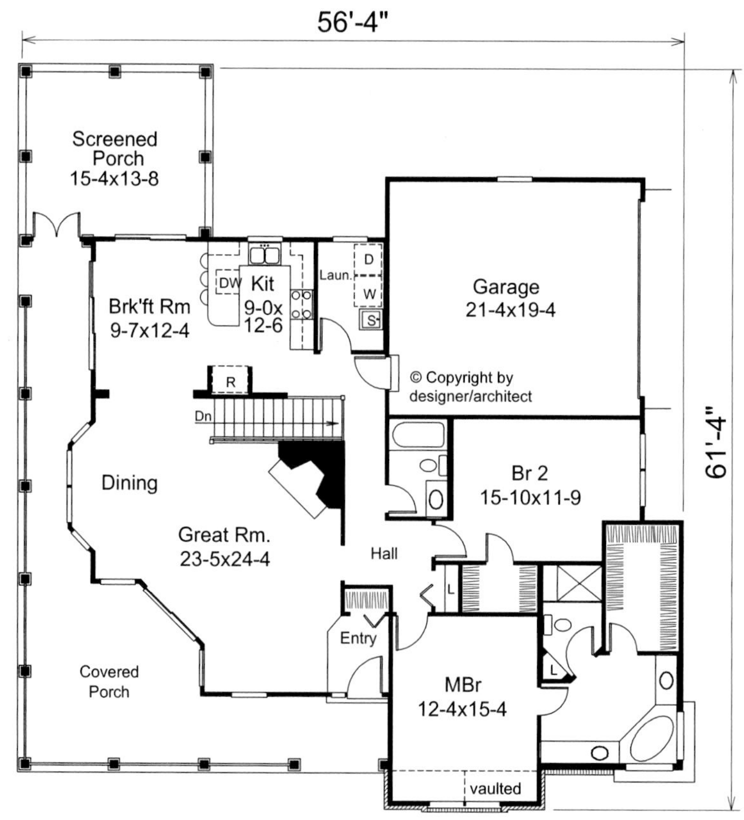

56'-4"
61'-4"
Screened Porch 15-4x13-8
Brk'ft Rm 9-7x12-4
DW
Kit 9-0x 12-6
Laun.
D
W
S
Garage 21-4x19-4
© Copyright by designer/architect
R
Dn
Dining
Great Rm. 23-5x24-4
Hall
Br 2 15-10x11-9
L
Entry
Covered Porch
MBr 12-4x15-4
vaulted

To order plans, visit the Menards Building Materials Desk or visit www.Menards.com.

MENARDS®

BUCHANAN

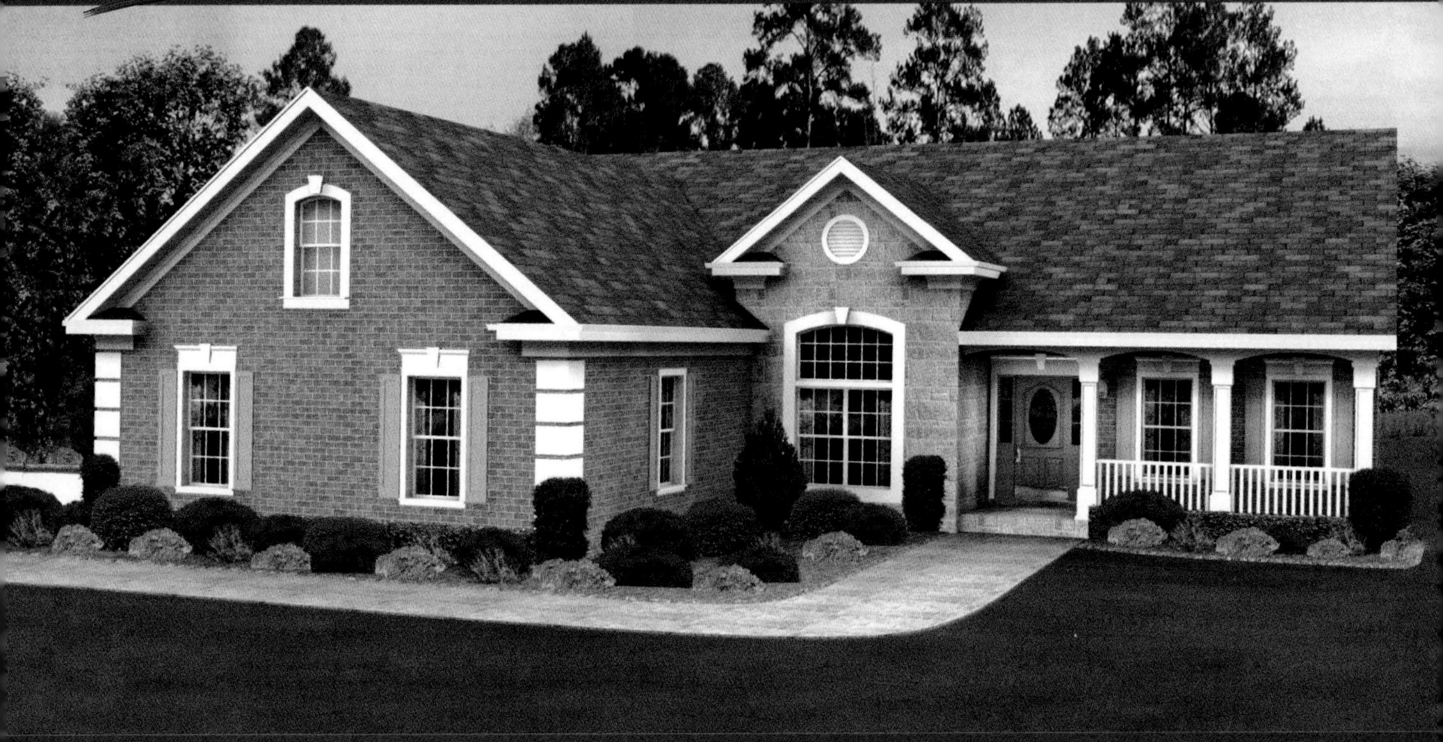

Plan #M06-013L-0160

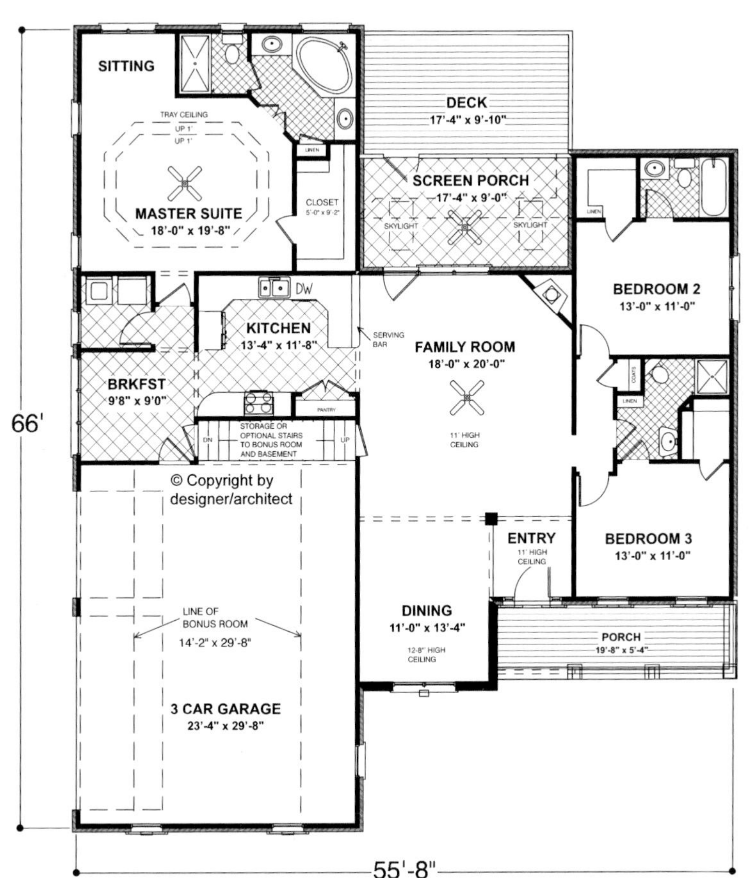

SITTING
DECK
17'-4" x 9'-10"
SCREEN PORCH
17'-4" x 9'-0"
SKYLIGHT
SKYLIGHT
TRAY CEILING
MASTER SUITE
18'-0" x 19'-8"
CLOSET
DW
KITCHEN
13'-4" x 11'-8"
SERVING BAR
FAMILY ROOM
18'-0" x 20'-0"
11' HIGH CEILING
BEDROOM 2
13'-0" x 11'-0"
BRKFST
9'8" x 9'0"
PANTRY
STORAGE OR OPTIONAL STAIRS TO BONUS ROOM AND BASEMENT
DN
UP
66'
© Copyright by designer/architect
ENTRY
11' HIGH CEILING
BEDROOM 3
13'-0" x 11'-0"
LINE OF BONUS ROOM
14'-2" x 29'-8"
DINING
11'-0" x 13'-4"
12'-8" HIGH CEILING
PORCH
19'-8" x 5'-4"
3 CAR GARAGE
23'-4" x 29'-8"
55'-8"

To order plans, visit the Menards Building Materials Desk or visit www.Menards.com.

STYLISH ONE-LEVEL LIVING

1,898 total square feet of living area

3 bedrooms, 3 baths

3-car side entry garage

Basement foundation

SPECIAL FEATURES

A large and open family room has a corner fireplace and screen porch access

A stunning corner whirlpool tub provides the ultimate escape in the master suite

A cozy and comforting breakfast area is perfect for intimate meals anytime of the day

Bonus room above the garage has an additional 474 square feet of living space

PRICE CODE B

HILLTOP

MENARDS®

Plan #M06-008D-0110

PALLADIAN WINDOWS DOMINATE FACADE

1,500 total square feet of living area

3 bedrooms, 2 baths

2-car garage

Basement foundation

SPECIAL FEATURES

The living room features a cathedral ceiling and opens to the breakfast room

The breakfast room has a spectacular bay window and adjoins a well-appointed kitchen with generous storage

The laundry room is convenient to the kitchen and includes a large closet

The large walk-in closet gives the master bedroom abundant storage

PRICE CODE B

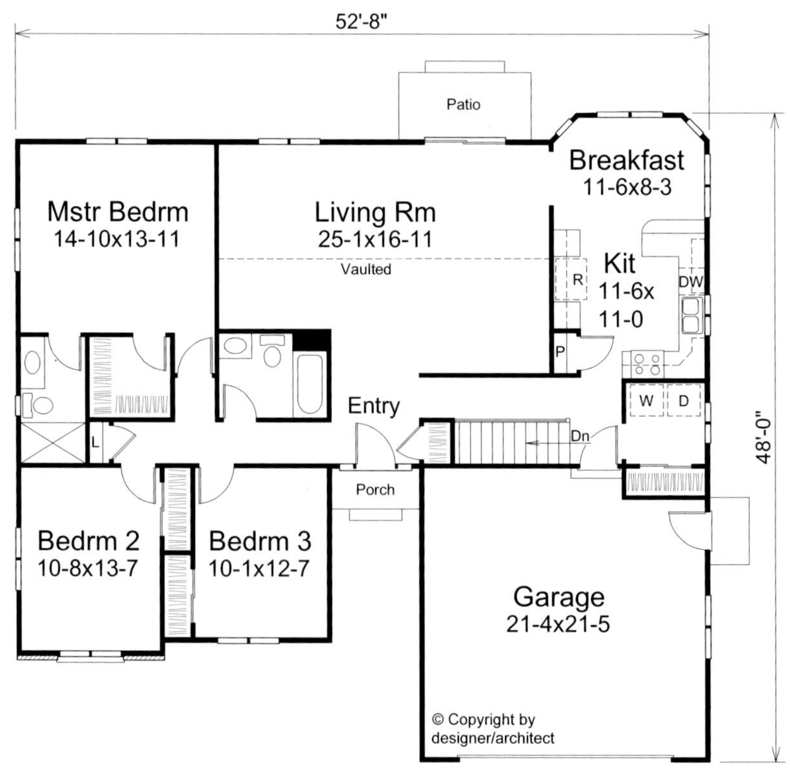

52'-8"
Patio
Breakfast
11-6x8-3
Mstr Bedrm
14-10x13-11
Living Rm
25-1x16-11
Vaulted
Kit
11-6x
11-0
R
DW
P
W
D
L
Entry
Dn
Porch
Bedrm 2
10-8x13-7
Bedrm 3
10-1x12-7
Garage
21-4x21-5
48'-0"
© Copyright by
designer/architect

To order plans, visit the Menards Building Materials Desk or visit www.Menards.com.

MENARDS®

OAKBURY

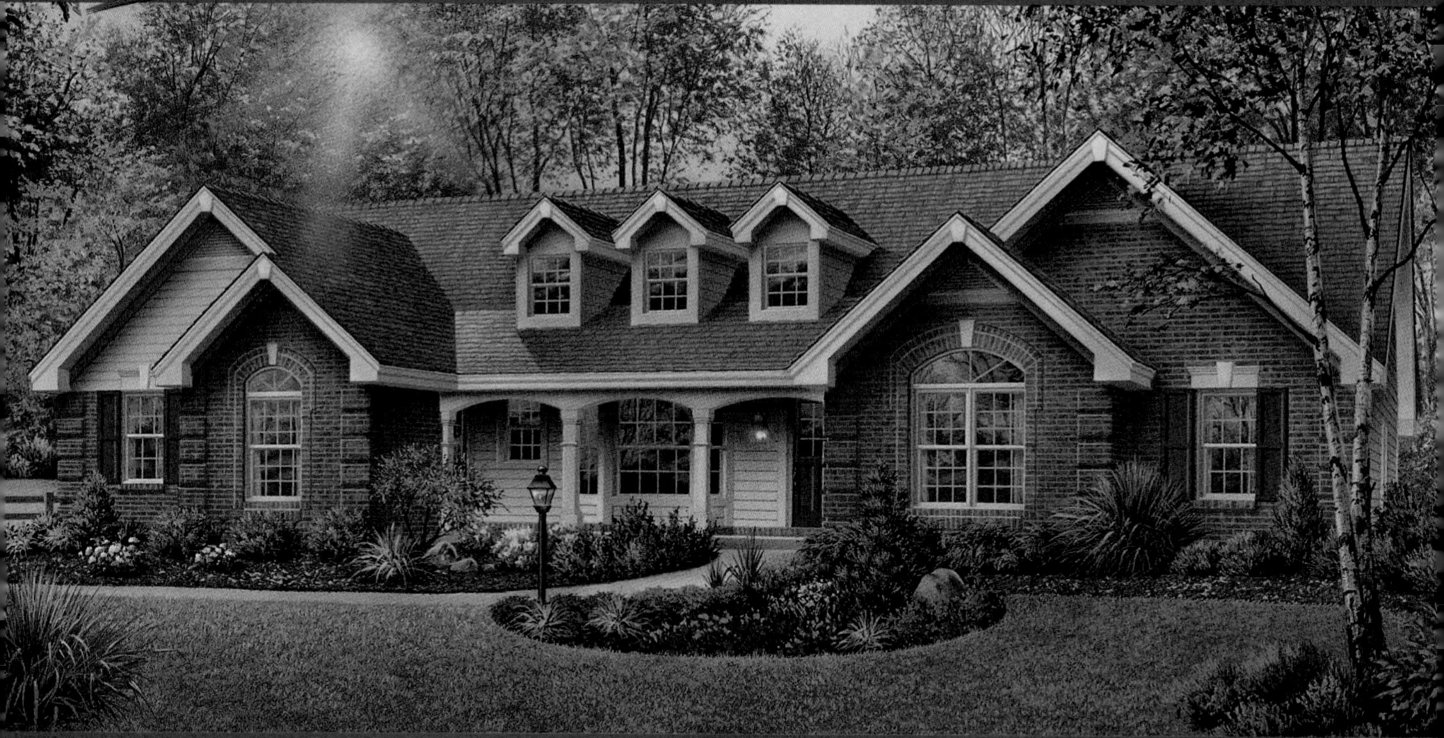

Plan #M06-007D-0146

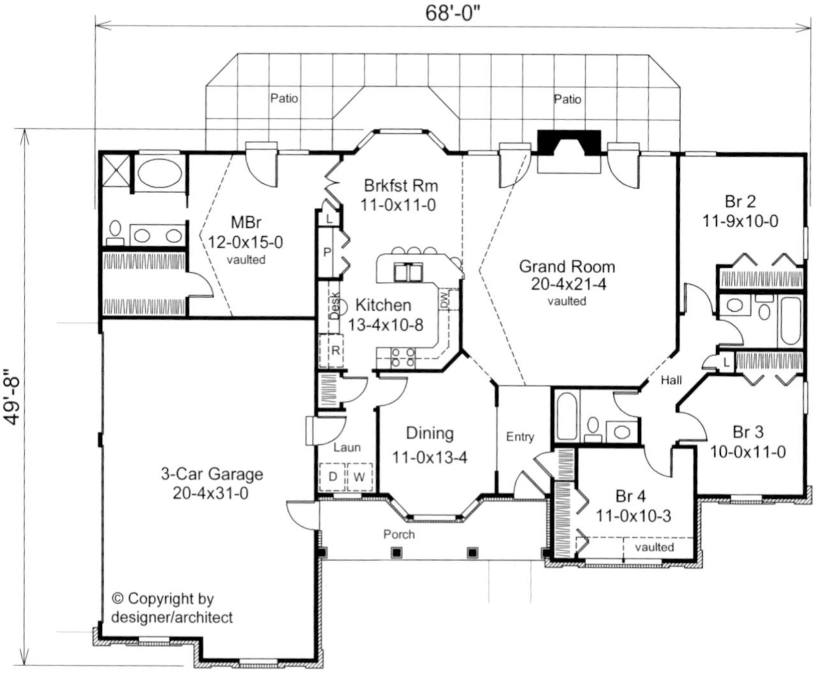

68'-0"

49'-8"

Patio

Patio

MBr
12-0x15-0
vaulted

Brkfst Rm
11-0x11-0

Grand Room
20-4x21-4
vaulted

Br 2
11-9x10-0

Kitchen
13-4x10-8

Hall

Br 3
10-0x11-0

Dining
11-0x13-4

Entry

Laun

3-Car Garage
20-4x31-0

Br 4
11-0x10-3

vaulted

Porch

To order plans, visit the Menards Building Materials Desk
or visit www.Menards.com.

THE PLAN THAT HAS IT ALL

1,929 total square feet of living area

4 bedrooms, 3 baths

3-car side entry garage

Crawl space foundation, drawings also include slab and basement foundations

SPECIAL FEATURES

More than a great room for this size home, the grand room features a vaulted ceiling and a brick and wood mantle fireplace flanked by doors to the rear patio

State-of-the-art U-shaped kitchen has a built-in pantry, computer desk, snack bar and breakfast room with bay window

The master bedroom includes a vaulted ceiling, large walk-in closet, luxury bath and access to the rear patio

PRICE CODE C

Rear View

ROSEDALE

MENARDS

Plan #M06-048D-0008

STATELY COVERED FRONT ENTRY

2,089 total square feet of living area

4 bedrooms, 3 baths

2-car garage

Slab foundation

SPECIAL FEATURES

The family room features a fireplace, built-in bookshelves and triple sliding glass doors opening to the covered patio

The kitchen overlooks the family room and features a pantry and desk

Separated from the three secondary bedrooms, the master bedroom becomes a quiet retreat with patio access

The master bedroom features an oversized bath with walk-in closet and corner tub

PRICE CODE C

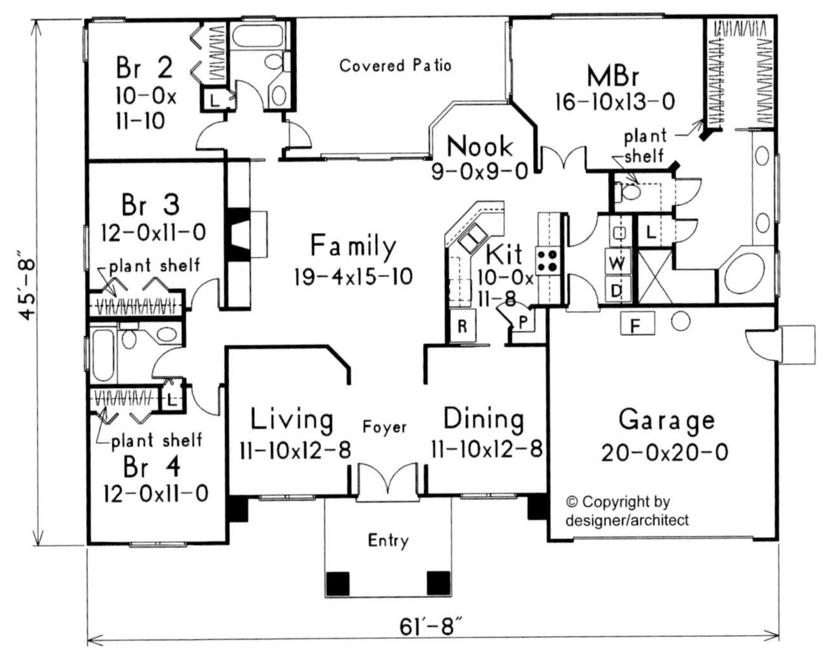
Br 2
10-0x
11-10
Covered Patio
MBr
16-10x13-0
Nook
9-0x9-0
plant shelf
Br 3
12-0x11-0
plant shelf
Family
19-4x15-10
Kit
10-0x
11-8
L
W
D
R
P
F
Living
11-10x12-8
Foyer
Dining
11-10x12-8
Garage
20-0x20-0
plant shelf
Br 4
12-0x11-0
© Copyright by
designer/architect
Entry
45′-8″
61′-8″

To order plans, visit the Menards Building Materials Desk or visit www.Menards.com.

MENARDS

WHITEHAVEN

Plan #M06-007D-0229

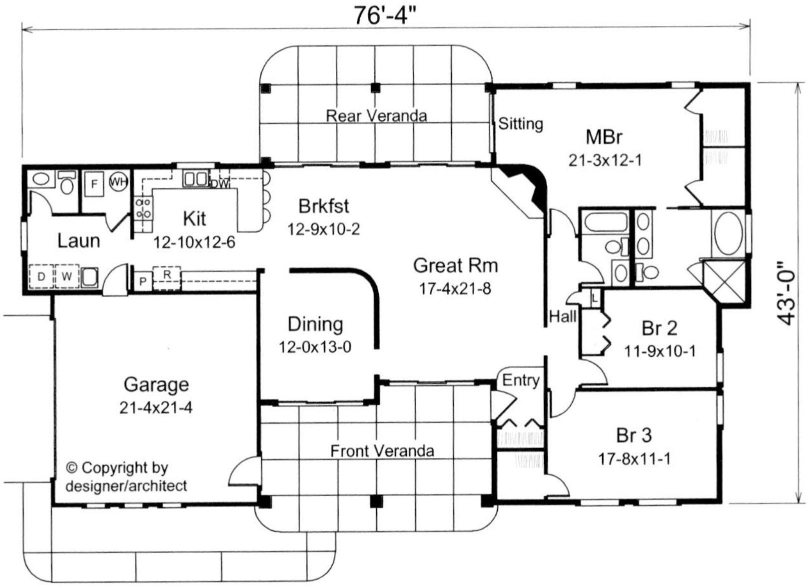

76'-4"

Rear Veranda
Sitting
MBr
21-3x12-1
Brkfst
12-9x10-2
Kit
12-10x12-6
Laun
Great Rm
17-4x21-8
Dining
12-0x13-0
Hall
Br 2
11-9x10-1
Entry
Garage
21-4x21-4
Br 3
17-8x11-1
Front Veranda
© Copyright by designer/architect

43'-0"

EXCITING DESIGN FOR VIEWS

2,014 total square feet of living area

3 bedrooms, 2 1/2 baths

2-car side entry garage

Slab foundation

SPECIAL FEATURES

The front veranda, with its 15' high volume ceiling receives abundant light from the dormer windows above

A curved wall around the dining, separate entry with closet and two 9' wide sliding glass doors are some of the awesome features of the spacious great room

The kitchen excels in cabinet storage and includes a useful snack bar

The master bedroom enjoys two walk-in closets and a luxury bath

PRICE CODE D

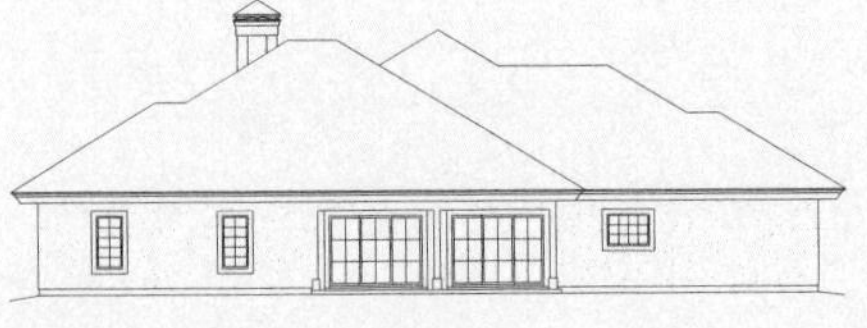

Rear View

To order plans, visit the Menards Building Materials Desk or visit www.Menards.com.

SPRINGATE

MENARDS®

Plan #M06-058D-0067

LUXURIOUS MASTER BEDROOM

1,587 total square feet of living area

3 bedrooms, 2 baths

2-car garage

Basement foundation

SPECIAL FEATURES

The spacious family room features a vaulted ceiling, a fireplace and a convenient coat closet

The kitchen/breakfast area is brightened by large windows and includes a centrally located pantry

The secondary bedrooms are generously sized and share a full bath

PRICE CODE B

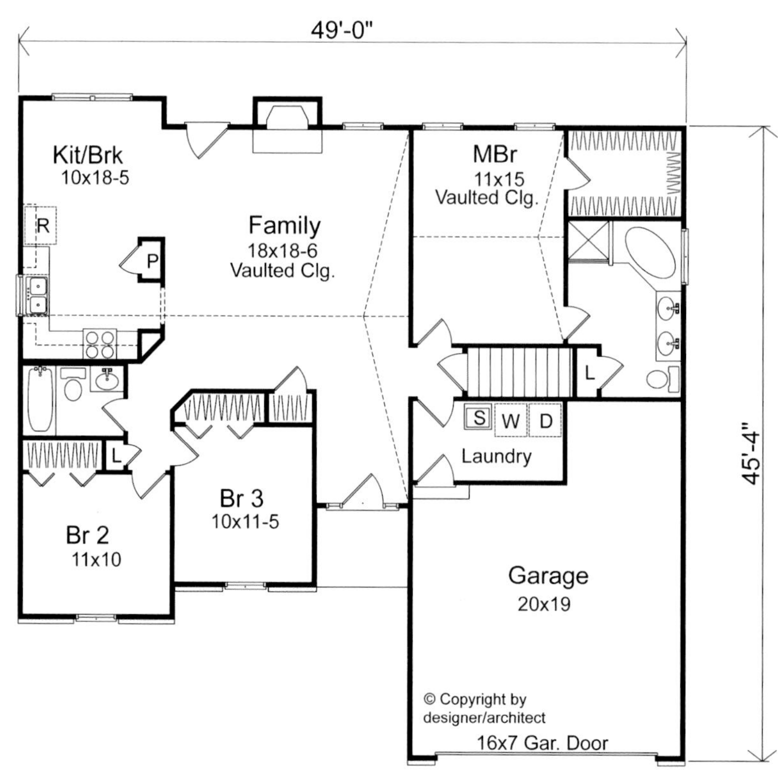
49'-0"
45'-4"
Kit/Brk
10x18-5
R
P
Family
18x18-6
Vaulted Clg.
MBr
11x15
Vaulted Clg.
L
S W D
Laundry
L
Br 3
10x11-5
Br 2
11x10
Garage
20x19
© Copyright by designer/architect
16x7 Gar. Door

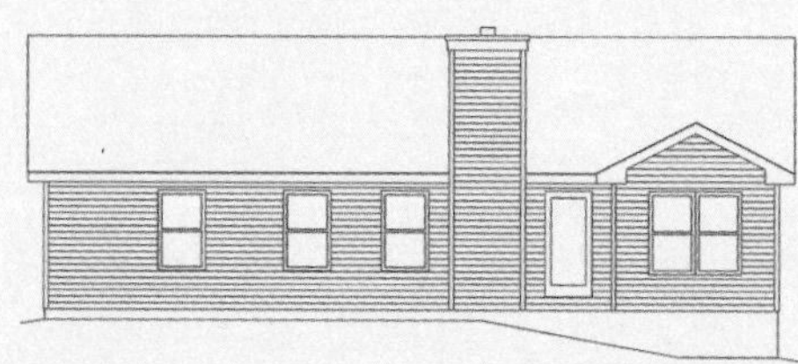

Rear View

To order plans, visit the Menards Building Materials Desk or visit www.Menards.com.

MENARDS®

KASINGTON

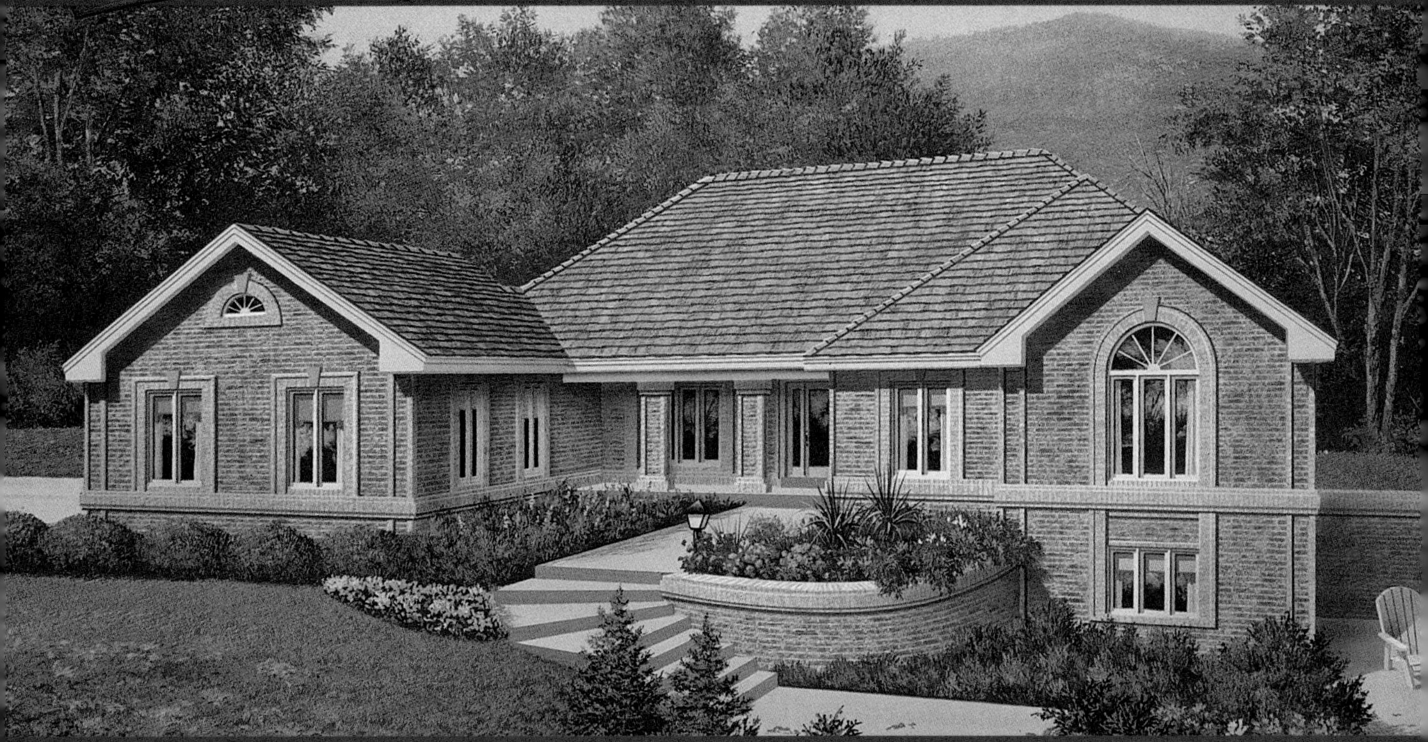

Plan #M06-007D-0080

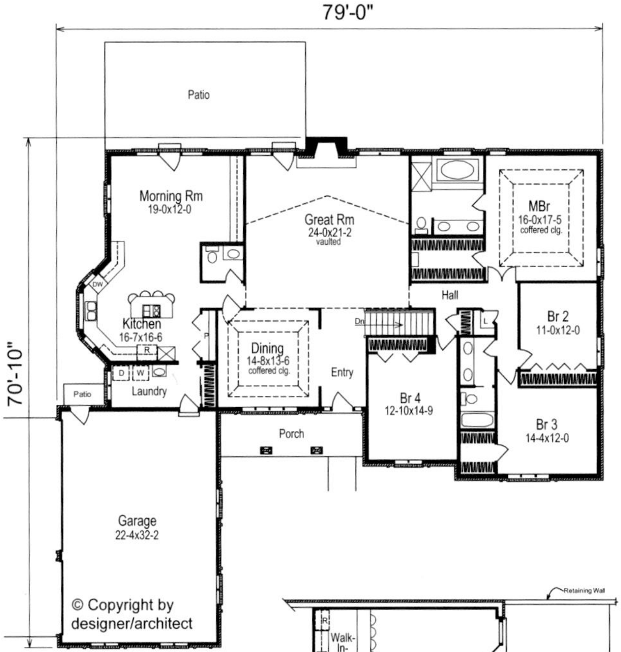

79'-0"

70'-10"

Patio

Morning Rm 19-0x12-0

Great Rm 24-0x21-2 vaulted

MBr 16-0x17-5 coffered clg.

Hall

Kitchen 16-7x16-6

Dining 14-8x13-6 coffered clg.

Entry

Br 2 11-0x12-0

Br 4 12-10x14-9

Br 3 14-4x12-0

Patio

Laundry

Porch

Garage 22-4x32-2

First Floor
2,900 sq. ft.

Retaining Wall

Walk-In-Bar

storage

Family Room 19-8x30-9

Patio

Unfinished Basement

Br 5 14-4x12-0

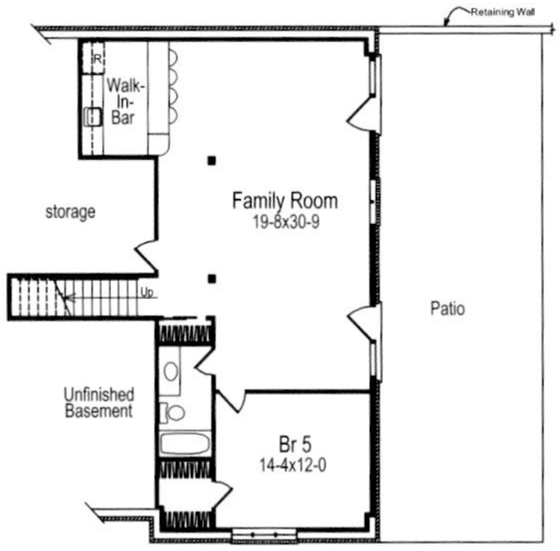

Optional
Lower Level

To order plans, visit the Menards Building Materials Desk or visit www.Menards.com.

CONTEMPORARY WRAPPED IN BRICK

2,900 total square feet of living area

4 bedrooms, 2 1/2 baths

3-car side entry garage

Walk-out basement foundation

SPECIAL FEATURES

Energy efficient home with 2" x 6" exterior walls

The grand-scale great room offers a vaulted ceiling and palladian windows flanking an 8' wide brick fireplace

The built-in-a-bay kitchen features a picture window above sink, 12' of cabinetry, huge pantry, cooktop island and is open to a large morning room

1,018 square feet of optional living area on the lower level with family room, walk-in bar and a fifth bedroom with a bath

PRICE CODE E

Rear View

RILEY

MENARDS

Plan #M06-121D-0021

COVERED COUNTRY FRONT PORCH

1,562 total square feet of living area

3 bedrooms, 2 baths

2-car garage

Basement foundation

SPECIAL FEATURES

The vaulted breakfast room sits in a sunny bay window with sliding glass doors that access the rear patio

A convenient eating bar in the kitchen is perfect for casual meals

The spacious great room boasts a vaulted ceiling and warming corner fireplace

PRICE CODE A

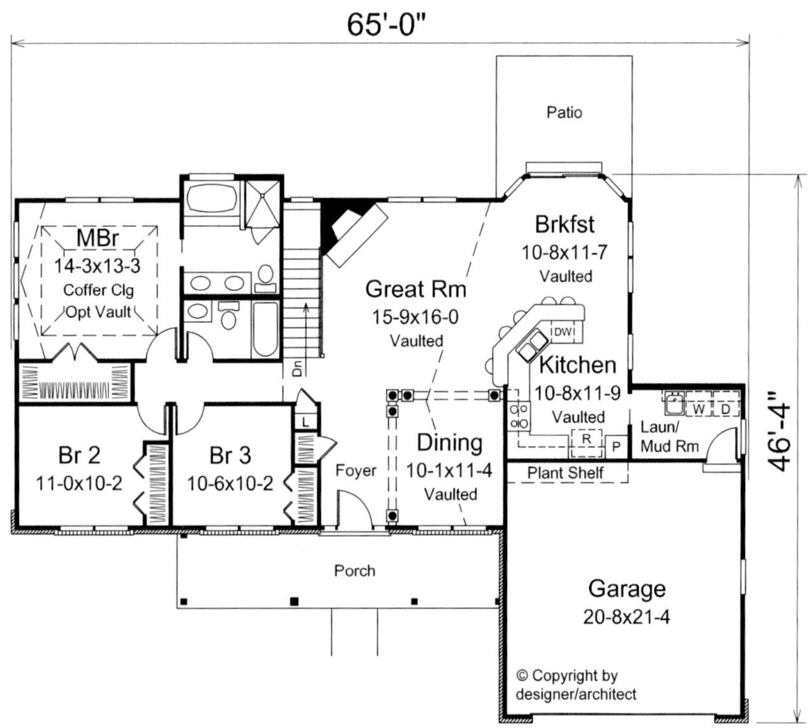

65'-0"
46'-4"
Patio
Brkfst
10-8x11-7
Vaulted
MBr
14-3x13-3
Coffer Clg
Opt Vault
Great Rm
15-9x16-0
Vaulted
Dn
DW
Kitchen
10-8x11-9
Vaulted
W
D
R
P
Laun/
Mud Rm
L
Br 2
11-0x10-2
Br 3
10-6x10-2
Foyer
Dining
10-1x11-4
Vaulted
Plant Shelf
Porch
Garage
20-8x21-4
© Copyright by
designer/architect

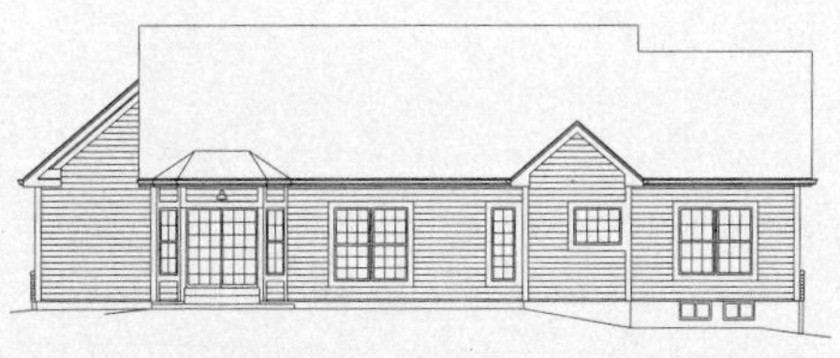

Rear View

To order plans, visit the Menards Building Materials Desk or visit www.Menards.com.

MENARDS

SANTA CLARA

Plan #M06-022D-0005

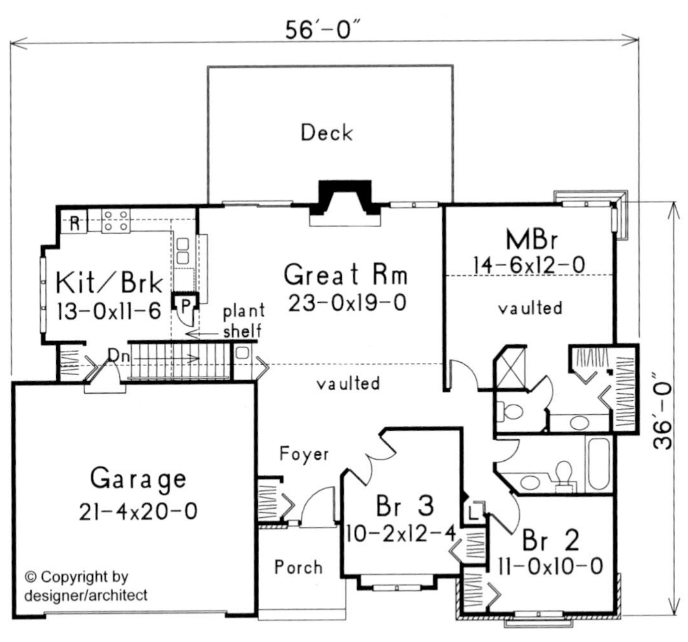

56'-0"
Deck
MBr
14-6x12-0
vaulted
R
Kit/Brk
13-0x11-6
P
Great Rm
23-0x19-0
plant shelf
Dn
vaulted
36'-0"
Garage
21-4x20-0
Foyer
Br 3
10-2x12-4
L
Br 2
11-0x10-0
Porch
© Copyright by designer/architect

DISTINCTIVE RANCH

1,360 total square feet of living area

3 bedrooms, 2 baths

2-car garage

Basement foundation

SPECIAL FEATURES

Double-gabled front facade has large windows

The foyer opens to the vaulted great room with a fireplace and access to the rear deck

A vaulted ceiling and large windows add openness to the kitchen/breakfast room

Bedroom #3 could easily convert to a den

PRICE CODE A

FORISTELL

Plan #M06-058D-0172

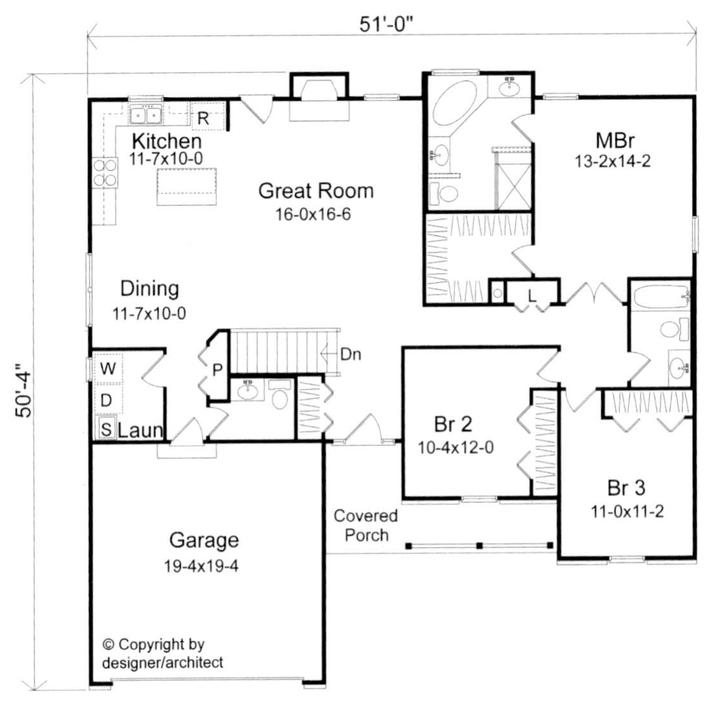

51'-0"
R
Kitchen
11-7x10-0
Great Room
16-0x16-6
MBr
13-2x14-2
Dining
11-7x10-0
L
50'-4"
W
D
S Laun
P
Dn
Br 2
10-4x12-0
Br 3
11-0x11-2
Garage
19-4x19-4
Covered Porch
© Copyright by designer/architect

STUNNING FAMILY HOME

1,635 total square feet of living area

3 bedrooms, 2 1/2 baths

2-car garage

Basement foundation

SPECIAL FEATURES

The covered porch creates an inviting facade

A whirlpool tub and twin vanities add elegance to the master bedroom's private bath

The kitchen island provides extra workspace and also offers an easy way to serve buffet dinners

PRICE CODE AA

To order plans, visit the Menards Building Materials Desk or visit www.Menards.com.

BRIARFIELD

Plan #M06-008D-0010

MENARDS

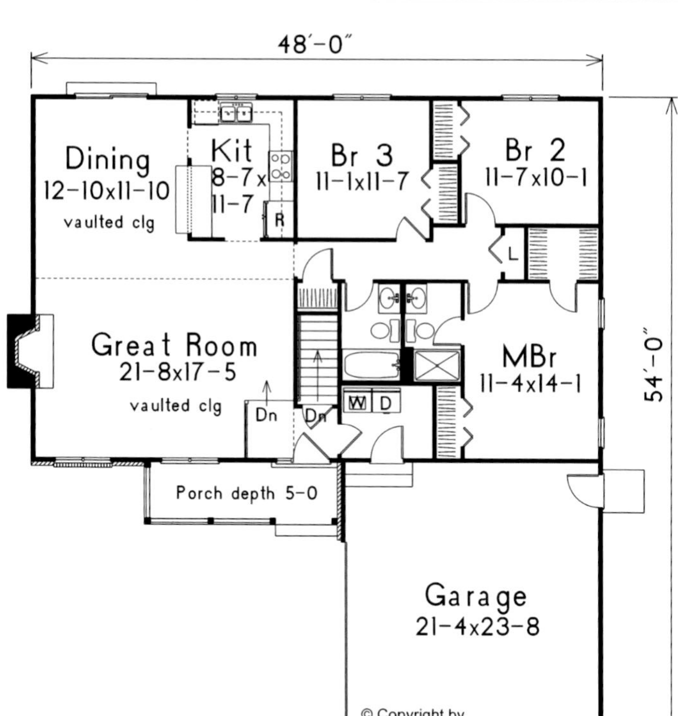

48'-0"
Dining
12-10x11-10
vaulted clg
Kit
8-7x
11-7
R
Br 3
11-1x11-7
Br 2
11-7x10-1
L
Great Room
21-8x17-5
vaulted clg
Dn
Dn
W
D
MBr
11-4x14-1
54'-0"
Porch depth 5-0
Garage
21-4x23-8
© Copyright by
designer/architect

LOVELY RANCH HOME

1,440 total square feet of living area

3 bedrooms, 2 baths

2-car side entry garage

Basement foundation, drawings also include crawl space and slab foundations

SPECIAL FEATURES

The foyer adjoins the massive-sized great room with a sloping ceiling and tall masonry fireplace

The kitchen connects to the spacious dining room and features a pass-through to the breakfast bar

An oversized two-car side entry garage offers plenty of storage for bicycles, lawn equipment, etc.

PRICE CODE A

GRANTWAY

Plan #M06-065L-0095

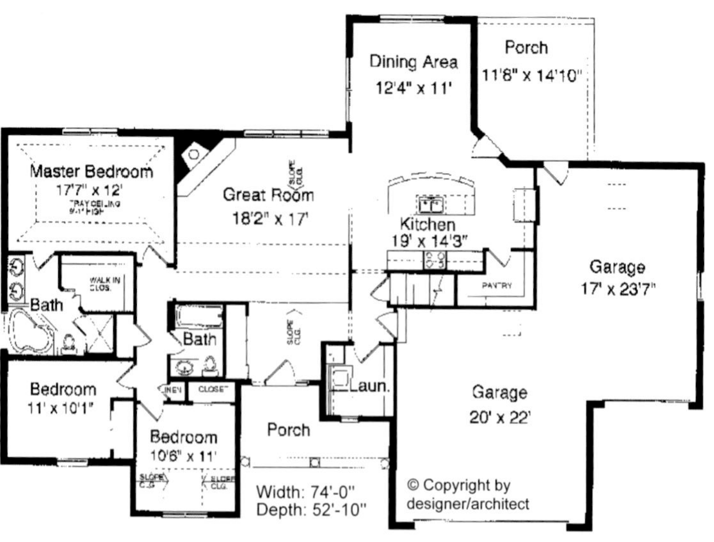

Dining Area
12'4" x 11'
Porch
11'8" x 14'10"
Master Bedroom
17'7" x 12'
Great Room
18'2" x 17'
Kitchen
19' x 14'3"
Garage
17' x 23'7"
Bath
Bath
Laun.
Garage
20' x 22'
Bedroom
11' x 10'1"
Bedroom
10'6" x 11'
Porch
Width: 74'-0"
Depth: 52'-10"
© Copyright by
designer/architect

INVITING ARCHED ENTRY

1,824 total square feet of living area

3 bedrooms, 2 baths

3-car garage

Basement foundation

SPECIAL FEATURES

A curved island with seating makes the kitchen an easy spot for quick meals

The bedrooms are set apart from the rest of the house with a hallway, making them more private

PRICE CODE C

To order plans, visit the Menards Building Materials Desk or visit www.Menards.com.

LULOW

Plan #M06-001D-0120

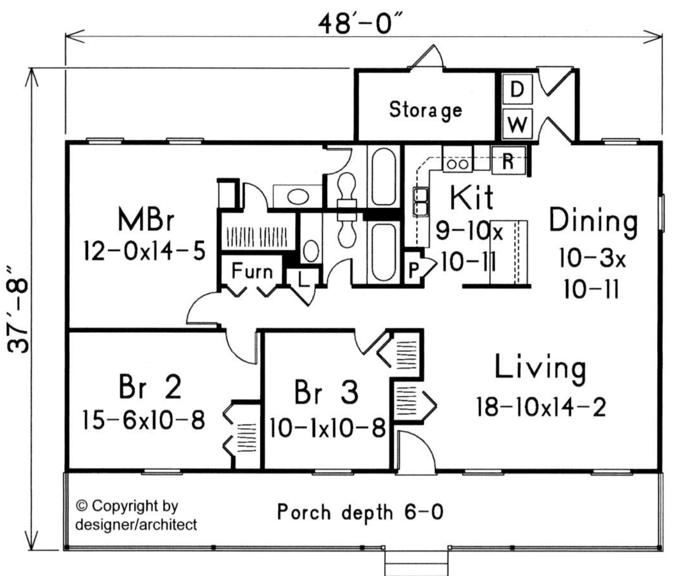

48′-0″
37′-8″
Storage
D
W
R
Kit
9-10x
10-11
Dining
10-3x
10-11
MBr
12-0x14-5
Furn
L
P
Br 2
15-6x10-8
Br 3
10-1x10-8
Living
18-10x14-2
© Copyright by
designer/architect
Porch depth 6-0

OPEN LIVING AREA

1,285 total square feet of living area

3 bedrooms, 2 baths

Crawl space foundation, drawings also include basement and slab foundations

SPECIAL FEATURES

Energy efficient home with 2" x 6" exterior walls

Accommodating home with ranch style porch

The master bedroom includes a dressing area, private bath and built-in bookcase

The kitchen features a pantry, breakfast bar and complete view to the dining room

PRICE CODE B

STOVALL

Plan #M06-077L-0019

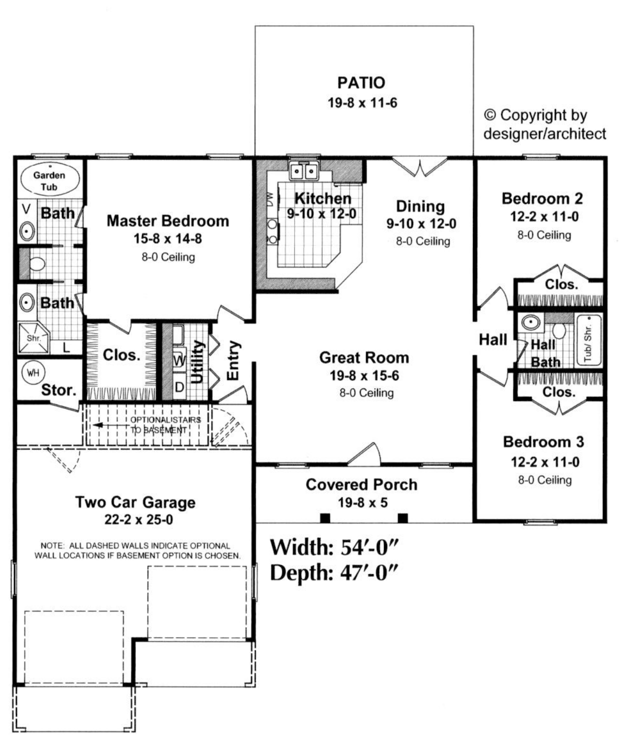

PATIO
19-8 x 11-6
© Copyright by
designer/architect
Garden Tub
Bath
Master Bedroom
15-8 x 14-8
8-0 Ceiling
Kitchen
9-10 x 12-0
Dining
9-10 x 12-0
8-0 Ceiling
Bedroom 2
12-2 x 11-0
8-0 Ceiling
Clos.
Bath
Clos.
W
D
Utility
Entry
Great Room
19-8 x 15-6
8-0 Ceiling
Hall
Hall
Bath
Tub/ Shr.
Clos.
Stor.
WH
OPTIONAL STAIRS TO BASEMENT
Bedroom 3
12-2 x 11-0
8-0 Ceiling
Covered Porch
19-8 x 5
Two Car Garage
22-2 x 25-0
NOTE: ALL DASHED WALLS INDICATE OPTIONAL WALL LOCATIONS IF BASEMENT OPTION IS CHOSEN.
Width: 54′-0″
Depth: 47′-0″

PLEASANT FRONT PORCH

1,400 total square feet of living area

3 bedrooms, 2 baths

2-car garage

Slab, basement or crawl space foundation, please specify when ordering

SPECIAL FEATURES

The efficient kitchen has plenty of counterspace

French doors lead from the dining room to the patio

The master bedroom is set apart from the rest of the house for additional privacy

PRICE CODE C

To order plans, visit the Menards Building Materials Desk or visit www.Menards.com.

AMBERDALE

MENARDS

Plan #M06-007D-0240

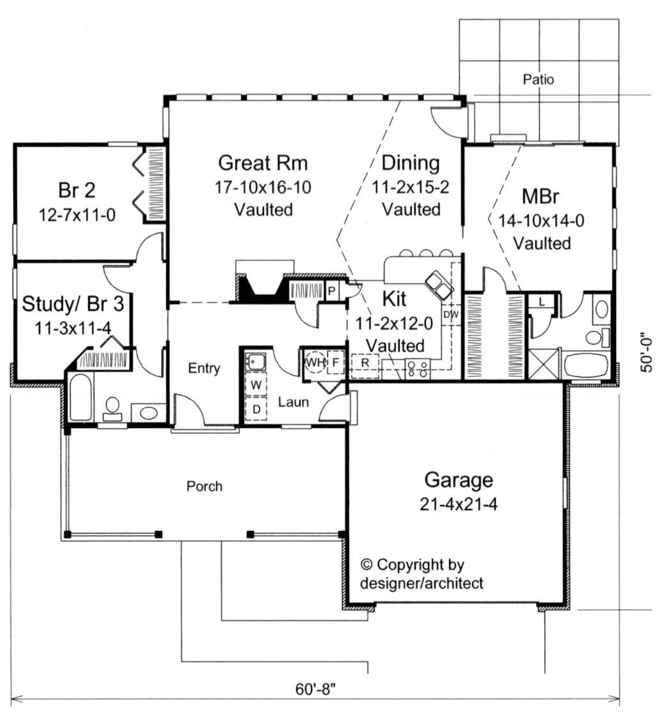
Patio
Br 2
12-7x11-0
Great Rm
17-10x16-10
Vaulted
Dining
11-2x15-2
Vaulted
MBr
14-10x14-0
Vaulted
Study/ Br 3
11-3x11-4
Kit
11-2x12-0
Vaulted
Entry
Laun
Porch
Garage
21-4x21-4
© Copyright by
designer/architect
50'-0"
60'-8"

ENCHANTING DORMERS

1,663 total square feet of living area

3 bedrooms, 2 baths

2-car garage

Crawl space or slab foundation, please specify when ordering

SPECIAL FEATURES

The vaulted great room of grand scale offers wonderful views through a 30' wide window wall

A snack bar, built-in pantry and vaulted ceiling are a few features of the efficient U-shaped kitchen

The vaulted master bedroom has showcase windows, a walk-in closet and a roomy bath

PRICE CODE C

DELMAR

Plan #M06-053D-0037

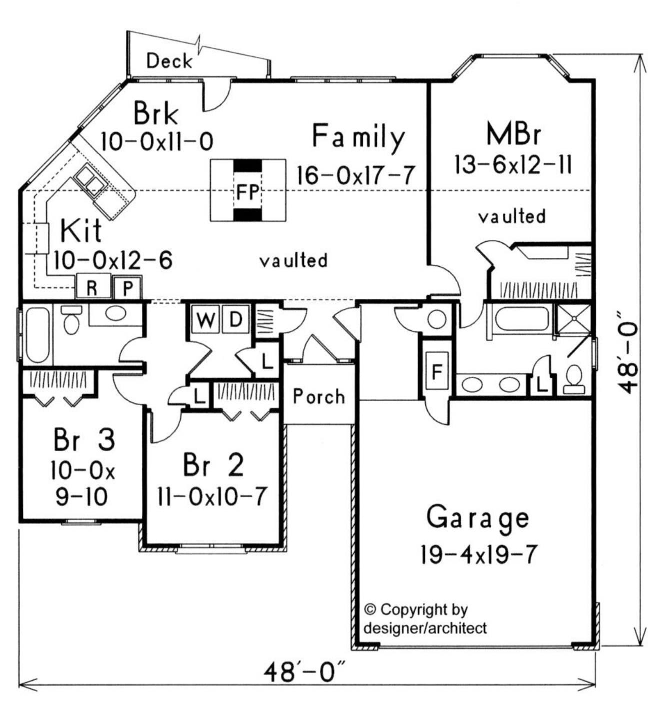
Deck
Brk
10-0x11-0
Family
16-0x17-7
MBr
13-6x12-11
vaulted
FP
Kit
10-0x12-6
vaulted
Br 3
10-0x
9-10
Br 2
11-0x10-7
Porch
Garage
19-4x19-7
© Copyright by
designer/architect
48'-0"
48'-0"

FABULOUS FAMILY LIVING

1,388 total square feet of living area

3 bedrooms, 2 baths

2-car garage

Crawl space foundation, drawings also include slab foundation

SPECIAL FEATURES

A handsome see-through fireplace offers a gathering point for the kitchen, family and breakfast rooms

A dramatic angular wall and large windows add brightness to the kitchen and breakfast room

PRICE CODE A

To order plans, visit the Menards Building Materials Desk or visit www.Menards.com.

MENARDS

EDGEWATER

Plan #M06-008D-0094

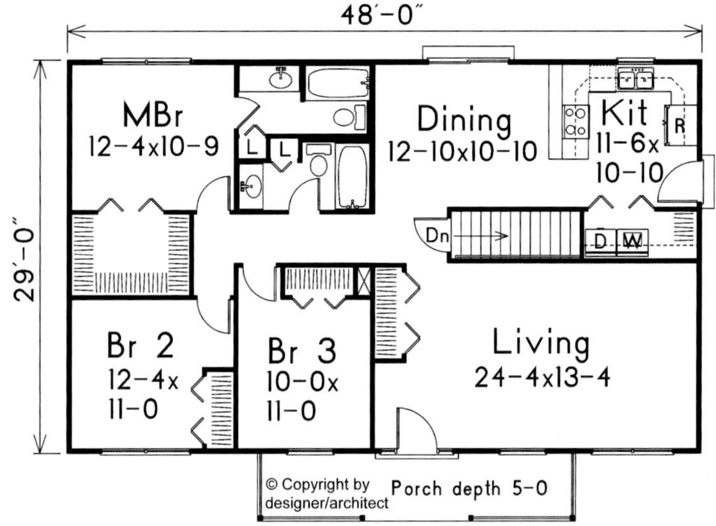
48'-0"
29'-0"
MBr
12-4x10-9
Dining
12-10x10-10
Kit
11-6x
10-10
R
L
L
Dn
D
W
Br 2
12-4x
11-0
Br 3
10-0x
11-0
Living
24-4x13-4
© Copyright by
designer/architect
Porch depth 5-0

EFFICIENT RANCH

1,364 total square feet of living area

3 bedrooms, 2 baths

Optional 2-car garage

Basement foundation, drawings also include crawl space foundation

SPECIAL FEATURES

The master bedroom features a spacious walk-in closet and private bath

The living room is highlighted with several windows

The kitchen with snack bar is adjacent to the dining area

Plenty of storage space throughout this home

PRICE CODE A

IMPERIAL

Plan #M06-008D-0057

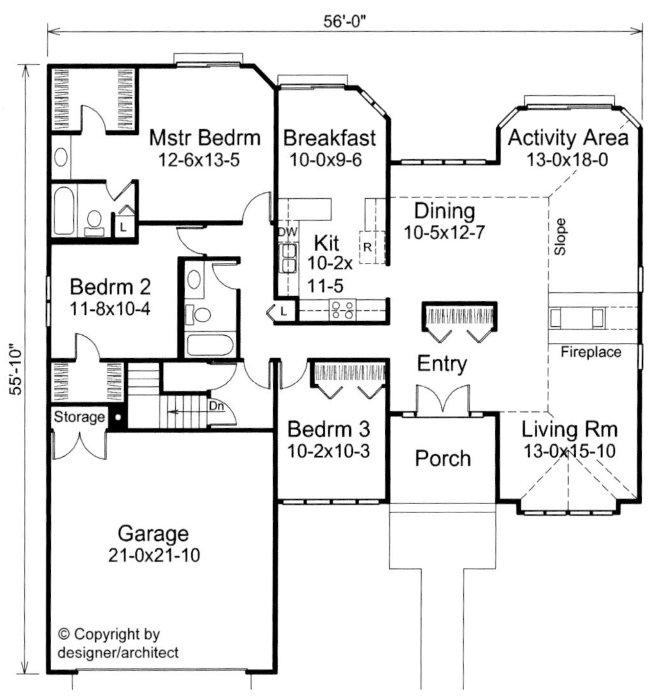
56'-0"
55'-10"
Mstr Bedrm
12-6x13-5
Breakfast
10-0x9-6
Activity Area
13-0x18-0
Dining
10-5x12-7
Slope
DW
Kit
10-2x
11-5
R
L
Bedrm 2
11-8x10-4
Fireplace
Entry
Storage
Dn
Bedrm 3
10-2x10-3
Porch
Living Rm
13-0x15-10
Garage
21-0x21-10
© Copyright by
designer/architect

STYLISH RANCH LIVING

1,850 total square feet of living area

3 bedrooms, 2 baths

2-car garage

Partial basement/crawl space foundation, drawings also include slab foundation

SPECIAL FEATURES

The well-equipped kitchen enjoys an eating bar next to the sunny breakfast room

The master bedroom enjoys a compartmented bath and walk-in closet

PRICE CODE C

To order plans, visit the Menards Building Materials Desk or visit www.Menards.com.

CHILDRESS

MENARDS

Plan #M06-058D-0050

69'-4"

65'-4"

MBr 15-4x14-8

Great Rm 18-9x19-5

Breakfast 18-0x13-10

Br 2 13-0x11-9

Kit. 20-0x 10-3

Br 3 13-0x11-8

Study 13-4x13-8

Dining 12-0x13-0

Covered Porch

Garage 2-04x23-8

OPEN FLOOR PLAN FOR FAMILY ACTIVITIES

2,598 total square feet of living area

3 bedrooms, 2 1/2 baths

2-car side entry garage

Basement foundation

SPECIAL FEATURES

A see-through fireplace warms the spacious great room, kitchen and breakfast area

The private master bedroom enjoys two walk-in closets and a private bath with a whirlpool tub

The study features a fireplace and is ideal for a home office

PRICE CODE D

ASHMONT PLACE

Plan #M06-007D-0164

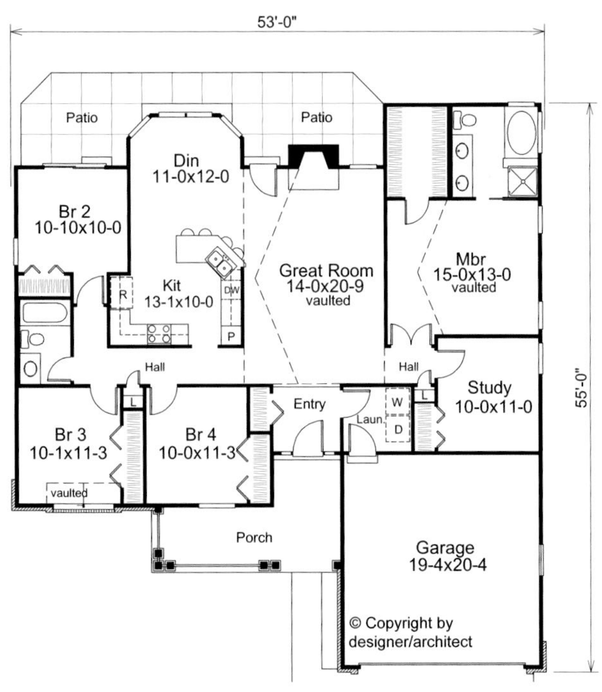
53'-0"
55'-0"
Patio
Patio
Din 11-0x12-0
Br 2 10-10x10-0
Kit 13-1x10-0
Great Room 14-0x20-9 vaulted
Mbr 15-0x13-0 vaulted
Hall
Hall
Study 10-0x11-0
Entry
Laun.
Br 3 10-1x11-3
vaulted
Br 4 10-0x11-3
Porch
Garage 19-4x20-4
© Copyright by designer/architect

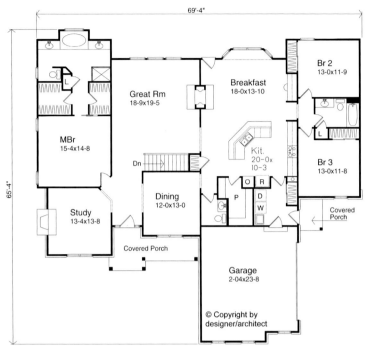

STYLISH RANCH WITH STUDY

1,741 total square feet of living area

4 bedrooms, 2 baths

2-car garage

Crawl space foundation, drawings also include slab and basement foundations

SPECIAL FEATURES

The great room offers a fireplace, vaulted ceiling and is open to the bayed dining area and kitchen

The master bedroom boasts a vaulted ceiling, large walk-in closet and luxury bath

PRICE CODE B

To order plans, visit the Menards Building Materials Desk or visit www.Menards.com.

MENARDS

SUMMERSET

Plan #M06-007D-0055

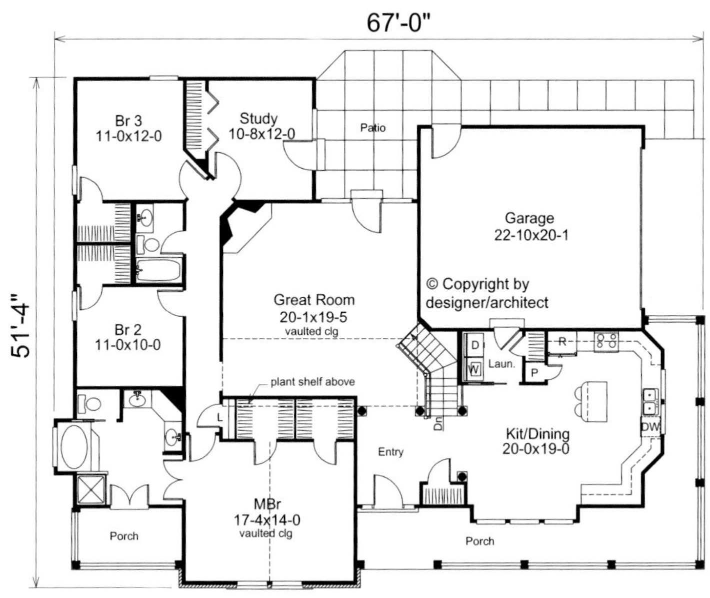

67'-0"
51'-4"
Br 3
11-0x12-0
Study
10-8x12-0
Patio
Garage
22-10x20-1
© Copyright by
designer/architect
Great Room
20-1x19-5
vaulted clg
Br 2
11-0x10-0
D
W
Laun.
R
P
plant shelf above
L
Dn
DW
Kit/Dining
20-0x19-0
Entry
MBr
17-4x14-0
vaulted clg
Porch
Porch

LOVELY COUNTRY HOME

2,029 total square feet of living area

3 bedrooms, 2 baths

2-car side entry garage

Basement foundation, drawings also include crawl space and slab foundations

SPECIAL FEATURES

The kitchen/dining area enjoys an island snack bar, a built-in pantry and multiple tall windows

2" x 6" exterior walls available, please order plan #M06-007E-0055

PRICE CODE D

CONWAY GLEN

Plan #M06-077L-0030

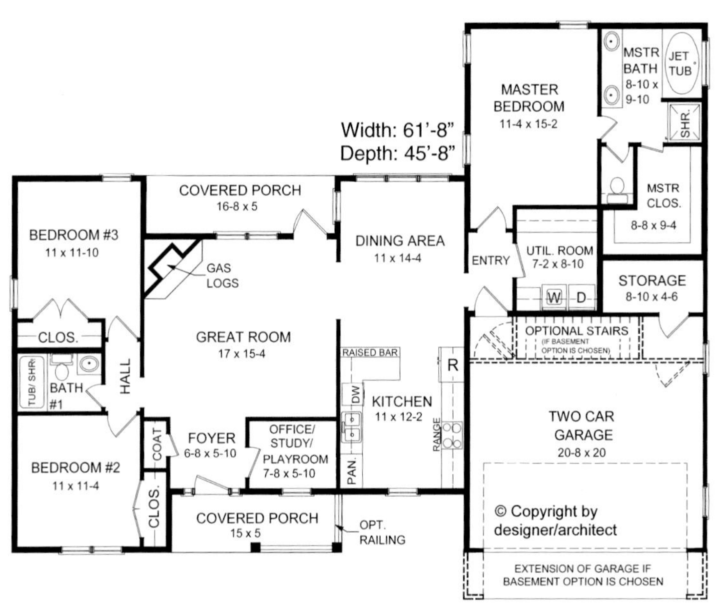

Width: 61'-8"
Depth: 45'-8"
MASTER
BEDROOM
11-4 x 15-2
MSTR
BATH
8-10 x
9-10
JET
TUB
SHR.
MSTR
CLOS.
8-8 x 9-4
COVERED PORCH
16-8 x 5
BEDROOM #3
11 x 11-10
DINING AREA
11 x 14-4
ENTRY
UTIL. ROOM
7-2 x 8-10
STORAGE
8-10 x 4-6
GAS
LOGS
W
D
CLOS.
GREAT ROOM
17 x 15-4
OPTIONAL STAIRS
(IF BASEMENT OPTION IS CHOSEN)
RAISED BAR
R
TUB/SHR
BATH
#1
HALL
DW
KITCHEN
11 x 12-2
TWO CAR
GARAGE
20-8 x 20
RANGE
COAT
FOYER
6-8 x 5-10
OFFICE/
STUDY/
PLAYROOM
7-8 x 5-10
BEDROOM #2
11 x 11-4
PAN.
CLOS.
COVERED PORCH
15 x 5
OPT.
RAILING
© Copyright by
designer/architect
EXTENSION OF GARAGE IF
BASEMENT OPTION IS CHOSEN

BEAUTIFUL, OPEN DESIGN

1,600 total square feet of living area

3 bedrooms, 2 baths

2-car garage

Basement, crawl space or slab foundation, please specify when ordering

SPECIAL FEATURES

Energy efficient home with 2" x 6" exterior walls

The office/study/playroom is a flexible space that can adapt to any need

PRICE CODE D

To order plans, visit the Menards Building Materials Desk or visit www.Menards.com.

SANDUSKY

MENARDS

Plan #M06-051L-0027

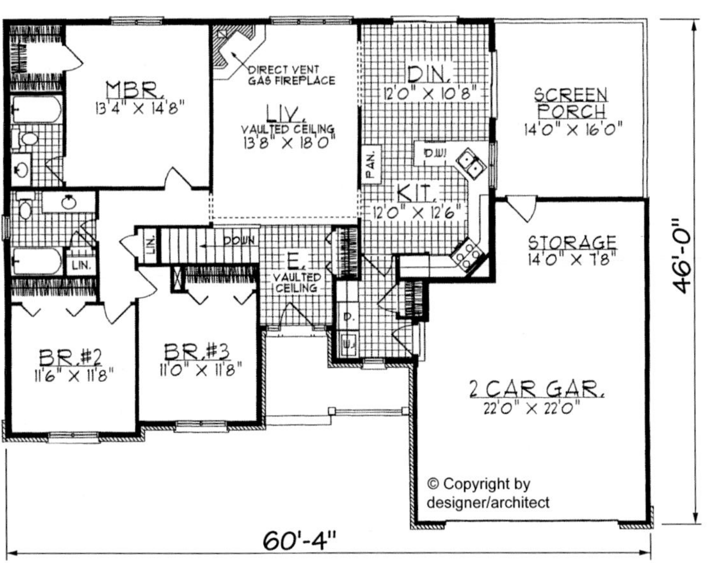

MBR.
13'4" X 14'8"
DIRECT VENT GAS FIREPLACE
LIV.
VAULTED CEILING
13'8" X 18'0"
DIN.
12'0" X 10'8"
SCREEN PORCH
14'0" X 16'0"
PAN.
D.W.
KIT.
12'0" X 12'6"
LIN.
LIN.
DOWN
E.
VAULTED CEILING
STORAGE
14'0" X 7'8"
BR.#2
11'6" X 11'8"
BR.#3
11'0" X 11'8"
2 CAR GAR.
22'0" X 22'0"
© Copyright by designer/architect
60'-4"
46'-0"

TERRIFIC RANCH

1,520 total square feet of living area

3 bedrooms, 2 baths

2-car garage

Basement foundation

SPECIAL FEATURES

Energy efficient home with 2" x 6" exterior walls

The spacious master bedroom has a large walk-in closet and sweeping windows overlooking the yard

The laundry room is conveniently located between the garage and kitchen

The living room features a cathedral ceiling and corner fireplace

PRICE CODE B

STRATFORD

Plan #M06-003D-0002

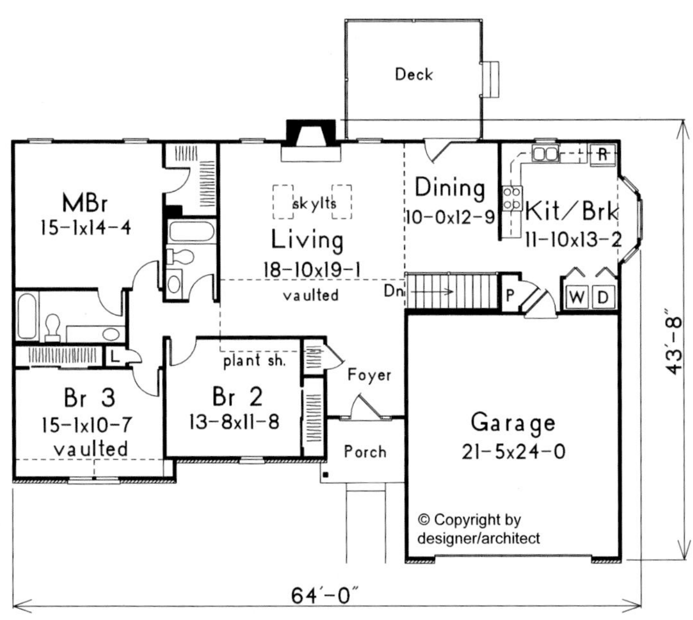

Deck
MBr
15-1x14-4
skylts
Living
18-10x19-1
vaulted
Dining
10-0x12-9
Kit/Brk
11-10x13-2
R
Dn
P
W
D
L
plant sh.
Br 3
15-1x10-7
vaulted
Br 2
13-8x11-8
Foyer
Porch
Garage
21-5x24-0
© Copyright by designer/architect
64'-0"
43'-8"

SKYLIGHTS PROVIDE LIGHT

1,676 total square feet of living area

3 bedrooms, 2 baths

2-car garage

Basement foundation, drawings also include crawl space and slab foundations

SPECIAL FEATURES

The living area skylights and large kitchen/breakfast area with bay window provide plenty of sunlight

The master bedroom has a walk-in closet and both the secondary bedrooms have large closets

PRICE CODE B

To order plans, visit the Menards Building Materials Desk or visit www.Menards.com.

MENARDS CRAIGLAND HILLS
Plan #M06-007D-0249

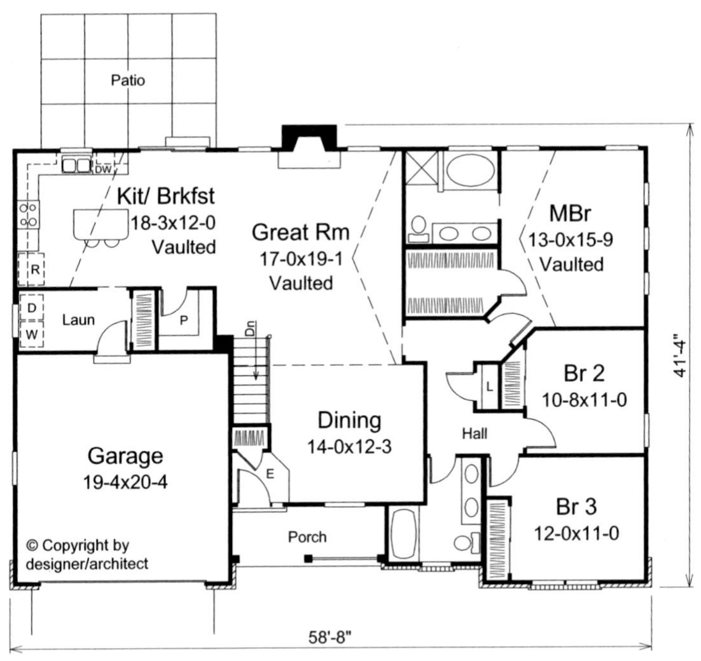
Patio
Kit/ Brkfst
18-3x12-0
Vaulted
DW
R
Great Rm
17-0x19-1
Vaulted
MBr
13-0x15-9
Vaulted
D
W
Laun
P
Dn
Br 2
10-8x11-0
L
41'-4"
Garage
19-4x20-4
Dining
14-0x12-3
Hall
E
Br 3
12-0x11-0
Porch
© Copyright by
designer/architect
58'-8"

COUNTRY RANCH

1,740 total square feet of living area

3 bedrooms, 2 baths

2-car garage

Basement foundation

SPECIAL FEATURES

A protective covered porch and separate entry with guest closet invite you into the vast open living areas

The great room offers a vaulted ceiling, a fireplace and is open to a semi-formal dining area

Decorative windows above the bed wall add sunlight to the master bedroom that also enjoys a luxury bath

PRICE CODE C

TWINBROOKE
Plan #M06-037D-0022

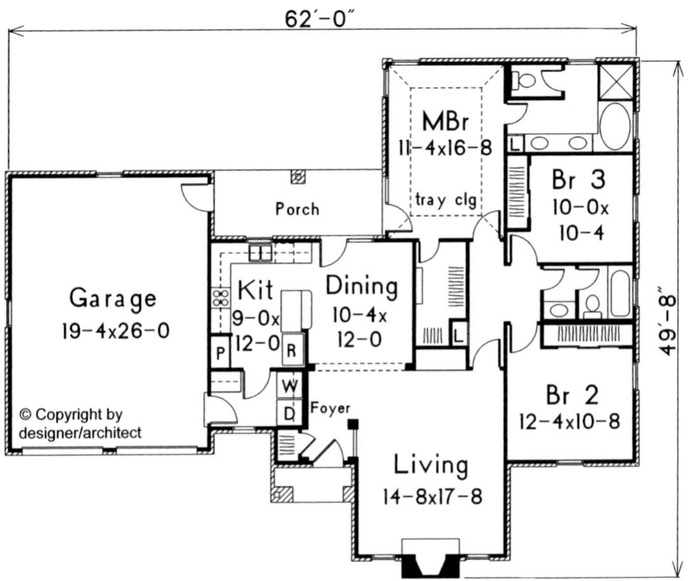
62'-0"
MBr
11-4x16-8
tray clg
Br 3
10-0x
10-4
L
Porch
Garage
19-4x26-0
Kit
9-0x
12-0
R
P
Dining
10-4x
12-0
L
49'-8"
W
D
Foyer
Br 2
12-4x10-8
© Copyright by
designer/architect
Living
14-8x17-8

FIREPLACE IS FOCAL POINT

1,539 total square feet of living area

3 bedrooms, 2 baths

2-car garage

Slab foundation

SPECIAL FEATURES

The master bedroom has a 10' tray ceiling, access to the porch, ample closet space and a full bath

Serving counter separates the kitchen and dining room

A foyer with handy coat closet opens to the living area with fireplace

PRICE CODE B

To order plans, visit the Menards Building Materials Desk or visit www.Menards.com.

MADISON MANOR

MENARDS

Plan #M06-007D-0113

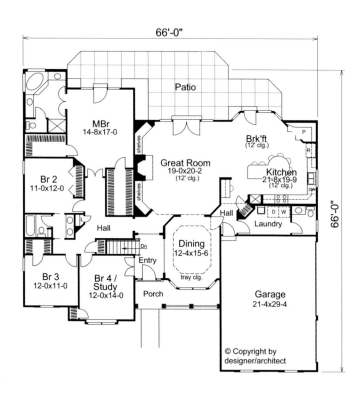

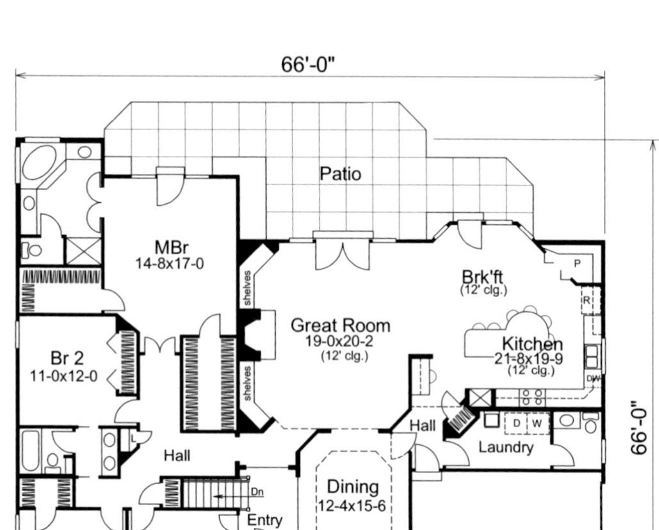

66'-0"
Patio
MBr
14-8x17-0
Br 2
11-0x12-0
shelves
Great Room
19-0x20-2
(12' clg.)
Brk'ft
(12' clg.)
Kitchen
21-8x19-9
(12' clg.)
Hall
Laundry
Hall
Dining
12-4x15-6
tray clg.
Entry
Br 3
12-0x11-0
Br 4 /
Study
12-0x14-0
Porch
Garage
21-4x29-4
© Copyright by
designer/architect
66'-0"

COUNTRY HOME FOCUSES ON PATIO VIEWS

2,547 total square feet of living area

4 bedrooms, 2 1/2 baths

3-car side entry garage

Basement foundation

SPECIAL FEATURES

Grand-sized great room features a 12' volume ceiling, fireplace with built-in wrap-around shelving and patio doors with sidelights and transom windows

The walk-in pantry, computer desk, large breakfast island for seven and bayed breakfast area are the many features of this outstanding kitchen

PRICE CODE D

SYCAMORE

Plan #M06-022D-0011

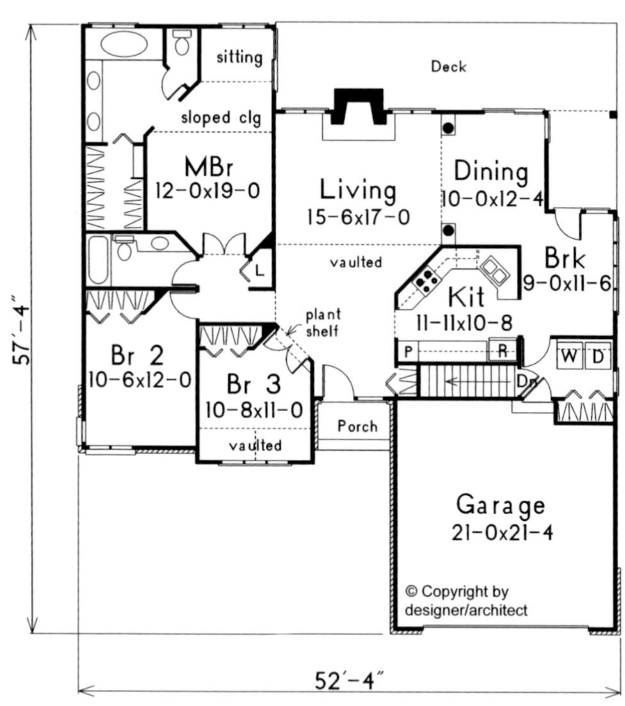

sitting
Deck
sloped clg
MBr
12-0x19-0
Living
15-6x17-0
Dining
10-0x12-4
Brk
9-0x11-6
vaulted
Kit
11-11x10-8
plant
shelf
Br 2
10-6x12-0
Br 3
10-8x11-0
vaulted
Porch
Garage
21-0x21-4
© Copyright by
designer/architect
57'-4"
52'-4"

OPEN RANCH DESIGN

1,630 total square feet of living area

3 bedrooms, 2 baths

2-car garage

Basement foundation

SPECIAL FEATURES

Wrap-around rear deck is accessible from the breakfast room, dining room and master bedroom

Vaulted ceilings top the living room and master bedroom

PRICE CODE B

To order plans, visit the Menards Building Materials Desk or visit www.Menards.com.

MENARDS

WOODFORD

Plan #M06-008D-0126

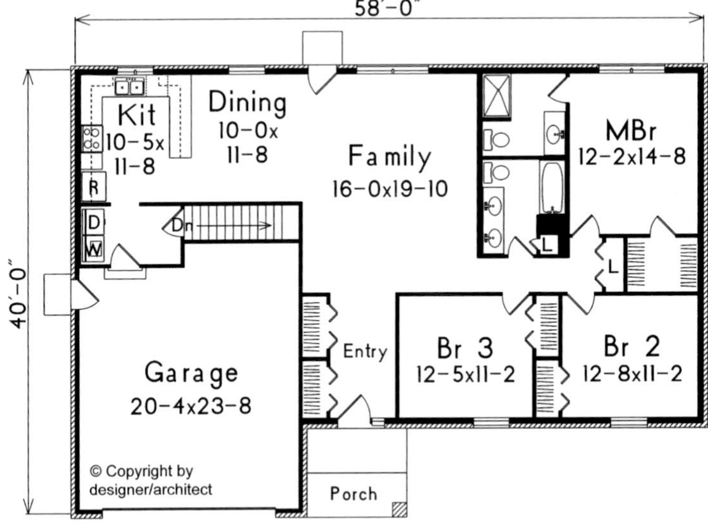
58'-0"
40'-0"
Kit
10-5x
11-8
Dining
10-0x
11-8
Family
16-0x19-10
MBr
12-2x14-8
R
D
W
Dn
L
L
Entry
Br 3
12-5x11-2
Br 2
12-8x11-2
Garage
20-4x23-8
© Copyright by
designer/architect
Porch

DISTINCTIVE ONE-LEVEL HOME

1,605 total square feet of living area

3 bedrooms, 2 baths

2-car garage

Basement foundation, drawings also include crawl space and slab foundations

SPECIAL FEATURES

Detailed entry is highlighted with a stone floor and double guest closets

The well-designed kitchen includes an open view to the family room

Bedroom #3 can be easily utilized as a den

PRICE CODE B

SEYMOUR

Plan #M06-058D-0170

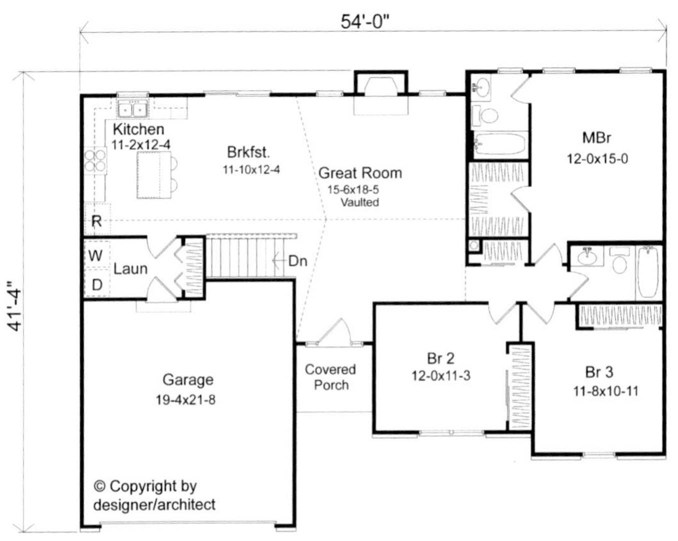
54'-0"
41'-4"
Kitchen
11-2x12-4
Brkfst.
11-10x12-4
Great Room
15-6x18-5
Vaulted
MBr
12-0x15-0
R
W
Laun
D
Dn
Garage
19-4x21-8
Covered
Porch
Br 2
12-0x11-3
Br 3
11-8x10-11
© Copyright by
designer/architect

CHEERFUL RANCH

1,418 total square feet of living area

3 bedrooms, 2 baths

2-car garage

Basement foundation

SPECIAL FEATURES

The kitchen, breakfast and great rooms combine for an easy flow of family functions

A coat closet at the garage entrance helps organization

All bedrooms are generous in size and the master bedroom enjoys a walk-in closet and private bath

PRICE CODE AA

To order plans, visit the Menards Building Materials Desk or visit www.Menards.com.

DARWIN

MENARDS

Plan #M06-001D-0021

PLEASANT COVERED PORCH

1,416 total square feet of living area

3 bedrooms, 2 baths

2-car garage

Crawl space foundation, drawings also include basement foundation

SPECIAL FEATURES

The master bedroom features a private bath

The foyer opens to both a formal living room and an informal great room

The great room has access to the outdoors through sliding doors

PRICE CODE A

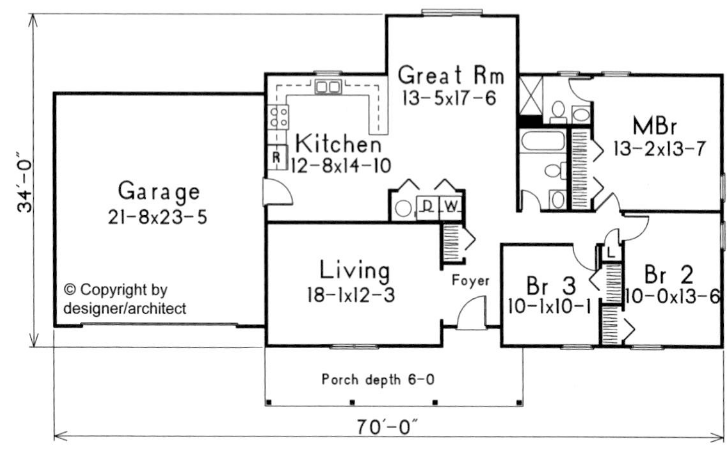

Great Rm
13-5x17-6
MBr
13-2x13-7
Kitchen
12-8x14-10
R
D W
Garage
21-8x23-5
34'-0"
Living
18-1x12-3
Foyer
Br 3
10-1x10-1
L
Br 2
10-0x13-6
© Copyright by
designer/architect
Porch depth 6-0
70'-0"

MAPLE GROVE

Plan #M06-051L-0053

COUNTRY FLAIR IN A RANCH

1,461 total square feet of living area

3 bedrooms, 2 baths

2-car garage

Basement foundation

SPECIAL FEATURES

The casual dining room enjoys close proximity to the kitchen for easy serving

Cathedral ceilings in the great room and dining area give the home a spacious feel

A relaxing master bedroom boasts an expansive bath

PRICE CODE A

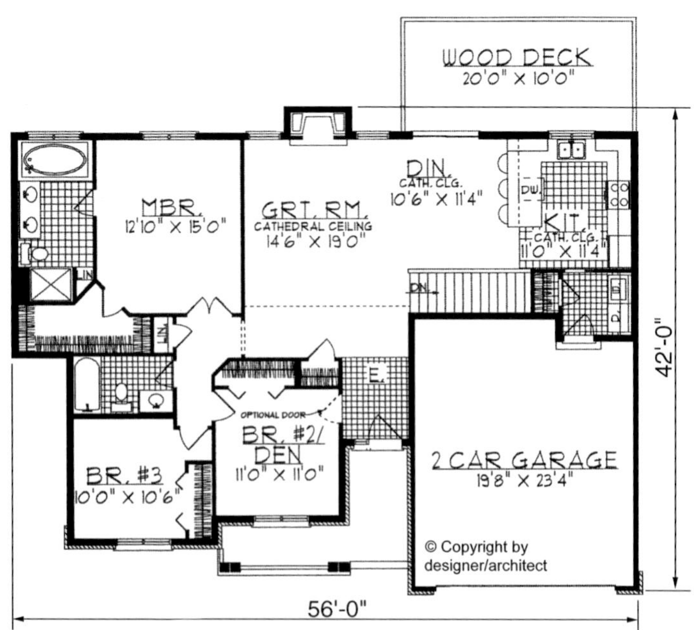

WOOD DECK
20'0" X 10'0"
MBR.
12'10" X 15'0"
GRT. RM.
CATHEDRAL CEILING
14'6" X 19'0"
DIN.
CATH. CLG.
10'6" X 11'4"
DW
KIT.
CATH. CLG.
11'0" X 11'4"
DN
LN
E.
OPTIONAL DOOR
BR. #2/
DEN
11'0" X 11'0"
BR. #3
10'0" X 10'6"
2 CAR GARAGE
19'8" X 23'4"
© Copyright by
designer/architect
42'-0"
56'-0"

To order plans, visit the Menards Building Materials Desk or visit www.Menards.com.

MENARDS®

Multi-Family HOME PLANS

Multi-family home plans are a popular option for families of all sizes and can range from a two-unit duplex to a plan with over twelve dwellings. A multi-family plan can be a great source of income, an energy efficient option and economical to build. They are also a great option for those who need a dwelling that includes in-law quarters. Browse our stylish selection of multi-family home designs in this special collection and find the perfect plan for your needs.

Plan #M06-007D-0022 can be found on page 223.

Plan #M06-007D-0091 can be found on page 218.

Plan #M06-007D-0190 can be found on page 215.

CORAL GABLES

Plan #M06-007D-0076

ATRIUM DUPLEX WITH ROOM TO GROW

3,484 total square feet of living area

Each unit has 3 bedrooms, 2 baths

Each unit has a 2-car garage

Walk-out basement foundation

SPECIAL FEATURES

Inviting porch and foyer lead to the vaulted living room/dining balcony with atrium window wall

Bedroom #2 doubles as a study with access to the deck through sliding glass doors

Atrium opens to the large family room and third bedroom

Duplex has 1,742 square feet of living space per unit

PRICE CODE H

Rear View

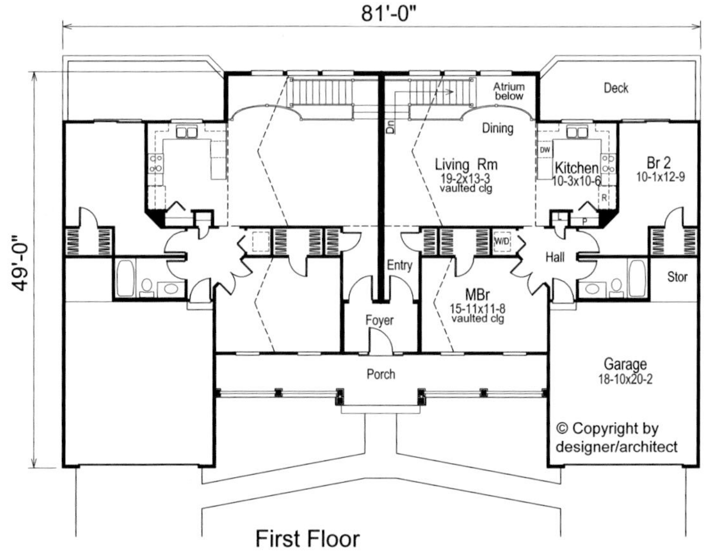
81'-0"
49'-0"
Atrium below
Deck
Dn
Dining
Living Rm
19-2x13-3
vaulted clg
DW
Kitchen
10-3x10-6
Br 2
10-1x12-9
W/D
Entry
Hall
Stor
MBr
15-11x11-8
vaulted clg
Foyer
Porch
Garage
18-10x20-2
© Copyright by designer/architect

First Floor
1,104 sq. ft. per unit

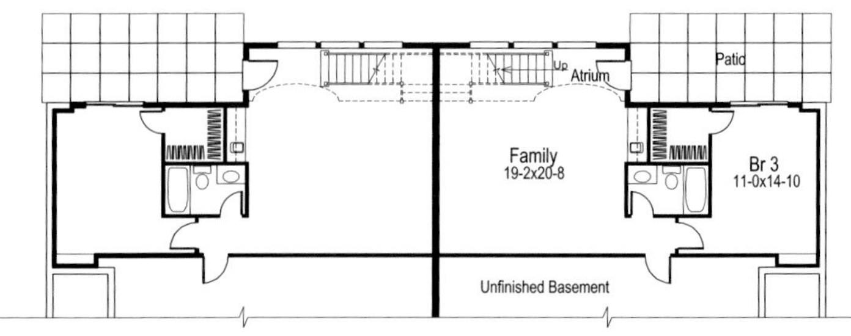
Up
Atrium
Patio
Family
19-2x20-8
Br 3
11-0x14-10
Unfinished Basement

Lower Level
638 sq. ft. per unit

To order plans, visit the Menards Building Materials Desk or visit www.Menards.com.

MENARDS

HICKORY MANOR

Multi-Family Plans

Plan #M06-007D-0190

Mbr 11-6x18-0
Br #2 9-5x12-6
Hall
Br #3 13-8x11-7

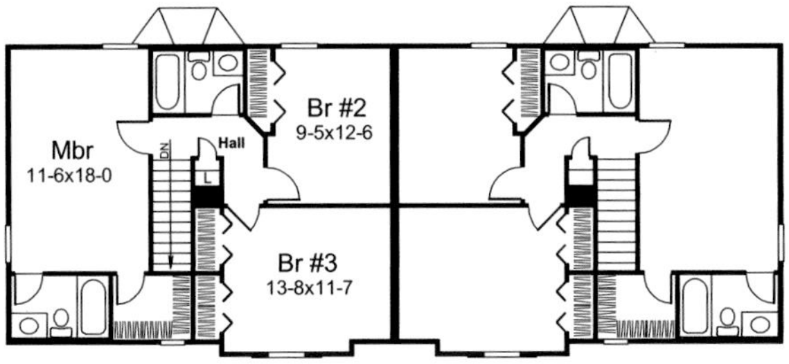

Second Floor
779 sq. ft.
per unit

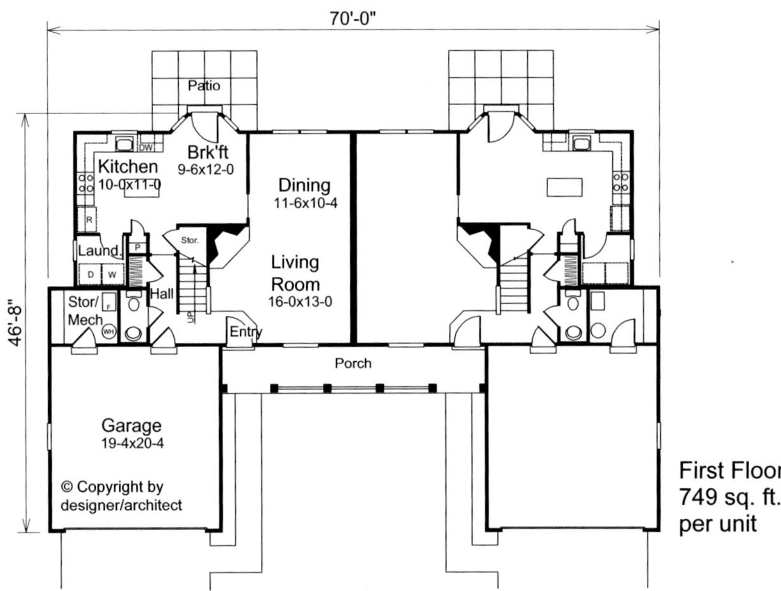

70'-0"
46'-8"
Patio
Kitchen 10-0x11-0
Brk'ft 9-6x12-0
Dining 11-6x10-4
Living Room 16-0x13-0
Laund.
Stor./Mech
Hall
Entry
Porch
Garage 19-4x20-4
© Copyright by designer/architect

First Floor
749 sq. ft.
per unit

To order plans, visit the Menards Building Materials Desk or visit www.Menards.com.

TRADITIONAL TWO-STORY DUPLEX

3,056 total square feet of living area

Each unit has 3 bedrooms, 2 1/2 baths

Each unit has a 2-car garage

Crawl space foundation

SPECIAL FEATURES

Multiple gables, a hipped roof and an elongated porch all help to create this handsome exterior

The large living room has a corner fireplace and is open to the dining area

The laundry room, built-in pantry and island cabinetry are amenities of the kitchen

Duplex has 1,528 square feet of living space per unit

PRICE CODE D

Rear View

PATTERSON PLACE

MENARDS

Plan #M06-007D-0094

COMPACT TWO-STORY DUPLEX

2,408 total square feet of living area

Each unit has 2 bedrooms, 1 1/2 baths

Each unit has a 1-car garage

Basement foundation

SPECIAL FEATURES

The large great room offers a fireplace and dining area with a view of the patio

Each unit enjoys its own private garage, front porch and rear patio

The second floor bedrooms are large in size and feature spacious walk-in closets

Duplex has 1,204 square feet of living space per unit

PRICE CODE F

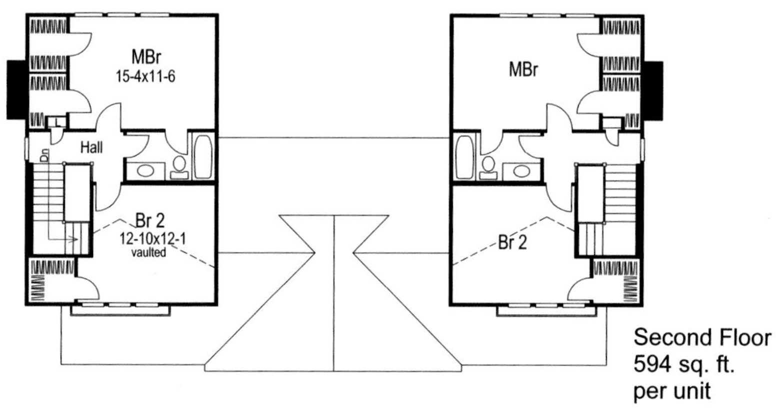
MBr
15-4x11-6
Hall
Dn
Br 2
12-10x12-1
vaulted
MBr
Br 2

Second Floor
594 sq. ft.
per unit

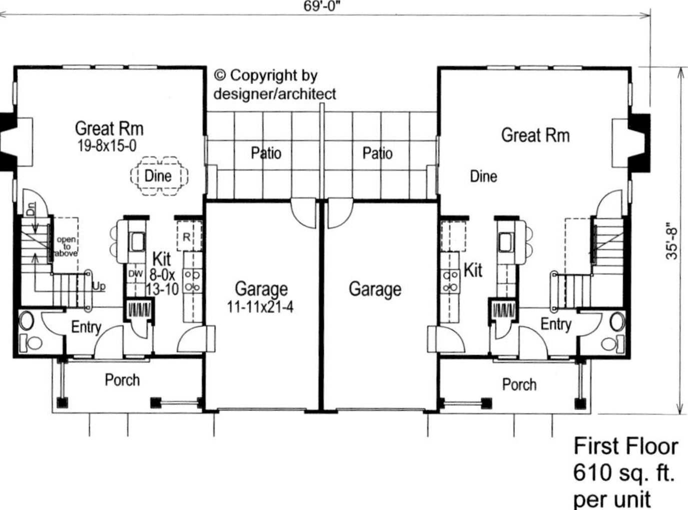
69'-0"
© Copyright by designer/architect
Great Rm
19-8x15-0
Dine
Patio
Patio
Great Rm
Dine
Dn
open to above
Kit
8-0x
13-10
DW
R
Up
Garage
11-11x21-4
Garage
Kit
Entry
Entry
Porch
Porch
35'-8"

First Floor
610 sq. ft.
per unit

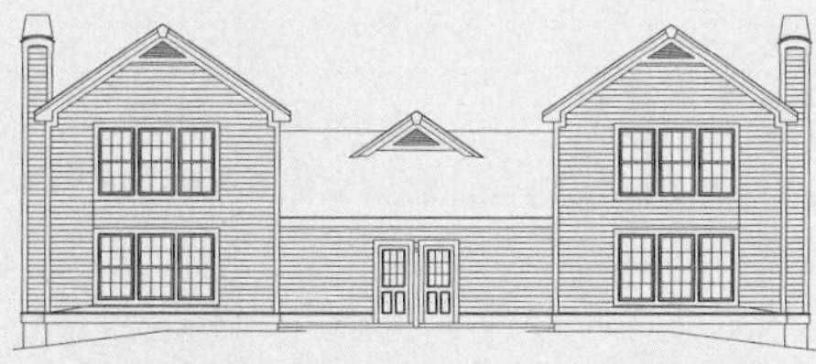

Rear View

To order plans, visit the Menards Building Materials Desk or visit www.Menards.com.

MENARDS

SHADYDALE

Multi-Family Plans

Plan #M06-007D-0020

VAULTED CEILINGS ADD SPACIOUSNESS TO LIVING AREAS

2,318 total square feet of living area

Each unit has 3 bedrooms, 2 baths

Each unit has a 1-car garage

Basement foundation

SPECIAL FEATURES

The great room and dining area are complemented with a fireplace and patio access

The breakfast bar has a corner sink that overlooks the great room

A plant shelf graces the vaulted entry

The master bedroom provides a walk-in closet and private bath

Duplex has 1,159 square feet of living space per unit

PRICE CODE F

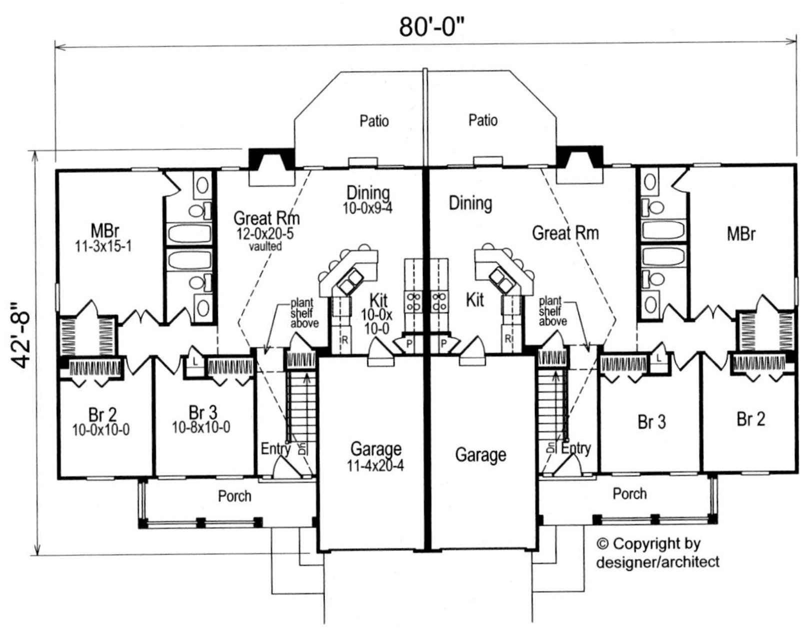
80'-0"
42'-8"
Patio
Patio
MBr
11-3x15-1
Great Rm
12-0x20-5
vaulted
Dining
10-0x9-4
Dining
Great Rm
MBr
plant shelf above
Kit
10-0x
10-0
Kit
plant shelf above
Br 2
10-0x10-0
Br 3
10-8x10-0
Entry
Garage
11-4x20-4
Garage
Entry
Br 3
Br 2
Porch
Porch
© Copyright by designer/architect

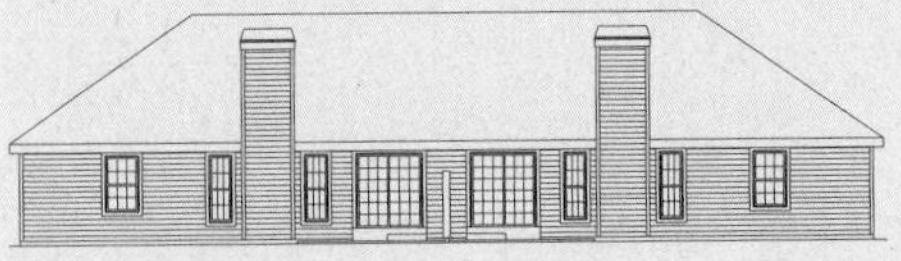

Rear View

To order plans, visit the Menards Building Materials Desk or visit www.Menards.com.

BEDFORD HEIGHTS

MENARDS

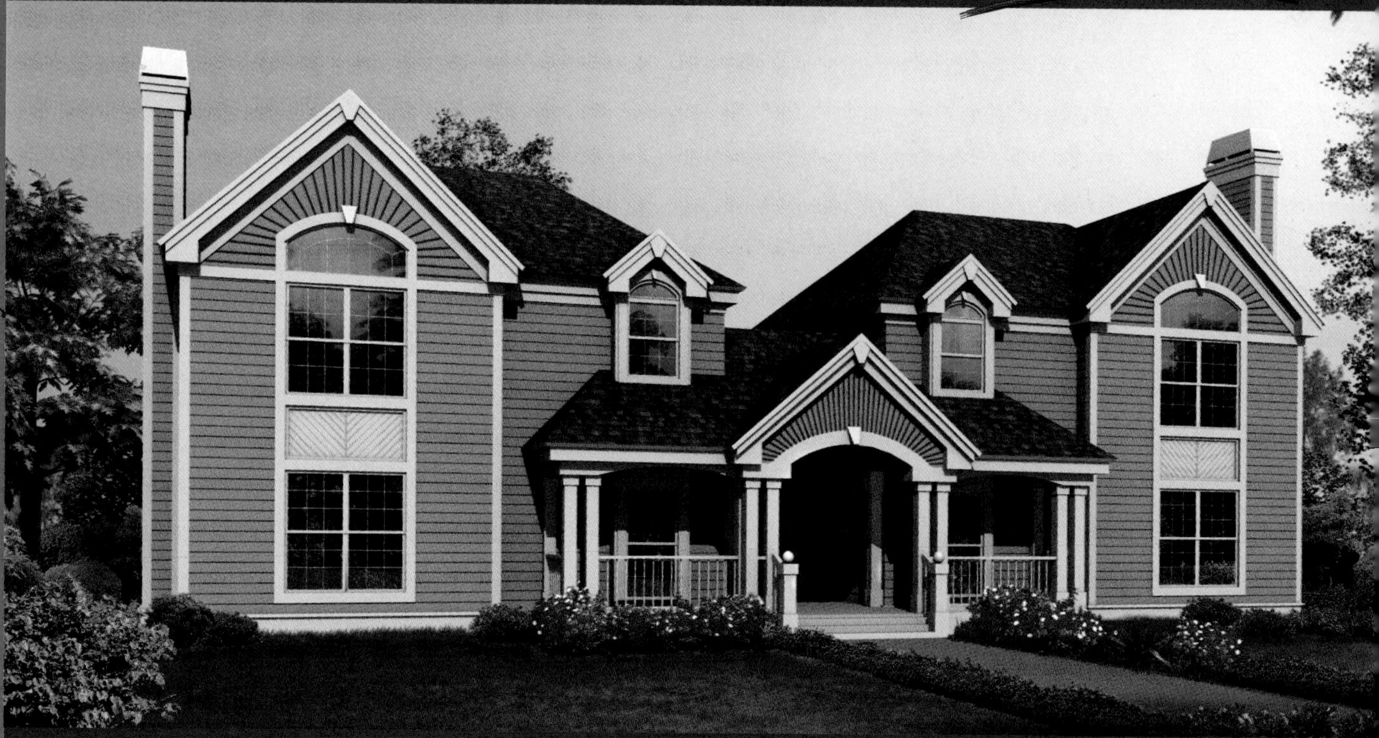

Plan #M06-007D-0091

DUPLEX WITH A GRAND-SCALE COUNTRY PORCH

3,502 total square feet of living area

Each unit has 3 bedrooms, 2 1/2 baths

Each unit has a 2-car drive under garage

Walk-out basement foundation

SPECIAL FEATURES

Two-story entry has a staircase that leads to the living room with a fireplace

The breakfast room enjoys a bay window, sliding glass doors to an outdoor balcony and a pass-through to the kitchen

Duplex has 1,751 square feet of living space per unit

PRICE CODE H

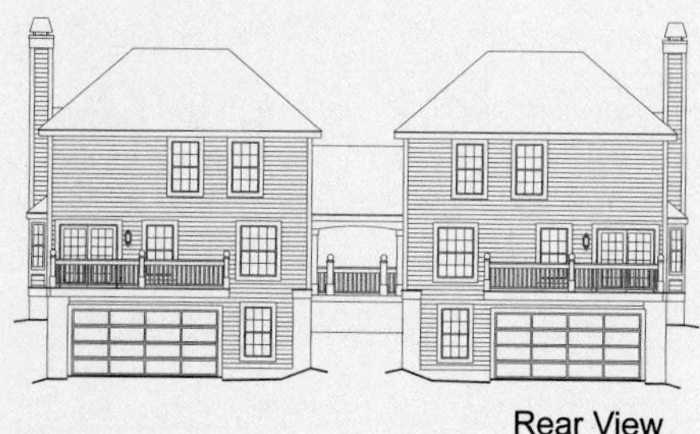

Rear View

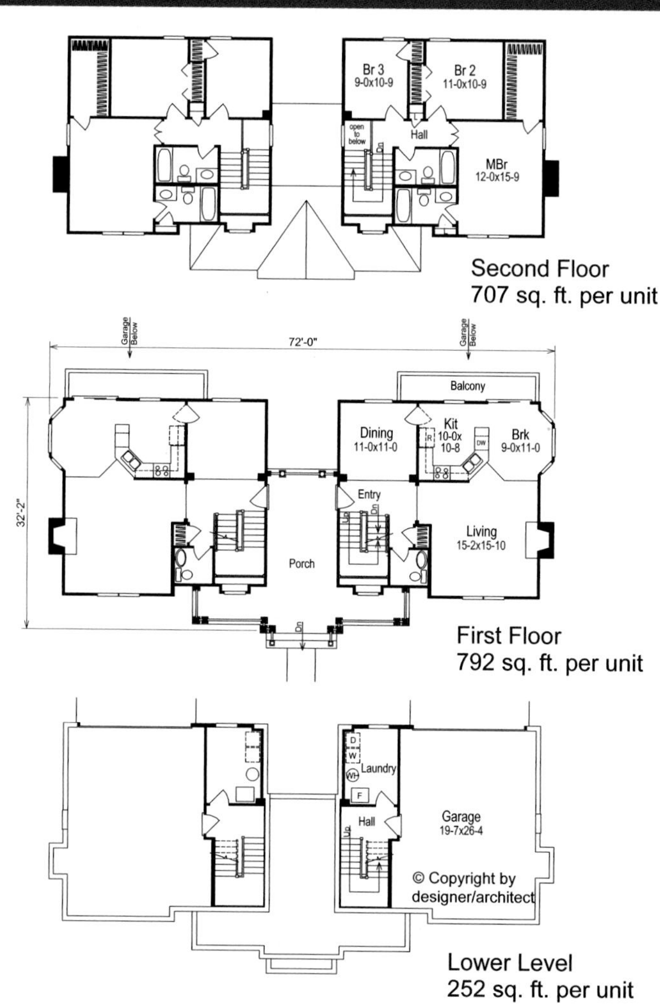

Br 3
9-0x10-9
Br 2
11-0x10-9
open to below
Hall
MBr
12-0x15-9

Second Floor
707 sq. ft. per unit

Garage Below
72'-0"
Garage Below
Balcony
Dining
11-0x11-0
Kit
10-0x
10-8
Brk
9-0x11-0
Entry
32'-2"
Living
15-2x15-10
Porch
Dn

First Floor
792 sq. ft. per unit

D
W
WH
Laundry
F
Hall
Up
Garage
19-7x26-4

© Copyright by designer/architect

Lower Level
252 sq. ft. per unit

To order plans, visit the Menards Building Materials Desk or visit www.Menards.com.

COUNTRYRIDGE

Plan #M06-007D-0024

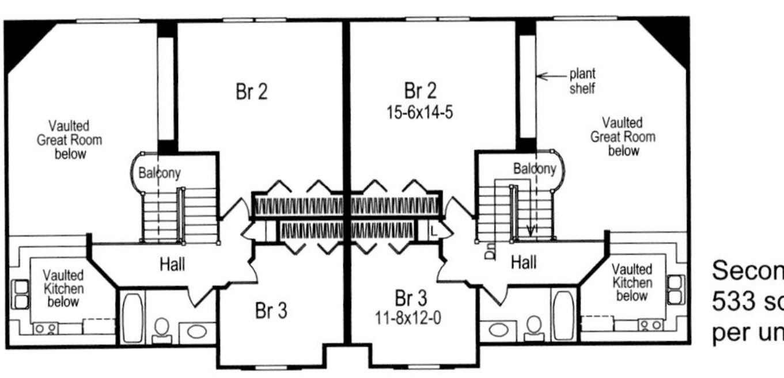
Br 2
Br 2
15-6x14-5
plant shelf
Vaulted Great Room below
Vaulted Great Room below
Balcony
Balcony
Hall
Hall
Vaulted Kitchen below
Vaulted Kitchen below
Br 3
Br 3
11-8x12-0

Second Floor
533 sq. ft.
per unit

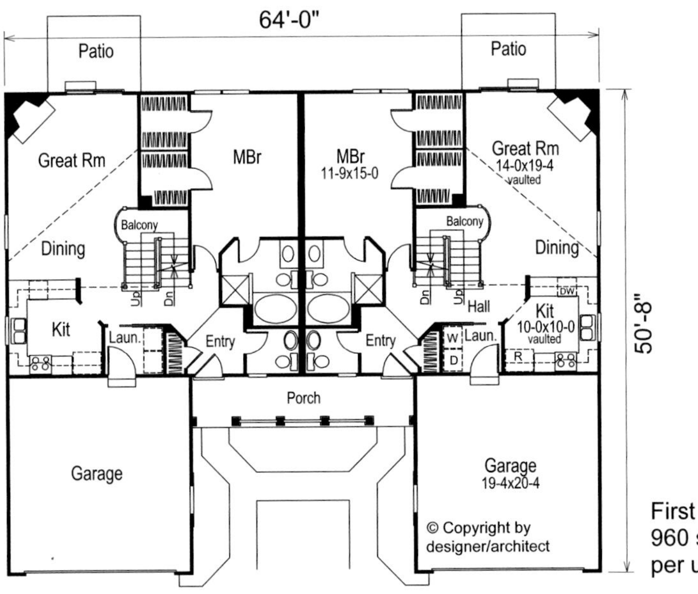
64'-0"
Patio
Patio
Great Rm
MBr
MBr
11-9x15-0
Great Rm
14-0x19-4
vaulted
Balcony
Balcony
Dining
Dining
Kit
Laun.
Entry
Entry
Laun.
Hall
Kit
10-0x10-0
vaulted
DW
W
D
R
Porch
Garage
Garage
19-4x20-4
50'-8"
© Copyright by designer/architect

First Floor
960 sq. ft.
per unit

To order plans, visit the Menards Building Materials Desk
or visit www.Menards.com.

COUNTRY CHARM IN A DOUBLE FEATURE

2,986 total square feet of living area

Each unit has 3 bedrooms, 2 1/2 baths

Each unit has a 2-car garage

Basement foundation

SPECIAL FEATURES

Vaulted great room, kitchen and two balconies define architectural drama

First floor master bedroom boasts a lavish bath and double walk-in closets

An impressive second floor features two large bedrooms, spacious closets, hall bath and balcony overlook

Duplex has 1,493 square feet of living space per unit

PRICE CODE G

Rear View

LAKESIDE

MENARDS

Plan #M06-008D-0032

DUTCH HIP ROOF CREATES ATTRACTIVE FACADE

3,674 total square feet of living area

Each unit has 3 bedrooms, 2 1/2 baths

Each unit has a 2-car garage

Basement foundation, drawings also include crawl space and slab foundation

SPECIAL FEATURES

The spacious second floor master bedroom has a large walk-in closet

The kitchen has a snack counter that opens to the dining area and great room

Duplex has 1,837 total square feet of living space per unit

PRICE CODE H

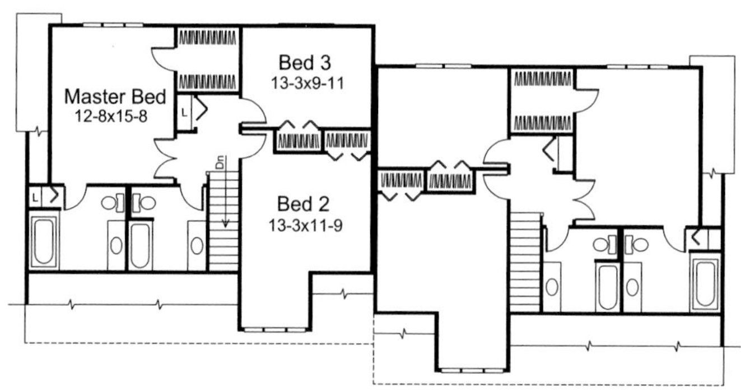

Master Bed
12-8x15-8
Bed 3
13-3x9-11
Bed 2
13-3x11-9
Dn

Second Floor
905 sq. ft. per unit

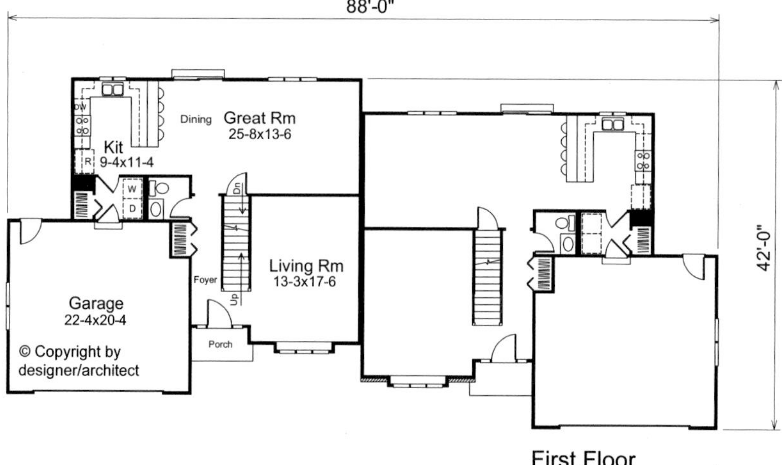

88'-0"
42'-0"
Dining
Great Rm
25-8x13-6
Kit
9-4x11-4
Living Rm
13-3x17-6
Foyer
Porch
Garage
22-4x20-4
© Copyright by designer/architect

First Floor
932 sq. ft. per unit

To order plans, visit the Menards Building Materials Desk or visit www.Menards.com.

FOREST HILL

Plan #M06-007D-0023

Unit B, C
Second Floor

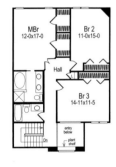

MBr 12-0x17-0
Br 2 11-0x15-0
Hall
Br 3 14-11x11-5
entry below
plant shelf
Dn

116'-0"
58'-0"
72'-6"

Deck
MBr 13-4x14-0
Deck
Living 13-8x22-0
Din
Kit 8-0x11-2
Entry
Porch
Br 2 9-11x11-0
Brk 12-0x15-4
Living 15-5x18-1
Kit 11-5x13-1
Laun.
Dining 15-5x12-0
Entry
Porch
Garage 18-4x20-4
Garage 18-4x21-10

Unit A, D
First Floor

Unit B, C
First Floor

Unit A, D
Lower Level

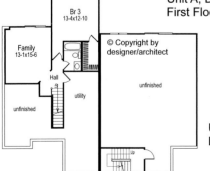

Br 3 13-4x12-10
Family 13-1x15-6
Hall
utility
unfinished
unfinished

Unit B, C
Lower Level

LOVELY FOURPLEX

7,372 total square feet of living area

Walk-out basement foundation

SPECIAL FEATURES

Units A and D feature a living/dining combination and master bedroom with lower level family room and third bedroom

Units A and D include 3 bedrooms, 3 baths, 2-car garage in a ranch plan with 1,707 square feet of living area with 1,149 on the first floor and 558 on the lower level

Units B and C feature a luxurious living area and second floor with spacious master bedroom featuring two walk-in closets and a lavish bath

Units B and C include 3 bedrooms, 2 1/2 baths, 2-car garage in a two-story plan with 1,979 square feet of living area with 1,055 on the first floor and 924 on the second floor

PRICE CODE H

Rear View

To order plans, visit the Menards Building Materials Desk or visit www.Menards.com.

HIGHLAND

MENARDS

Plan #M06-007D-0025

STYLISH LIVING, OPEN DESIGN

1,992 total square feet of living area

Each unit has 2 bedrooms, 2 baths

Each unit has a 1-car garage

Basement foundation

SPECIAL FEATURES

A graciously designed ranch duplex with alluring openness

The vaulted kitchen with accent on spaciousness features a huge pantry, plenty of cabinets and a convenient laundry room

The master bedroom includes its own cozy bath and oversized walk-in closet

Duplex has 996 square feet of living space per unit

PRICE CODE E

Rear View

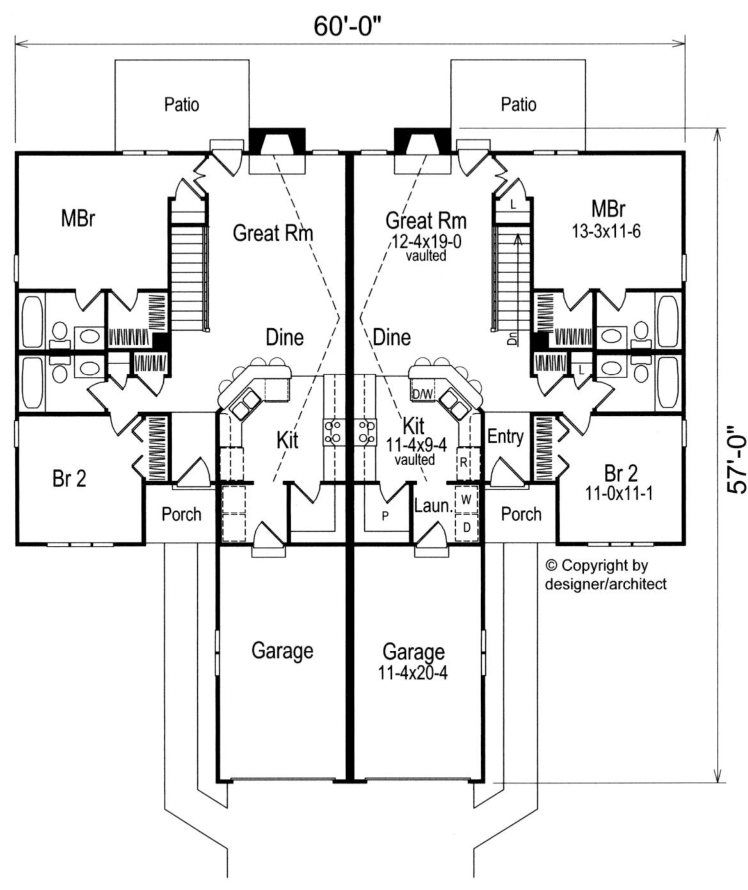
60'-0"
57'-0"
Patio
Patio
MBr
Great Rm
Great Rm
12-4x19-0
vaulted
MBr
13-3x11-6
Dine
Dine
Kit
D/W
Kit
11-4x9-4
vaulted
Entry
Br 2
Porch
Laun.
Porch
Br 2
11-0x11-1
Garage
Garage
11-4x20-4
© Copyright by
designer/architect

To order plans, visit the Menards Building Materials Desk or visit www.Menards.com.

PASADENA

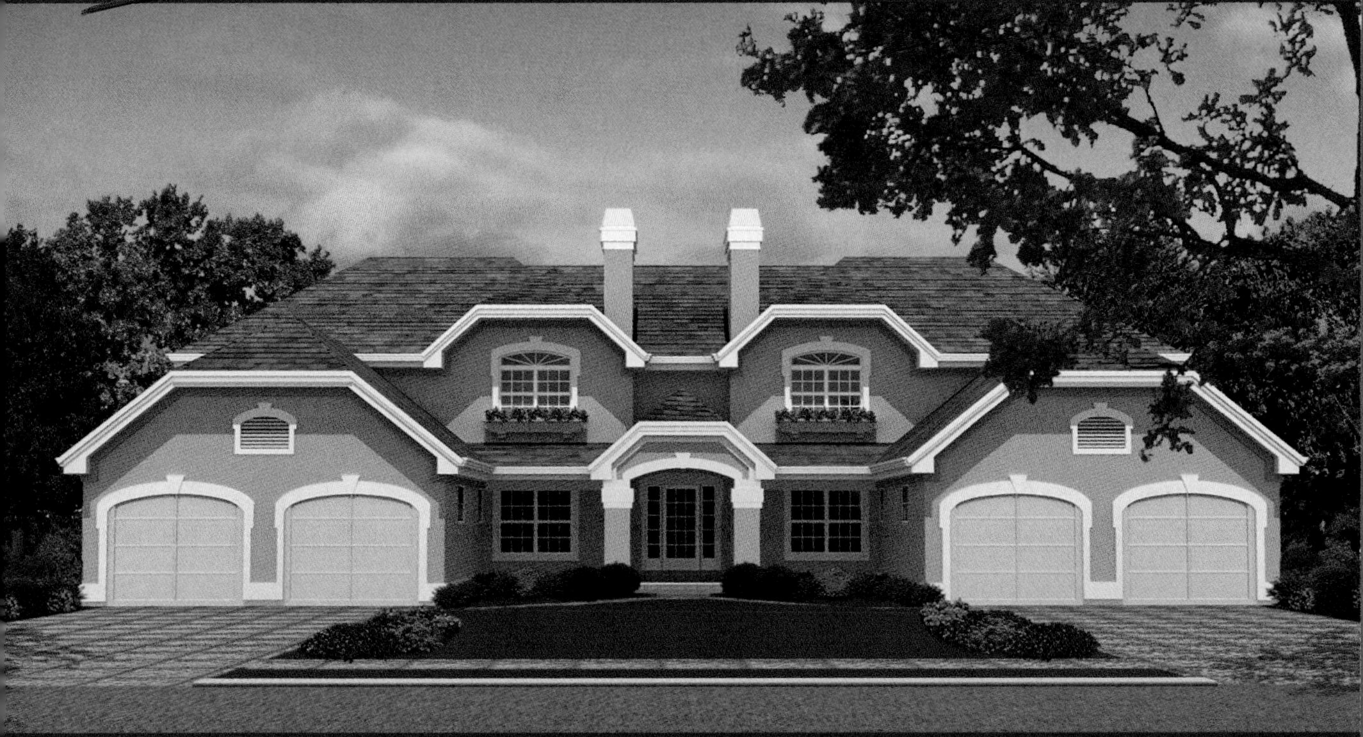

Plan #M06-007D-0022

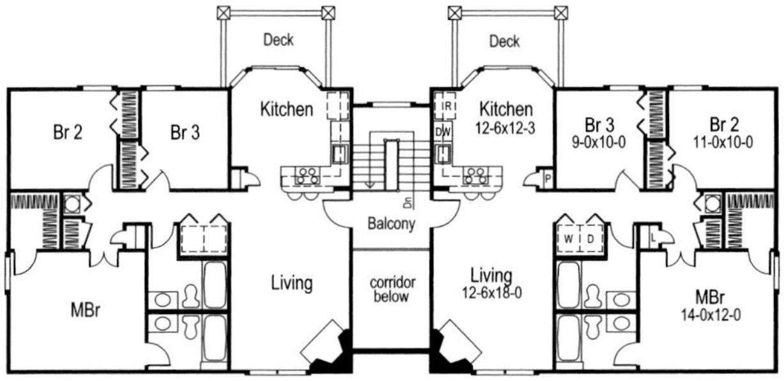

Second Floor
1,060 sq. ft.
per unit

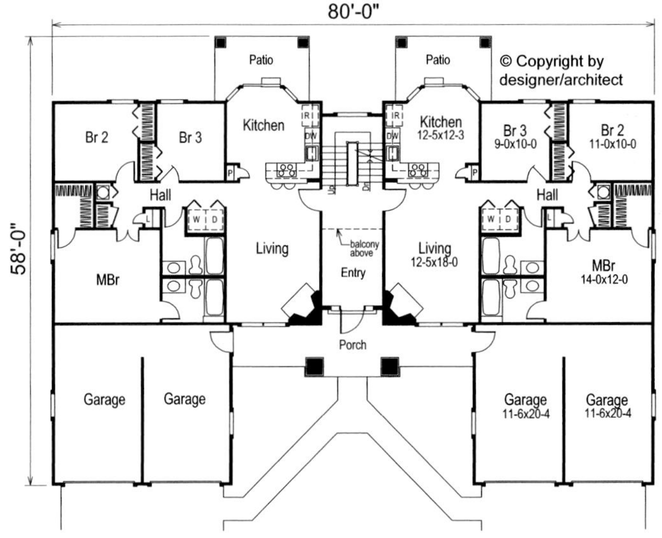
80'-0"
58'-0"
Patio
Patio
© Copyright by designer/architect
Br 2
Br 3
Kitchen
Kitchen
12-5x12-3
Br 3
9-0x10-0
Br 2
11-0x10-0
Hall
Hall
Living
balcony above
Entry
Living
12-5x18-0
MBr
MBr
14-0x12-0
Porch
Garage
Garage
Garage
11-6x20-4
Garage
11-6x20-4

First Floor
1,060 sq. ft.
per unit

To order plans, visit the Menards Building Materials Desk
or visit www.Menards.com.

WELL-DESIGNED FACADE, WELCOMING AND DISTINCTIVE

4,240 total square feet of living area

Each unit has 3 bedrooms, 2 baths

Each unit has a 1-car garage

Basement foundation

SPECIAL FEATURES

The kitchen, brightened by a large bay window, accesses a patio on first floor units and a deck on second floor units

A corner fireplace provides warmth

Bedrooms are separated from living areas

The laundry area is located off hall for accessibility

Fourplex has 1,060 square feet of living space per unit

PRICE CODE H

Rear View

HOME PLAN INDEX